Laboratory Experiments in CHEMISTRY

H. Clark Metcalfe
John E. Williams
Joseph F. Castka

Holt, Rinehart and Winston, Inc.

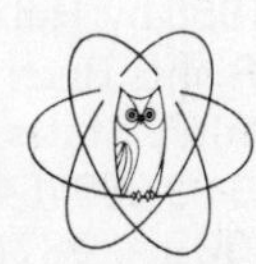

NEW YORK TORONTO LONDON SYDNEY

Printed in the United States of America
ISBN-0-03-089454-9
789 008 98765

Preface

The list of experiments in LABORATORY EXPERIMENTS IN CHEMISTRY is comprehensive and varied. From this the teacher may select the appropriate experiments for one school year. The experiments may be used to supplement and complement classroom work. The teacher should select the experiments to fit the aims of the course, the needs of the students, and the time and facilities available for the laboratory program.

Each experiment gives a list of apparatus and materials required. These are usually available. The directions are clear and concise. Certain experiments can be used as teacher demonstrations to supplement the basic laboratory program. Instructor's experiments are given within many of the experiments. Many experiments include a section entitled Further Investigations which may serve to stimulate and guide student project activity.

The arrangement of the 65 experiments follows the sequence of topics in MODERN CHEMISTRY, 1974 edition. This provides experimental background for each chapter. Experiments should precede classroom treatment of topics when feasible. This emphasizes the experimental approach to the study of chemistry. The Introduction to each experiment sets the stage for the experimental investigation of the problems stated under the section labeled Purpose. Many of the experiments are of the open-ended type in which the student cannot find the answer by referring to the textbook. The experiments involve varying degrees of challenge so that the student is involved in a scientific inquiry and real experimentation.

The 65 experiments can be divided roughly into the following categories:

1. Descriptive-observational, in which the students observe, summarize, and draw conclusions.
2. Qualitative, in which the students record observations in data tables and draw conclusions on the basis of qualitative comparison.
3. Quantitative, in which the students measure various quantities, and make computations based on these quantitative observations.

The distribution follows the sequence of material in MODERN CHEMISTRY 1974, where most of the quantitative-theoretical material is concentrated in the early parts of the book with descriptive chemistry most heavily concentrated in the later parts.

The form of laboratory report required depends on the discretion of the teacher. The minimum essentials consist of an essay-type report based on observations, purpose or problem, questions, equations, etc. as they appear in the manual under appropriately numbered procedures and headings. The Data Tables usually give headings and arrangement, indicating how the data may be set up in tabular form. These should be a required part of the report. A more extensive report may require more details and possibly some restatement of fundamental procedures employed.

The *Teacher's Edition to Exercises and Experiments in Chemistry* contains lists of student apparatus and additional laboratory equipment, lists of needed chemicals, directions for preparation of solutions, and answers to the questions, and where feasible the Data Tables are completed.

Contents

TECHNIQUES AND SAFETY SKETCHES

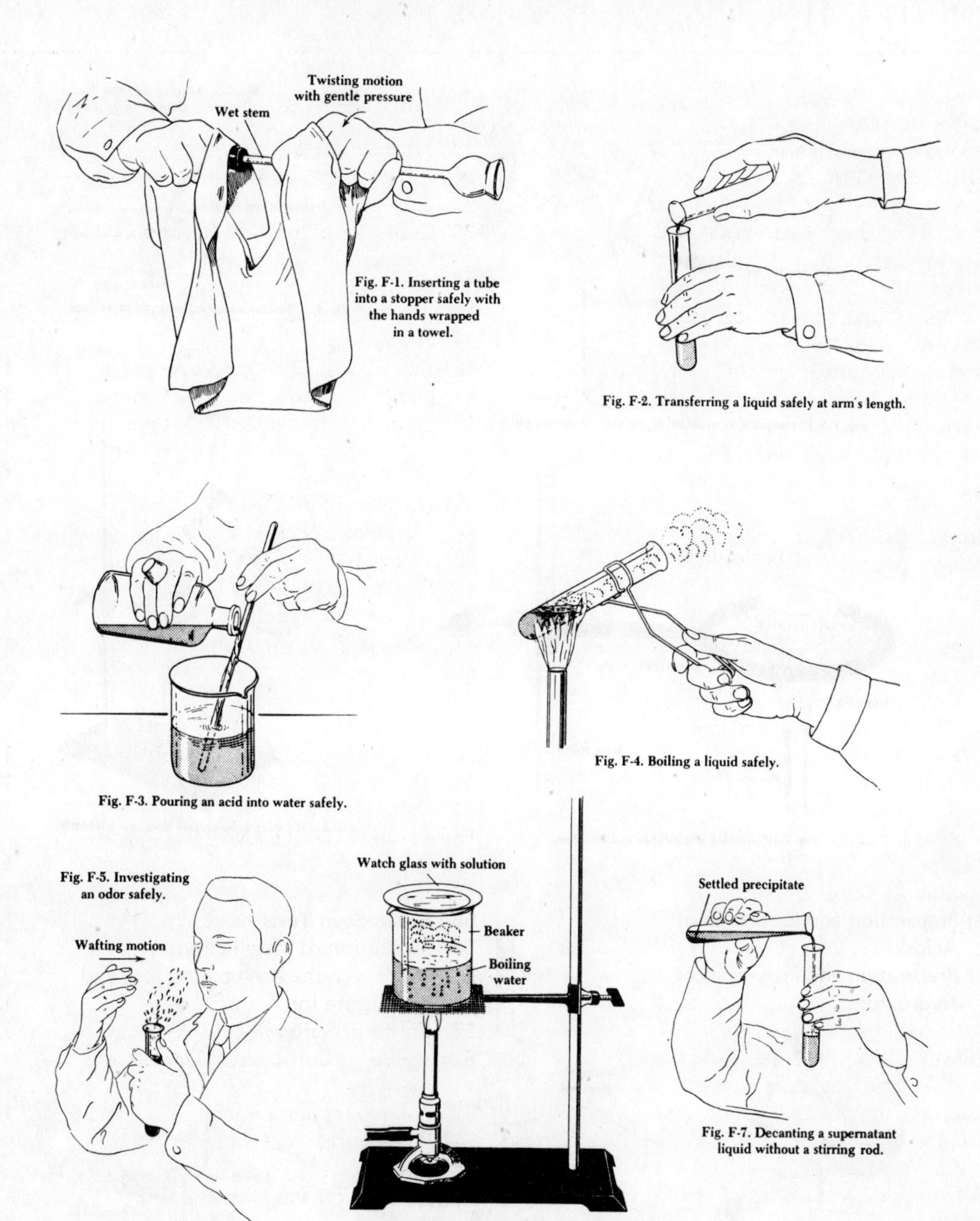

Fig. F-1. Inserting a tube into a stopper safely with the hands wrapped in a towel.

Fig. F-2. Transferring a liquid safely at arm's length.

Fig. F-3. Pouring an acid into water safely.

Fig. F-4. Boiling a liquid safely.

Fig. F-5. Investigating an odor safely.

Fig. F-6. Evaporating over a water bath.

Fig. F-7. Decanting a supernatant liquid without a stirring rod.

TECHNIQUES AND SAFETY SKETCHES

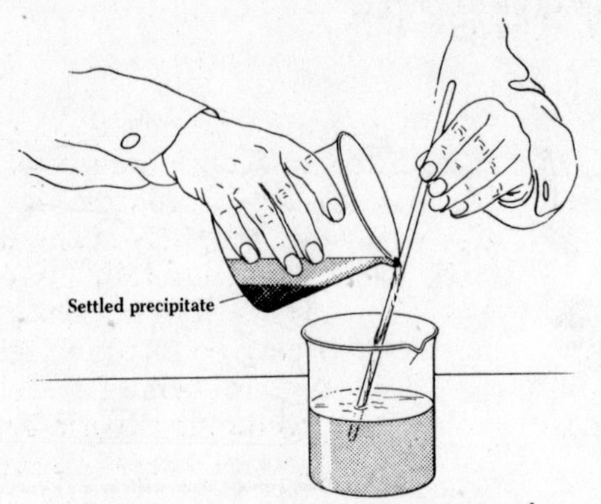

Fig. F-8. Decanting a supernatant liquid using a stirring rod.

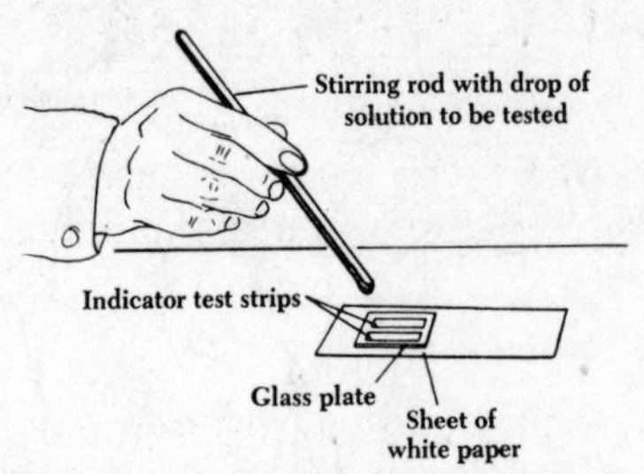

Fig. F-9. Testing a solution with indicator paper.

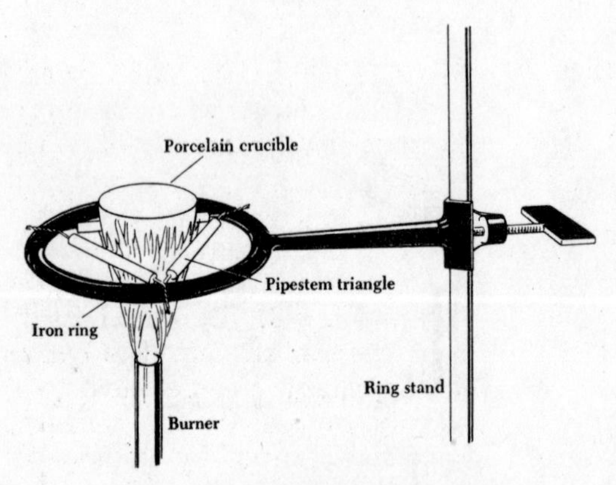

Fig. F-10. Heating a substance in a crucible.

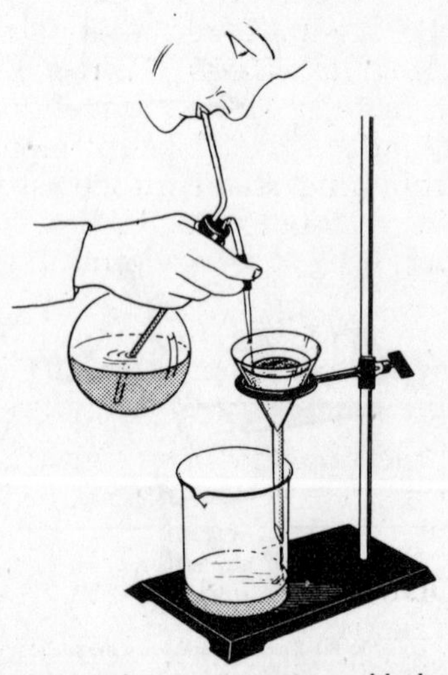

Fig. F-11. Washing a precipitate using a wash bottle.

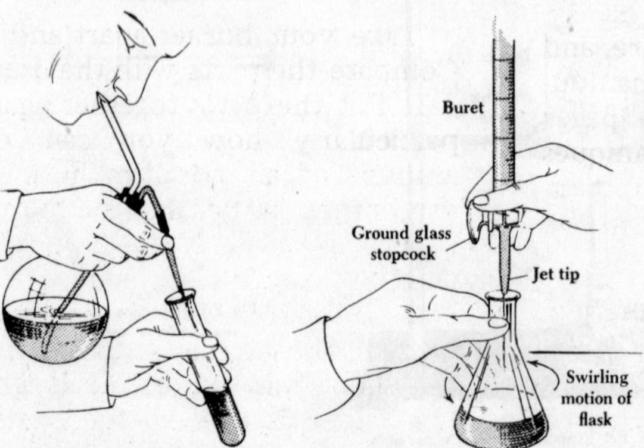

Fig. F-12. Using a wash bottle.

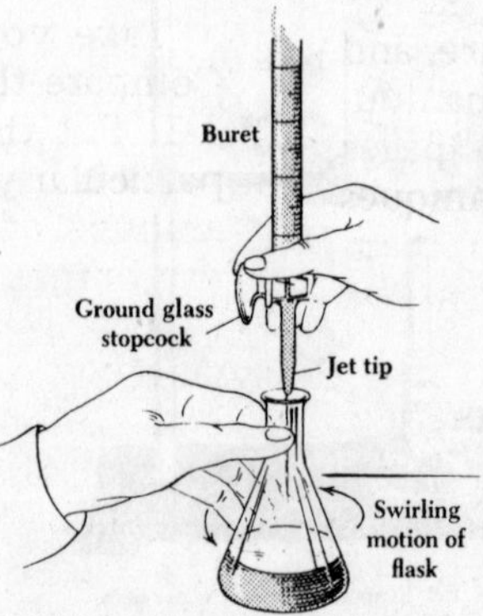

Fig. F-13. Titrating a solution using a buret.

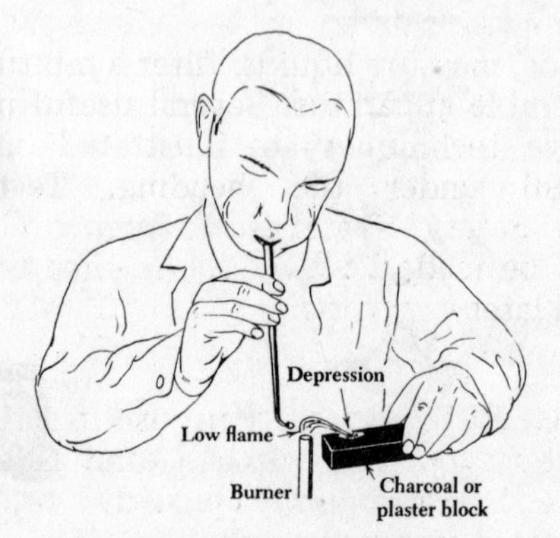

Fig. F-14. Using a blowpipe.

Experiment 1 Laboratory Procedures

PURPOSE: To become acquainted with laboratory apparatus and laboratory techniques.

APPARATUS: Asbestos square; beakers, 250 ml, 400 ml; balance, platform, buret; burner and tubing; calorimeter (plastic cups and lid); clamp, buret; dish, evaporating; file, triangular; flasks, Florence, 250 ml, 500 ml; forceps; funnel; funnel tube; graduated cylinder; pinch clamp; pipet, 25 ml; ring, iron; ring stand; rubber stoppers, 2-hole No. 4, 2-hole No. 5; test tube; thermometer; wing top; wire gauze.

MATERIAL: Copper wire, 18 gauge; filter paper, glass rod, 6 mm; glass tubing, 6 mm; potassium permanganate; sand; sodium chloride.

INTRODUCTION: The best way to become familiar with chemical apparatus is to actually handle the pieces yourself in the laboratory. In this experiment, you will learn how to adjust the bas burner, manipulate glass tubing, make weighings, handle solids, measure liquids, filter a mixture, and assemble apparatus. Several useful manipulative techniques are illustrated on pages 95-96 under the heading, Techniques and Safety Sketches. Reference to them will be made in this experiment and in several later experiments.

SUGGESTION: If you use plastic wash bottles you may wish to omit this procedure. However it does provide a project for those students who do the glass bending, cutting, and fire polishing. Wash bottles, once made, may be stored in a wall case where they are readily accessible for use. In multiple-section laboratories the instructor may wish to store one set of wash bottles with solid stoppers in the wall case and have each student retain his own stopper assembly in his locker. Other subassemblies which may be stored in sets or in individual student lockers (Fig. 1-14) are time savers in subsequent experiments. Two full laboratory periods are needed for this experiment.

PROCEDURE: 1. *The burner.* The Bunsen or Tirrell burner is commonly used in laboratory heating operations. While the details of construction vary among burners, each has a gas inlet located in the base, a vertical tube or barrel in which the gas is mixed with air, and adjustable openings or ports in the base of the barrel to introduce air into the gas stream. The burner may have an adjustable needle valve to regulate the supply of gas, or the gas supply may be regulated simply by adjusting the valve on the supply line. The burner is always turned off at the gas valve, never at the needle valve.

Take your burner apart and examine it. Compare the parts with the drawing in Fig. 1-1. Put the parts together again and note particularly how you can control the amount of air admitted near the base of the burner. In lighting the burner, partially close the ports at the base of the barrel, turn the gas full on, and hold the lighted match about 5 cm above the top of the burner. The gas may then be regulated until the flame has the desired height. If a very low flame is needed, the ports should be kept partly closed when the gas pressure is reduced. Otherwise the flame may "strike back" and burn inside the base of the barrel.

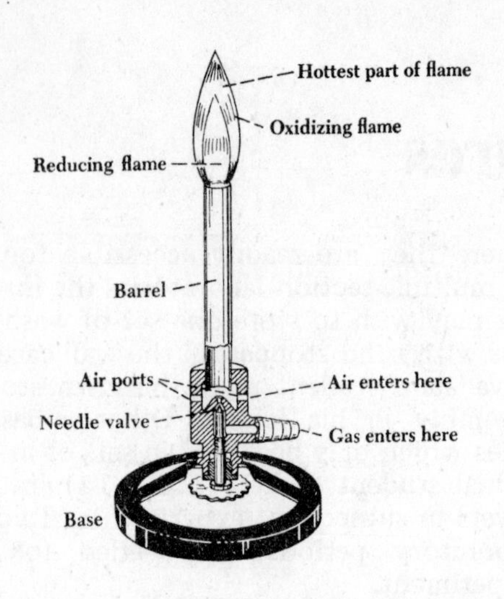

Fig. 1-1

If this happens, turn off the gas, decrease the amount of air admitted, and relight.

Close the holes at the base. What is the result? How would you describe the flame? Using the forceps, hold an evaporating dish in the tip of the flame. Result? Suggest a possible explanation. Such a flame is seldom used in the laboratory. Why? For laboratory work, you should adjust the burner so that the flame will be free of yellow color, and also free from the "roaring" sound caused by admitting too much air.

Regulate the flow of gas to give a flame extending roughly 8 cm above the barrel. Now adjust the supply of air until you have a quiet, steady flame with a sharply defined inner cone. This adjustment gives the highest temperature possible with your burner. Using the forceps, insert a 10-cm piece of copper wire into the flame just above the barrel. Lift the wire slowly up through the flame. Where is the hottest portion of the flame located? Hold the wire in this part of the flame for a few seconds. Result? The melting point of copper is 1083° C.

2. *Glass Manipulations. a. Cutting tubing.* Secure several pieces of glass tubing from the scrap supply to use for practice. At the point to be cut, make a deep scratch at right angles by pushing the edge of a triangular file away from you with *one* firm, steady stroke. Grasp the tubing with both hands, with your thumbs meeting opposite the scratch, and break it by pulling the ends toward you. Repeat until you have mastered this operation.

b. Fire polishing. The edges of the tubes you have just cut are very sharp, and they would cut a rubber stopper or rubber tubing if you tried to use the tube with either one. *Fire polish* the end of the tube by holding it in the burner flame, rolling it between the fingers to heat it uniformly. Recall the location of the hottest part of the burner flame as determined in Part 1. As the flame above the tubing yellows, the glass softens, and its sharp edges become rounded. **CAUTION:** *If the end of the tube is held in the flame too long, the size of the opening will be reduced.* Place hot glass tubing on an asbestos square to cool.

c. Bending tubing. Place a wing top on the barrel of your burner, in order to give a broad, flat flame. Select pieces of glass tubing from the scrap supply for practice. Hold the tubing in the flame so that it will be heated for about 5 cm of its length at the place where it is to be bent. Rotate the tubing constantly to heat all sides uniformly. When the flame above the tubing becomes an intense yellow, the glass will be soft enough to bend easily. Remove it from the flame, and bend it to make a smooth 90° bend similar to that shown in *b* of Fig. 1-2. Fire polish the ends and place the tube on the asbestos square to cool. Be sure that you have both arms of the bent tube in the same plane.

Repeat the procedure with additional pieces of scrap glass tubing until you are able to form a satisfactory bend. Now secure a length of tubing, 6 mm in diameter, and cut, bend, and fire polish 90° glass bends as follows: one 8 × 8 cm, one 8 × 15 cm, and one 8 × 30 cm. Secure a 15-cm length of 6-mm glass rod and fire polish both ends to form a *stirring rod*. Retain all 4 pieces in your locker for future use.

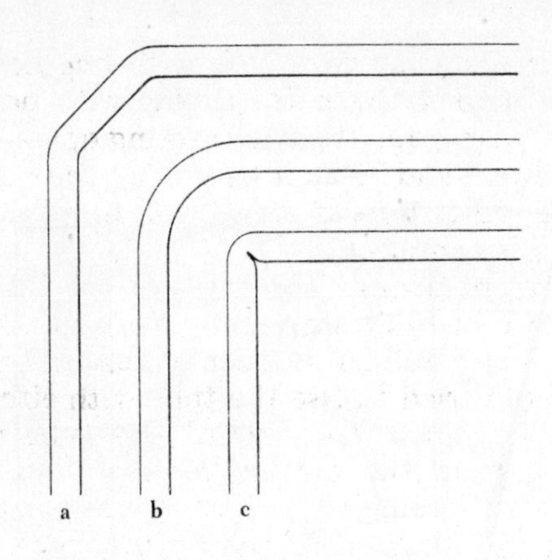

Fig. 1-2

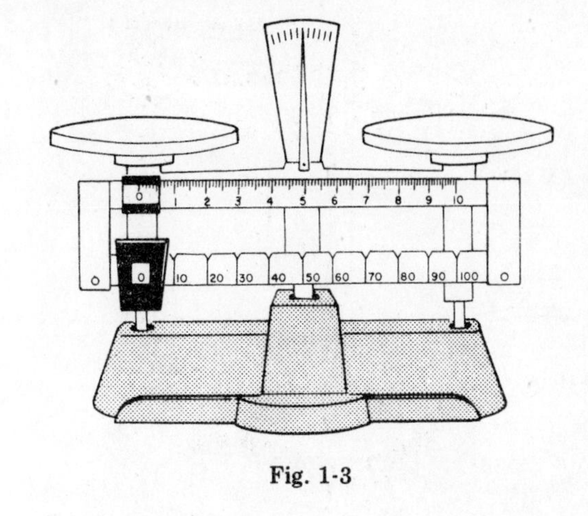

Fig. 1-3

d. Drawing glass tubing. Again secure a few picces of scrap tubing to use for practice. Remove the wing top from your burner and hold the middle region of a piece of tubing in the flame as you heat it a little hotter than necessary for bending. Allow the walls to thicken somewhat. Remove it from the flame and pull the two ends apart until the softened region is as small as desired, making the pull straight and with even tension. To make a *jet tip*, cut the constricted portion to leave a jet tip about 6 or 8 cm in length. Fire polish both ends, being careful not to seal the jet end. Using 6-mm glass tubing, make 3 well-formed jet tips to retain in your locker. To make a *closed tube*, cut off the constricted part as before, and then hold the jet end in the flame until it is melted shut.

3. *The balance.* For most purposes in general chemistry, the moderately accurate weighings possible on the ordinary platform balance are satisfactory. Such a balance is shown in Fig. 1-3. It is sensitive to 0.1 g.

More precise work in the laboratory may require a balance of greater sensitivity. Such a balance is shown in Fig. 1-4. It is sensitive to 0.01 g and is very useful in certain quantitative experiments. In order to carry out a weighing successfully, you should learn the following steps.

a. Determine the rest point. Inspect your platform balance to see that both pans are clean and that the pointer swings, or oscillates, freely over the range of the attached scale with the slider (slide weight) at zero. *The rest point is at the center of the range over which the pointer swings, determined to the nearest half-scale division.* It is not necessarily at the center of the attached scale. The rest point can be found only if the pointer is oscillating within the range of the fixed scale. A typical rest point determination is illustrated in Fig. 1-5. If a weighing paper is to be used in making a weighing, place a paper square on each platform before determining the rest point. If the rest point is more than 3 scale divisions from the center of the scale, or if the pointer sticks in any part of its oscillation, call this to the attention of your instructor. Do not attempt to make independent adjustments on your balance.

b. Balance the substance and known masses. Place a small square of glazed paper on each platform of the balance (discs of filter paper will do if glazed paper is not available). Determine the rest point. Examine the balance carefully to determine which pan should be used to support the material whose mass is to be measured. Put an appropriate amount of dry sand on this pan.

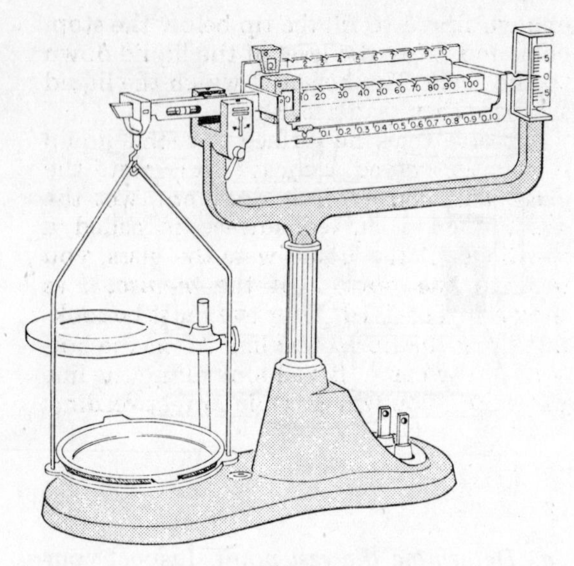

Fig. 1-4

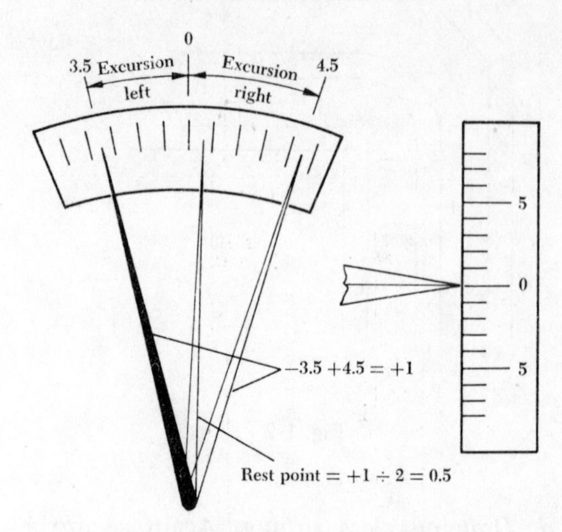

Fig. 1-5

Move the slider on the 0-100 g beam into the slot, which you judge, indicates the upper portion of the 10-g range within which the mass of the sand falls. For example, if use of this slider indicates that the mass of the sand is more than 10 g but less than 20 g, the slider is first placed in the 20-g position and then moved back to the lower part of the range, that is, the 10-g position. Now move the slider on the 0-10-g beam until the pointer oscillations remain within the range of the fixed scale. Adjust this slider so that the midpoint of the oscillation corresponds to the rest point of the balance. Record in your notebook the mass of the sand which is determined by the sum of the slider readings of both beams. For example, if the reading on the 0-100-g beam is 50 g and that on the 0-10 g beam is 4.3 g, the total mass which you are measuring is 54.3 g. For a balance accurate to 0.1 g, make sure that you record to one place to the right of the decimal point. Always label your record and retain it in your laboratory notes.

Sometimes only a close approximation is needed. Suppose you wish to use about 10 grams of a solid. Place a sheet of glazed paper on each pan, and move the slider to the extreme right, at the 10-g mark. Using a horn spoon or spatula, add the solid to the left pan until an approximate balance is reached. Such rough weighings are not usually recorded.

4. *Handling solids.* Solids are usually kept in wide-mouthed bottles. A porcelain or plastic spoon may be used to dip out the solid. *Never use more of a chemical than directed.*

In order to transfer a solid to a test tube, first place it on a piece of glazed paper about 10 cm square. Roll the paper into a cylinder and slide it into the test tube as it lies flat on the table. When you lift the tube to a vertical position, and tap the paper gently, the solid will slide down into the test tube. *Never try to pour a solid from a bottle into a test tube. As a precaution against contamination, never pour unused chemicals back into the reagent bottles without specific permission from the instructor.*

5. *Measuring liquids.* For approximate measurements, a graduated cylinder, as shown in Fig. 1-6, is generally used. These cylinders are usually graduated in milliliters (ml). Such a graduate may read from 0 to 10 ml, 0 to 25 ml, 0 to 50 ml, or more, from bottom

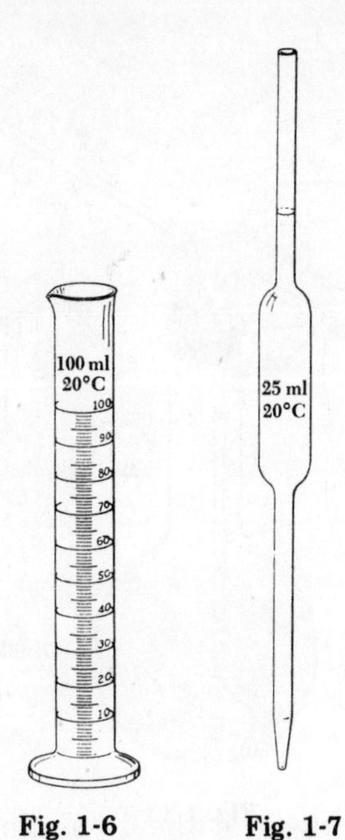

Fig. 1-6 Fig. 1-7

to top. It may also have a second row of graduations reading from top to bottom.

For more accurate measurements, either the pipet or the buret is used. See Figs. 1-7, 1-8, 1-9. The jet end of the pipet is thrust into the liquid, and the air is withdrawn from the pipet. When the liquid rises slightly above the graduated mark, a finger is placed quickly over the upper end of the pipet. As a little air is let in at the top, the liquid level falls slowly to the etched line. It is then held at that level, with the finger firmly against the top, and transferred to the vessel into which it is being measured. A bulb syringe is used with corrosive or poisonous liquids. Otherwise the mouth is commonly used to withdraw the air from the pipet. Pipets are made in many sizes and are used to deliver measured volumes of liquids.

Burets, fitted with either a stopcock, a pinch clamp, or a glass bead, are used for withdrawing any desired quantity of liquid to the capacity of the buret. Many burets are graduated in *tenths of milliliters.* In using a buret, you clamp it in position on a ring stand, fill it with liquid, and then draw off enough liquid to fill the tip below the stopcock and bring the level of the liquid down to the scale. The height at which the liquid stands is then read accurately.

Observe that the surface of such a liquid is slightly curved, concave if it wets the glass, and convex if it does not wet the glass. Such a curved surface is called a *meniscus*. If the liquid wets the glass, you read to the bottom of the *meniscus*, as shown in Fig. 1-10. Your eye must be looking along the horizontal line AC at the bottom of the curve. If you look along the line BC or DC, you will get an incorrect reading.

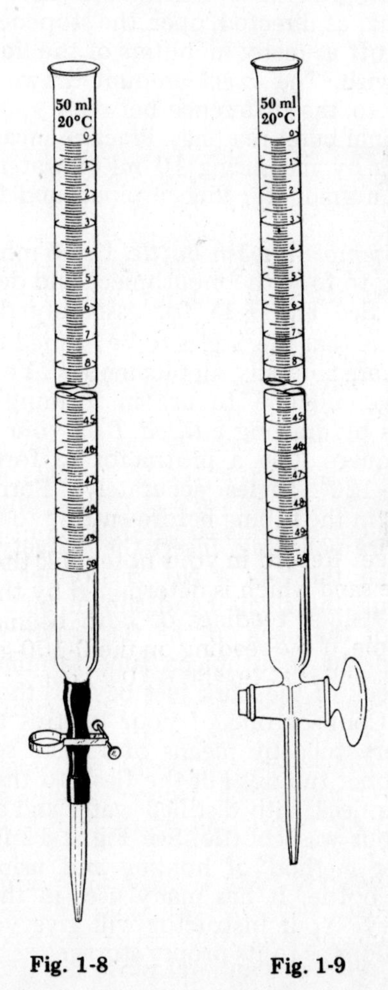

Fig. 1-8 Fig. 1-9

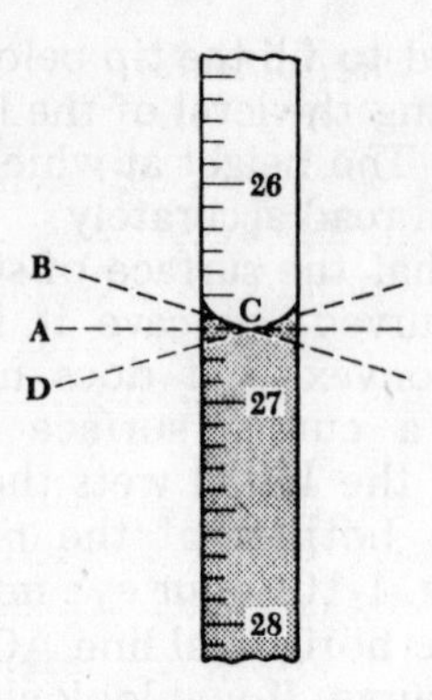

Fig. 1-10

After you have taken your first buret reading, as directed, open the stopcock and draw off as many milliliters of the liquid as you wish. The exact amount drawn off is equal to the difference between your first and final buret readings. Practice measuring liquids by measuring 10 ml of water, first using a graduate, then a pipet, and finally a buret.

6. *Assemble a wash bottle.* Use 6 mm glass tubing to form the mouthpiece and delivery tube. See Fig. 1-11 for assembly details. Observe that the angles to be formed by the tubes are mutually supplementary. You may arrange a guide to use in forming these angles by drawing a *tilted T* on your asbestos square. Use a protractor to form the 60° -120° angles accurately. Form the bends in the tubing before cutting to length and fire polishing. Insert the delivery tube through the 2-hole No. 5 stopper before forming the slight bend shown below the base of the neck of the flask. Why? Why should the mouthpiece tube terminate in the neck of the flask just beyond the stopper? Connect one of your jet tips to the delivery tube by means of a small section of rubber tubing. Fill the flask to the base of the neck with distilled water and assemble your wash bottle. See Fig. 1-12 for the proper method of holding and using the wash bottle. It has many uses in the laboratory. Your instructor will give you instructions as to its proper storage.

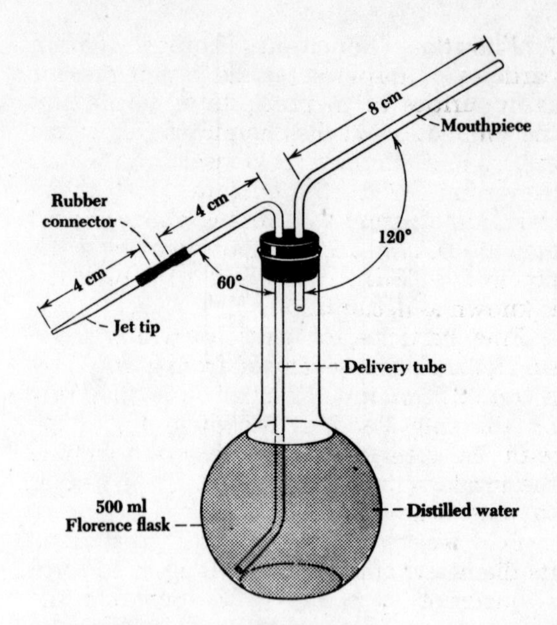

Fig. 1-11

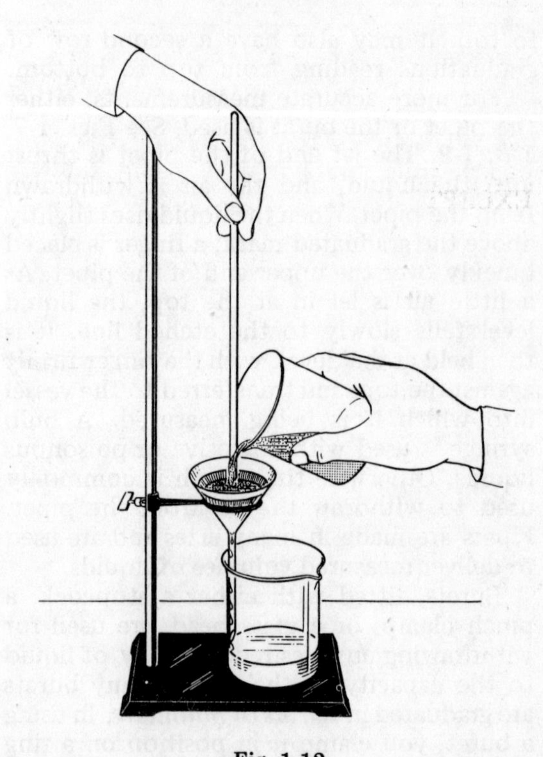

Fig. 1-12

7. *Filtration.* Sometimes liquids contain particles of insoluble solids, either present as impurities or as precipitates formed by the interaction of the chemicals used in the experiment. If they are denser than water, they soon sink to the bottom. Most of the clear, supernatant (swimming above) liquid may be poured off without disturbing the precipitate. Such a method of separation is known as *decantation*.

Fine particles, or particles which settle slowly, are often separated from a liquid by *filtration*. Support a funnel on a small ring on the ring stand as shown in Fig. 1-12, with the stem of the funnel just touching the inside wall of the beaker. Use a beaker to collect the *filtrate*.

Fold a circular piece of filter paper along its diameter, and then fold it again to form a quadrant. See Fig. 1-13. Separate the folds of the filter, with three thicknesses on one side and one on the other, then place in the funnel. The funnel should be wet before the paper is added. Use your wash bottle. Then wet the filter paper with a little water and press the edges firmly against the sides of the funnel so no air can get between the funnel and the filter paper while the liquid is being filtered. **EXCEPTION:** *A filter should not be wet with water when the liquid to be filtered is not miscible with water. Why?*

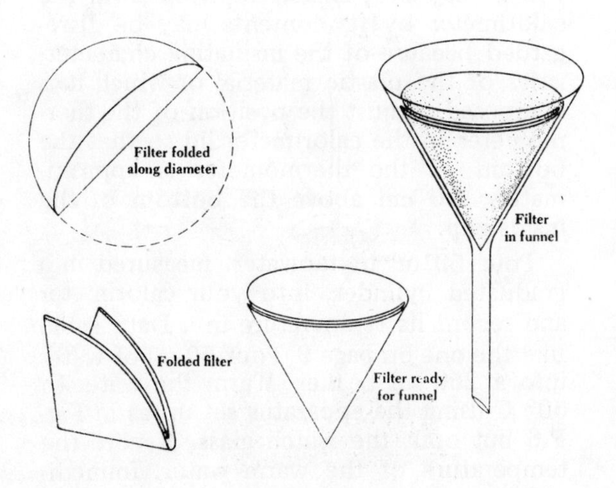

Fig. 1-13

Dissolve 2 or 3 g of salt in a beaker containing 50 ml of water, and stir into the solution an equal bulk of fine sand. Then filter out the sand by pouring the mixture into the filter, observing the following suggestions.

a. The filter paper should not extend above the edge of the funnel. It is better to use a filter disc which leaves about 1 cm of the funnel exposed.

b. Do not fill the filter. It must never overflow.

c. Try to establish a water column in the stem of the funnel, thus excluding air bubbles, and then add the liquid just fast enough to keep the level about 1 cm from the top of the filter.

d. When a liquid is poured from a beaker or other container, it may adhere to the glass and run down the outside wall. This may be avoided by holding a stirring rod against the tip of the beaker, as shown in Fig. F-8. The liquid will run down the rod and drop off into the funnel without running down the side of the beaker.

The sand suspended from the liquid is retained on the filter paper. What property of the sand enables it to be separated from the liquid by filtration? What does the filtrate contain? The salt may be recovered from the filtrate by pouring it into an evaporating dish, and evaporating it *nearly* to dryness. Remove the flame as soon as the liquid begins to spatter. What property of the salt prevents it from being separated from the water by filtration?

8. *Assembling apparatus.* Gases are usually generated in flasks or bottles and collected by water displacement, or if they are soluble, by air displacement. Vapors may be collected by condensation. A simple distilling apparatus to illustrate this method is shown in Fig. 1-14. The funnel tube and glass bend should be assembled through the 2-hole stopper (No. 4) before the stopper is placed in the neck of the 250-ml Florence flask. Why? Wet the glass surface and work

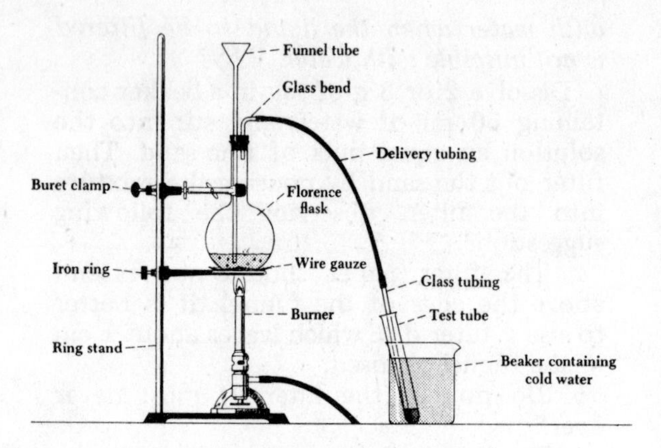

Fig. 1-14

the tubing through the stopper slowly with a twisting motion. Have both hands covered with a towel. See Fig. F-1 for safety precautions. The elbow tube extends just through the stopper and the funnel tube extends to within about 1 cm of the bottom of the flask. Clamp an iron ring on the ring stand at the proper height to allow the bottom of the flask to be just above the tip of the inner cone of the burner flame. Place a wire gauze on the ring and clamp the flask in place resting on the gauze. **CAUTION:** *Avoid clamping the neck of the flask more tightly than necessary to provide proper support. Why? Be sure the flask is Pyrex. Why?* How can you identify such glass? Next mount the funnel-tube-and-elbow assembly and attach a suitable length of rubber delivery hose. *Note that the ring, clamp, and flask are directly above the base of the ring stand.* Reason? Cut and fire polish a straight piece of 6-mm glass tubing slightly longer than the test tube to be used to collect the *distillate*. Place the test tube in a 400-ml beaker of cold water, attach the cooled glass tube to the delivery hose, and extend it to the bottom of the test tube.

Add a single crystal of potassium permanganate to 100 ml of water. Stir until dissolved; then pour into the flask by way of the funnel tube. Apply heat and bring the solution to boiling. As boiling begins, turn down the flame to just sustain the boiling action. What collects in the test tube? In what way does it appear to be different from the solution in the flask? How do you explain this difference?

After collecting several milliliters of distillate, shut off the burner and allow the apparatus to cool sufficiently to be disassembled. When it is cool, disassemble the apparatus, dry and put away. Always completely disassemble glass tubing in contact with rubber stoppers and hose immediately after use. Why? Have the glass surface thoroughly wet. Follow the same precautions as in assembly. Equipment stored in your locker should be clean, dry, and arranged in an orderly fashion. Reason?

9. *Measuring temperature and heat.* A thermometer (Fig. 1-15) is used to measure temperature and temperature changes. Examine your thermometer and the temperature range for the Celsius temperature scale. Compare the Celsius temperatures with those on the Fahrenheit scale which appear on the thermometer in the laboratory.

A calorimeter is an apparatus used in measurements involving heat, and heat transfer. For approximate measurements, a simple calorimeter, as shown in Fig. 1-16, may be used. The small quantities of heat which may be transferred to or from the calorimeter by its contents may be disregarded because of the insulating characteristics of the plastic material of which it is composed. Adjust the position of the thermometer in the calorimeter lid so that the bottom of the thermometer is approximately 1.0 cm above the bottom of the inside cup.

Pour $5\bar{0}$ ml of tapwater, measured in a graduated cylinder, into your calorimeter and record its temperature in a Data Table like the one on page 9. Pour $5\bar{0}$ ml of water into a 250 ml beaker. Warm the water to 60° C using the apparatus set up as in Fig. F-6 but omit the watch glass. Record the temperature of the warm water. Immediately transfer the warm water into the calorimeter cup. Replace the lid, insert the ther-

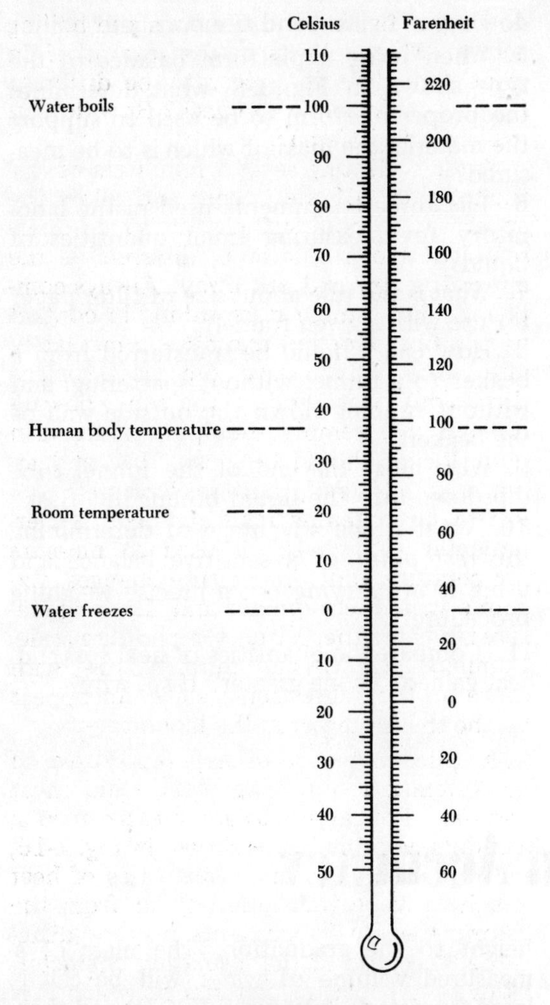

Fig. 1-15

mometer, and stir the contents gently until a fixed temperature is reached. Record this final temperature of the mixture of hot and cold water in the Data Table. The quantities of heat, Q, in calories, gained by the cold water and lost by the hot water may each be calculated from the equation:

$$Q = \textit{temperature change } (C^\circ) \times \textit{mass } (g) \times 1.0 \textit{ cal/g } C^\circ.$$

Using this equation, calculate Q for the heat gained by the $5\bar{0}$ g of cold water and Q for the heat lost by the hot water. Record these

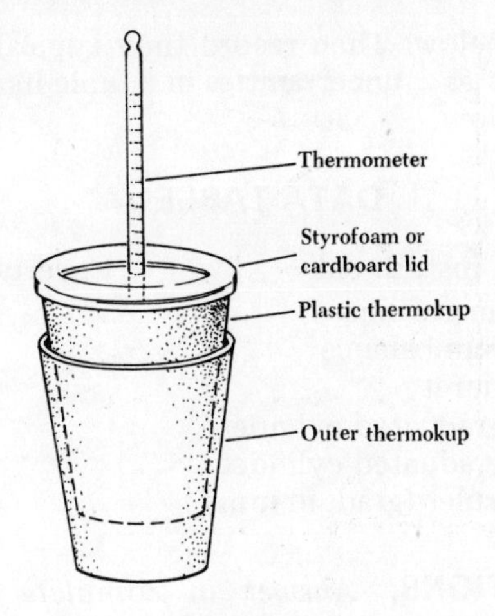

Fig. 1-16

quantities in the Data Table. How do these two quantities of heat compare?

DATA TABLE

Mass of cold water	g
Temperature of cold water	°C
Mass of hot water	g
Temperature of hot water	°C
Fixed temperature of mixture	°C
Temperature change of cold water (Fixed temperature — initial temperature)	C°
Temperature change of hot water (Initial temperature — fixed temperature)	C°
Heat gained by cold water	cal
Heat lost by hot water	cal

10. *Precision.* Precision is the agreement between the numerical values of two or more measurements that have been made in the same way. Precision refers to the reproducibiltiy of measurement data or the degree of detail — that is, the ± uncertainty — involved. The reproducibility of a measurement would not ordinarily be expected to exceed the tolerance of the instrument used. Carefully inspect the instruments listed below. Then record their typical tolerances as ± uncertainties in a table like the one below.

DATA TABLE

Instrument	Uncertainty
Platform balance	g
Centigram balance	g
50 ml buret	ml
10 ml graduated cylinder	ml
50 ml graduated cylinder	ml
15 cm ruler (grad. in mm)	cm

QUESTIONS: *Answer in complete sentences.*

1. What may cause the laboratory burner to strike back?
2. State two reasons why the luminous flame is less desirable than the nonluminous flame as a source of heat in the laboratory.
3. How is a piece of glass tubing cut into two pieces?
4. How is a glass bend fire polished?
5. When using a platform balance of the type shown in Fig. 1-3, what determines the proper platform to be used to support the material the mass of which is to be measured?
6. List three instruments used in the laboratory for measuring small quantities of liquids.
7. What is the rule about size of filter paper for use with a given funnel?
8. How can a liquid be transferred from a beaker to a funnel without spattering, and without running down the outside wall of the beaker.
9. Why must the end of the funnel tube dip down into the liquid boiling in a flask?
10. What is the advantage of determining the *rest point* of a sensitive balance and using it in carrying out a precise weighing procedure?
11. Compare the quantities of heat loss and heat gained? Is one greater? If so, why?

Experiment 2 Measurements and Accuracy

PURPOSE: To measure various physical properties of matter and to determine the accuracy of such measurements.

APPARATUS: Balance, platform; beaker, 100 ml; graduated cylinder, 50 ml; ruler, 15 cm, plastic; thermometer.

MATERIAL: Metal shot, aluminum, copper, lead.

INTRODUCTION: In this experiment the volume of the graduated cylinder to the 50-ml graduation will be calculated from measurements of its internal diameter and height to the graduation. The mass of a measured volume of water will be calculated from its density ($m = V \times D$) and then determined by weighing. The density of a metal will then be calculated from measurements of its mass and volume ($D = m/V$). You will calculate the error and percentage error in each part of the experiment on the basis of accepted values.

PROCEDURE: 1. Examine the centimeter scale of the plastic ruler. What are the smallest divisions? To what fraction of a centimeter are you expected to be able to make a measurement with such a ruler?

Measure the inside diameter of the graduated cylinder using the ruler. Similarly measure the inside height of the cylinder to the 50-ml graduation. Record these observations in a Data Table like the one below. Calculate the volume of the cylinder to the 50-ml graduation ($V = 3.14\ r^2 \times h$). Assume the capacity in ml of the cylinder (to the top graduation) to be equal to that numerical value in cm^3. Using this value in cm^3 as the *accepted value*, calculate the error and percentage error.

DATA TABLE

Inside diameter of cylinder	cm
Inside height of cylinder	cm
Volume of cylinder (computed)	cm^3
Volume of cylinder (accepted)	cm^3
Error	cm^3
Percentage error	% %

2. Examine the 0-10 gram scale of the platform balance. What are the smallest divisions? To what fraction of a gram may you make measurements with a platform balance? Is this compatible with its uncertainty?

Similarly examine the graduation on the graduated cylinder and determine the smallest fraction of a millimeter to which you could make a measurement? Is this compatible with the uncertainty of a 50-ml graduated cylinder?

Using the platform balance, determine the mass of the dry cylinder. Record the mass in a Data Table like the one below. Half fill the beaker with water and determine its temperature to the nearest degree. Look up the density of water for this temperature and record both the temperature and water density. Fill your graduated cylinder to some value between 40 and 50 ml, accurately read and record the volume. Determine the mass of this volume of water plus that of the cylinder by weighing. Then record. Calculate the mass of the water as determined by use of the balance. Calculate the mass of the water from its measured volume and its density ($m = D \times V$). Record these values in the Data Table. Using the mass determined by the use of the balance as the *accepted value*, calculate the error and percentage error.

DATA TABLE

Mass of cylinder and water	g
Mass of empty cylinder	g
Mass of water	g
Measured volume of water	ml(cm^3)
Temperature of water	°C
Density of water	g/cm^3
Mass of water ($m = D \times V$)	g
Error	g
Percentage error	%

3. Pour out some of the water in the cylinder until it contains between 25 and 30 ml. Measure and record this volume in a Data Table like the following. Determine the mass of the cylinder and the water and record. Add a sufficient quantity of the assigned metal shot (aluminum, copper, or lead) to the cylinder containing the water to increase the volume by at least 10 ml. Determine the volume and then the mass of the shot, water, and cylinder and record your measurements. Calculate the volume of the metal shot, its mass, and its density. Record the results of these calculations. Look up the specific

DATA TABLE

Volume of metal shot and water	ml
Volume of water	ml
Volume of metal shot (computed)	ml
Mass of metal shot + water + cylinder	g
Mass of water + cylinder	g
Mass of metal shot	g
Density of metal (computed: 1 ml = 1 cm^3)	g/cm^3
Density of metal (accepted)	g/cm^3
Error	g/cm^3
Percentage error	%

gravity of the metal in a Handbook or your textbook Appendix. The density of liquids and solids in the metric system is numerically equal to the specific gravity. Record this *accepted value*. Calculate the error and percentage error.

4. Precision is the agreement between the numerical values of two or more *measurements* that have been made in the same way. It is expressed in terms of *deviation*. An *absolute deviation* D_a is the difference between an observed value O and the arithmetic mean (average) M for set of identical measurements.

$$D_a = O - M$$

In a Data Table like the following record at least five results compiled by you and your classmates for the density of the same metal. Calculate the average for these results, and enter it in the Data Table. Compute the absolute deviation D_a for each measurement and enter these quantities in the Data Table. Do not enter the sign of the deviation. Calculate the average value of the deviations and enter this quantity at the bottom of the Deviation column in the Data Table. This quantity with a ± sign before it is the *uncertainty* in the measurements data. Now in the appropriate place in the Data Table express the result of this set of measurements as M ± average deviation.

DATA TABLE

Experiment	Measurement (Density: g/cm^3)	Deviation (D_a)
1		
2		
3		
4		
5		

Average: M =

Uncertainty = ± g/cm^3

Expression for set of experimental results = M ± uncertainty = ± g/cm^3

QUESTIONS: *Answer in complete sentences.*

1. What value of a measurement must be available if the accuracy of a measurement is to be determined?
2. What type of error must be calculated before the percentage error may be determined?
3. What are the possible sources of experimental errors in this experiment?
4. Why is it impossible to determine uncertainties in terms of precision in this experiment as it was performed?

Experiment 3 General Classes of Matter

PURPOSE: To recognize some differences in properties of two elements and between their mixture and a compound formed from these elements.

APPARATUS: Balance, platform; bar magnet; beaker, 250 ml; burner and tubing; clamp, test tube; funnel; graduated cylinder; magnifying lens; ring, iron; ring stand; stoppers, cork, to fit test tubes; test tubes; test tube, Pyrex; watch glass.

MATERIAL: Iron metal filings, 60–80 mesh; sulfur, powdered; filter paper; hydrochloric acid, dilute (1:4); carbon disulfide.

INTRODUCTION: In this experiment we shall use two common elements, iron and sulfur. We shall form a mixture of these elements and compare its properties with those of the elements themselves. Then we shall cause the elements to react to form a compound, and again compare the properties with those of the constituent elements.

PROCEDURE: 1. Spread approximately 5 g of iron filings on a small square of glazed paper. Try the effect of a magnet by passing the magnet back and forth under the paper. Result? Repeat this operation, using approximately 3 g of powdered sulfur. Result? Save these two quantities for use in Part 4.

2. Measure out 10 ml of carbon disulfide and idvide it equally into two test tubes. To one test tube, add 0.5 g of powdered sulfur; and to the other, add 0.5 g of iron filings. Stopper both test tubes and shake them gently to see if carbon disulfide will dissolve either of these substances. Results? CAUTION: *Keep carbon disulfide away from open flames as it is combustible! Avoid inhaling its vapors.*

3. Add 5 ml of dilute hydrochloric acid to each of two test tubes. To one, add 0.5 g of powdered sulfur; to the other 0.5 g of iron filings. In which tube(s) do you observe evidence of a chemical reaction? Describe. Test for odor of any gaseous product. CAUTION: *See Fig. F-5 for the proper technique of investigating odors.*

4. Mix thoroughly on a square of glazed paper the sulfur and iron filings of Part 1, using a spatula or stirring rod. Try the effect of a magnet on the mixture, again moving the magnet back and forth under the paper. Result? Inspect the mixture, using a magnifying lens. Describe. Remix and transfer half of the mixture to a test tube. Add 10 ml of carbon disulfide; stopper and shake vigorously. Filter the contents (dry filter paper), catching some of the filtrate on a watch glass. Recall the solubility test made in Part 2. What would you expect the filtrate to contain? Place the watch glass in the hood or on the ledge of an open window and allow the liquid to evaporate. Examine the residue with the magnifying lens. Were your expectations confirmed? Describe the residue. What does the residue remaining on the filter paper appear to be? How could you confirm this based on the characteristics of the elements you have observed?

5. To the other half of the mixture, Procedure 4, add 5 ml of hydrochloric acid in a test tube. Result? What do the results of Procedures 3 and 4 indicate about the effect of mixing on the properties of the elements involved?

6. Mix 7 g of iron filings and 4 g of powdered sulfur as before, transfer to a dry Pyrex test tube, and heat strongly until a definite red glow is observed within the contents of the tube. Remove the tube from the flame. Does the reaction stop? When all evidence of a reaction ceases, break the test tube by plunging the hot end into a beaker of cold water. Recover the solid product and examine it. Try the effect of a magnet. Result? Examine it closely with the magnifying lens. Result? Try the effect of 3 ml of carbon disulfide on it. Result?

7. To 5 ml of hydrochloric acid in a test tube add a small piece of the product obtained in Part 6. Describe any evidence of chemical reaction. Note any difference in odor of an observed gaseous product and compare with the results of the odor test in Part 3.

QUESTIONS: *Answer in complete sentences.*

1. What are three ways of distinguishing between iron and sulfur?
2. How do you know that the iron has not united with the sulfur when these two elements are merely mixed together?
3. In what proportions can a mixture of these two elements be made?
4. What evidence did you observe that the iron and sulfur reacted when the mixture was heated?
5. What is necessary to cause the iron and sulfur to react?
6. Why were you directed to use definite quantities of iron and sulfur for preparing

the compound of these two elements?

7. How did the hydrochloric acid test show that you had produced a compound with different properties from thsoe of either iron or sulfur?

Experiment 4 Physical and Chemical Changes

PURPOSE: To study the differences between physical and chemical changes in matter.

APPARATUS: Asbestos square; beakers, 100 ml, 150 ml; burner and tubing; forceps; funnel; ring, iron; ring stand; test tubes; thermometer; wash bottle; watch glass; wire gauze.

MATERIAL: Alka-seltzer tablets; baking powder; copper foil; magnesium ribbon; platinum wire test rod; sandpaper, fine grit; zinc, mossy; filter paper; hydrochloric acid, dilute (1:4); sulfuric acid, dilute (1:6); solution of silver nitrate (0.2 *M*); wooden splints.

SUGGESTION: Since fresh mossy zinc may react very slowly, pieces previously used and collected may be used. Provide receptacle(s) for any residual zinc pieces.

INTRODUCTION: Matter undergoes many changes. In some cases only the temperature, physical state, size of particle, or color is changed. Ice melts and water evaporates. *Such changes are physical.*

In other cases different substances with new characteristic properties are formed. Wood burns and metals tarnish. *Such changes are chemical.* Heat, light, electricity, and solution are often instrumental in *starting* chemical changes. In many cases, too, they are produced as the immediate result of such changes.

PROCEDURE: 1. Examine the platinum wire test rod. Observe the color and luster of the metal. Hold the wire in the flame of your burner for about two minutes. Recall Part 1 of Experiment 1 in which you determined the hottest part of the flame. Does the appearance of the platinum wire support your previous conslusion? Describe the appearance of the wire while held in the hottest part of the flame. Allow the wire to cool and re-examine it. Conclusion?

2. Sandpaper a piece of magnesium ribbon about 3 cm in length to remove the tarnish. Note the color, luster, and flexibility of the metal. Perform the next operation over the asbestos square. Holding one end with the forceps, ignite the other end in the burner flame. CAUTION: *Do not look directly at the magnesium while it is burning.* Compare the ash, which may be collected on the asbestos square, with the original metal.

3. Similarly clean a piece of copper foil and heat it in the outer cone of the burner flame for 1–2 minutes. Avoid melting. Let it cool and re-examine it. See if you can scrape off some of the black scale from the surface of the copper. Compare the properties of this scale with those of metallic copper. Heat the foil a second time. Result? Explain.

4. Place a thermometer into the liquid in a test tube containing 4 or 5 ml of dilute sulfuric acid. Observe carefully for any signs of chemical action. Result? Remove the platinum wire, flushing it with water before laying aside. Add a small piece of zinc to

the acid. Observe carefully for any signs of chemical action. Result? Let the action continue for about 5 minutes. Remove the thermometer and warm the tube gently, **CAUTION.**

When the reaction is proceeding vigorously, bring the flame of a burning splint to the mouth of the test tube. Result? The dilute sulfuric acid is a water solution of hydrogen sulfate. What gas do you think is being evolved during the reaction? Account for the appearance of a black suspension in the liquid. Filter to remove suspended matter, if present. Do you believe a second product of the reaction to be in solution in the filtrate? Using an appropriate technique, recover this product from a portion of the filtrate. Compare the product with the original acid and with the zinc. Suggest the probable name of the crystalline substance. Try writing a word equation to express your idea of the chemical reaction that has taken place.

5. To 3 or 4 ml of silver nitrate solution, add several drops of dilute hydrochloric acid. Result? Can you recognize a *precipitate*? Describe it. Hydrochloric acid is a water solution of hydrogen chloride. Consult the solubility table in your textbook and suggest the probable name of the insoluble product (the precipitate). Try writing a word equation to express your idea of the chemical reaction that has taken place. Was there any evidence of a gaseous product of this reaction? Transfer the entire contents of the test tube to a filter setup, flushing with small additions of water from the wash bottle, if necessary, to remove all of the precipitate. Discard the filtrate, unfold the filter paper and expose the precipitate to direct sunlight for several minutes. Result? Do you think this change is physical or chemical? Did you observe any evidence of an appreciable energy change during the reaction?

6. To one-half an Alka-seltzer tablet or to 2 grams of baking powder in a 100 ml beaker add 5 ml of water. Result? After the reaction proceeds for 15 seconds, thrust a burning splint into the upper portion of the beaker. Result? Both Alka-seltzer and baking powder contain a solid substance, which acts as an acid, and sodium hydrogen carbonate. What gas do you think is being evolved during the reaction? Why did the chemicals which did not react in the dry state begin to react?

QUESTIONS: *Answer in complete sentences.*

1. What kind of change occurs when platinum is heated?
2. Is a new substance formed as magnesium burns? Justify your answer.
3. How does the scale which forms when copper is heated differ from the copper?
4. What do you think would be the ultimate result of successive heatings and scrapings of the copper?
5. Does platinum interact with sulfuric acid?
Does zinc interact with sulfuric acid?
Do the crystals formed in Part 4 resemble either zinc or sulfuric acid?
6. Does the precipitate in Part 5 seem to be a new substance? Is this a chemical or physical change?
7. The precipitate in Part 5 is silver chloride. What effect does sunlight have on the precipitate? Do you think such a change may have some relation to photography?
8. Summarize the results of this experiment in a definite, concise conclusion.

Experiment 5 Oxygen: Catalysis

PURPOSE: To show that oxygen may be prepared from a number of chemical compounds and to show how catalysts play a part in chemical reactions.

APPARATUS: Balance, platform; clamp, buret; clamp, test tube; funnel tube; glass bend; 2 glass plates; graduated cylinder; ring stand; rubber stoppers, solid No. 3, 2-hole No. 4; test tubes, Pyrex (6), 200 mm, Pyrex (1); trough; tubing, delivery.

MATERIAL: Barium peroxide; calcium carbonate, powdered; charcoal, activated, pellets; lead(II)(IV) oxide; lead(IV) oxide; manganese dioxide C.P.; mercury(II) oxide; potassium permanganate; sodium peroxide; litmus papers, red and blue; wooden splints; yeast, dried; solution of hydrogen peroxide (6%). Optional: copper(II) oxide, powdered; iron(III) oxide; potassium chlorate, C.P., potassium dichromate.

INTRODUCTION: Oxygen may be prepared conveniently from other substances beside potassium chlorate without heating. These include sodium peroxide and hydrogen peroxide. A variety of substances will be added to hydrogen peroxide to determine their possible use as catalysts in bringing about its decomposition.

SUGGESTIONS: The instructor may wish to demonstrate the role of a catalyst in the decomposition of potassium chlorate. A 3–5 gram sample of potassium chlorate is heated until decomposition starts and the presence of oxygen is demonstrated with a glowing splint. The sample is permitted to cool until the evolution of oxygen apparently stops. The addition of 0.5 g of powdered manganese dioxide causes the reaction to occur at this lower temperature and the glowing splint test should be used again. The same procedure may be used to demonstrate the possible use of other catalysts: copper (II) oxide; iron(III) oxide; and potassium dichromate.

PROCEDURE: 1. Place 3 g of manganese dioxide in the large test tube using the technique of Experiment 1, Part 4. Clamp the test tube to the ring stand. Attach the rubber delivery tube to the two-hole stopper, funnel tube, glass bend assembly, and insert this assembly into the test tube, Fig. 5-1. Fill a test tube with water, cover the end with a glass plate, and place it mouth downward in the trough. Add 5 ml of hydrogen peroxide solution through the funnel tube. Permite the reaction to proceed for half a minute. Then collect a test tube of oxygen. Stopper the test tube while its mouth is still under water. Place the stoppered test tube in the test tube rack. Why was the collection of oxygen not started immediately upon the addition of hydrogen peroxide? Light a splint, blow out the flame, and insert the glowing splint in the oxygen. What result do you observe?

2. Into each of five test tubes in the test tube rack pour 3 ml of the hydrogen peroxide solution. To the first test tube add 4 pellets of activated charcoal. Report any evidence of gas evolution. If a gas is produced, test for oxygen by inserting a glowing splint into the space above the hydrogen peroxide. Repeat the above procedure using, in successive test tubes, 3 small crystals of potassium permanganate, 0.5 g of dried yeast, 0.5 g of powdered calcium carbonate, and 0.5 g of lead(II)(IV) oxide. Record your observations in a Data Table like the one on page 17.

Decant the hydrogen peroxide solution from the test tube containing the activated

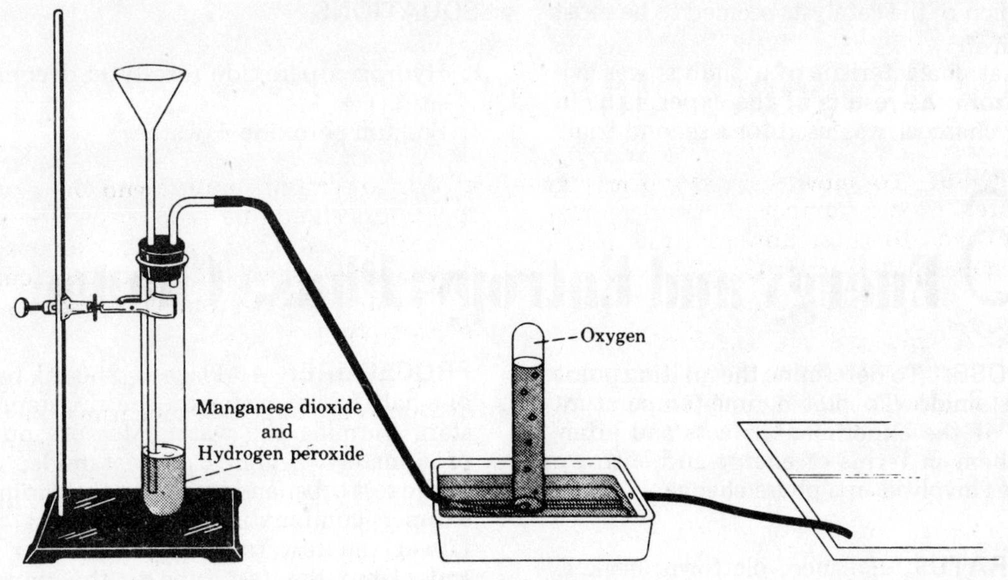

Fig. 5-1

charcoal pellets. Add another 3 ml of hydrogen peroxide solution. Result?

3. Place 1 g of sodium peroxide in a test tube. Add 5 ml of water. Result? Insert a glowing splint into the upper part of the test tube. Result? Dip a stirring rod into the test tube contents and touch the moistened end of the rod to a piece of blue litmus paper on a clean glass plate. Result? Repeat the procedure using a piece of red litmus paper. Result? (Basic solutions of metallic hydroxides turn red litmus to blue, while acidic solutions turn blue litmus red.)

Repeat the above procedure using, in successive test tubes, 1 g each of mercury(II) oxide, lead(IV) oxide, and barium peroxide. Results?

QUESTIONS: *Answer in complete sentences.*

1. Which of the solid substances added to hydrogen peroxide caused oxygen to be produced?
2. In which case or cases, if any, are you reasonably sure that the oxygen came from the hydrogen peroxide only?

DATA TABLE

Substance added	Evidence of evolution	Result of glowing splint test
Activated charcoal (C)		
Potassium permanganate ($KMnO_4$)		
Yeast		
Calcium carbonate ($CaCO_3$)		
Lead(II)(IV) oxide (Pb_3O_4)		

3. Which of the catalysts seemed to be most effective?
4. What characteristic of a catalyst was evident from the results of the experiment in which charcoal was used for a second trial?

EQUATIONS

1. Hydrogen peroxide (catalytic decomposition) →
2. Sodium peroxide + water →

Experiment 6 Energy and Entropy: Phase Change

PURPOSE: To determine the melting point of acetamide. To plot a time-temperature graph of the experimental facts and interpret them in terms of energy and entropy changes involved in a phase change.

APPARATUS: Balance, platform; beaker, 250 ml; burner and tubing; clamp, buret; clock; ring, iron; ringstand; rubber stopper, 1-hole No. 2; test tube; thermometer; wire gauze.

MATERIAL: Acetamide (practical grade).

SUGGESTION: You may wish to have half the class use another solid such as paradichlorobenzene.

INTRODUCTION: As a solid is heated its temperature rises. The continuous addition of energy finally results in a phase change, the solid melts at its melting point. Further addition of energy causes the temperature of the liquid to increase. Acetamide is a solid at room temperature. Its melting point is well below 100° C. In this experiment you will melt a sample of acetamide and record the temperature at stated time intervals as the liquid cools, solidification (crystallization) occurs, and the resultant solid undergoes subsequent cooling. The results of the experiment permit you to determine the melting point (actually the freezing point) of the substance and to interpret the changes in energy and entropy which have taken place.

PROCEDURE: 1. Place a 250-ml beaker one-half full of water on the ringstand and start warming the water. Measure out approximately 7 grams of acetamide, place in the test tube, and insert the thermometer-stopper combination into the test tube. Lower the test tube into the water bath and clamp the test tube to the ringstand (see Fig. 6-1). Heat the water until the contents of the test tube melt. To melt the acetamide, the water usually must be boiling. Remove the test tube from the heated water leaving it clamped to the ringstand, Fig. 6-2.

2. When the temperature indicated by the thermometer is approximately 100° C, read the temperature every minute and record the readings in a Data Table like the one on page 19. At the same time record when crystallization (freezing) starts, the places in which crystallization is taking place, and the extent of crystallization. Place these observations in the Data Table next to the appropriate times.

3. On a separate sheet of graph paper plot a graph of temperature versus time. Make time intervals the horizontal axis. Select and label the distinct portion of the graph during which crystallization (freezing) occurs.

4. If there is sufficient time, repeat the experiment using 30 second intervals.

5. Another interesting variation is to melt the acetamide, remove the thermometer, and when according to your initial data, crystallization should begin, drop several small seed crystals of acetamide into the liquid.

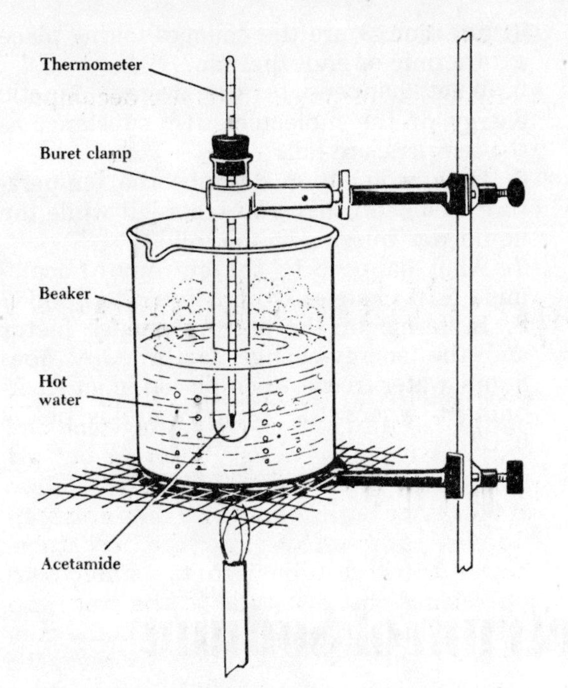

Fig. 6-1

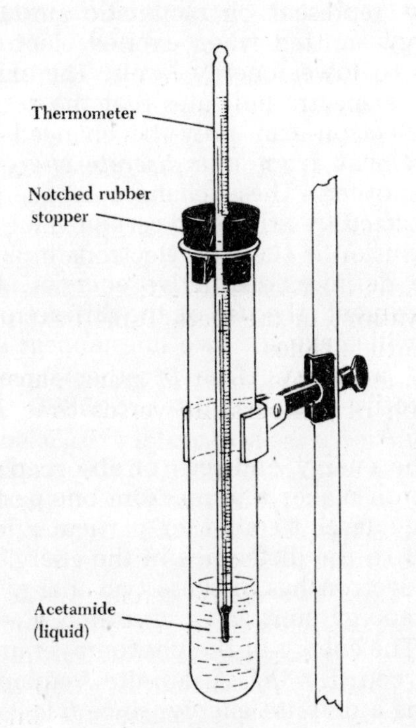

Fig. 6-2

DATA TABLE

Time (Minutes)	Temperature (°C)	Observations
0		Student answers.
1		
2		
3		
4		
5		
6		
7		
8		
9		
10		
11		
12		
13		
14		
15		
16		
17		
18		
19		
20		
21		
22		
23		
24		
25		

QUESTIONS: *Answer in complete sentences.*

1. What is the shape of the part of the graph which represents the cooling of the liquid?
2. What is happening to the kinetic energy of the acetamide molecules as the liquid cools?
3. How does the temperature of the acetamide sample compare with the temperature of the room (its external environment) while (a) the liquid is cooling, (b) very little, if any change in temperature occurs, (c) the solid is cooling?
4. In terms of the temperature differentials in question 3 are the changes taking place exothermic or endothermic?
5. What happens to the average kinetic energy of the molecules of a substance as the temperature fails?
6. How would you describe the temperature change(s) that you recorded while the liquid was freezing to the solid?
7. What happens to the entropy of acetamide as it changes from a liquid to a solid?
8. In terms of the entropy-change factor and the energy-change factor, why does liquid water freeze when placed in an environment where the temperature is below 0° C?

Experiment 7 Bright-Line Spectrum of Sodium

PURPOSE: To measure the wavelength of the bright-line spectrum of sodium.

APPARATUS: Bunsen burner and tubing (asbestos collar); cardboard screen with vertical slit; card-mounted diffraction grating, 1 lens support (Welch 3604 or 3606); meter stick and half-meter stick; 4 meter stick supports (Welch 3602); 2-screen supports (Welch 3610); Optional: sodium-arc light source with mount and transformer (Welch 3720 B).

MATERIAL: Sodium chloride.

Note: The asbestos collar is made from an asbestos sheet which is saturated with sodium chloride solution, dried, and then fastened around the top of the burner with thread or fine wire.

INTRODUCTION: Examination of the bright yellow flame, characteristic of a vaporized sodium compound, through a spectroscope reveals two closely spaced yellow lines. These lines constitute the bright-line emission spectrum of sodium. They represent characteristic amounts of energy emitted when excited electrons return to lower energy levels. The existence of line spectra indicates that the energy of an electron can only be changed by its movement from one *discrete energy level* to another. These changes in energy are *quantized* (restricted to certain values). The conclusion is that the electrons in an atom have definite, distinctive energies. In this experiment, the use of the diffraction grating will make the two lines appear as one. They are very close together since their respective wavelengths are 5890 Å and 5896 Å.

The energy emitted (or absorbed) as an electron makes a jump from one particular energy level to another particular level is equal to the difference in the energies that the electron has in these two energy levels. The energy emitted or absorbed, $E = E_2 - E_1$. The energy of the photon(s) emitted or absorbed, $E = hf$. A definite frequency (f) means a definite energy, since h is Planck's constant which is identical for all types of

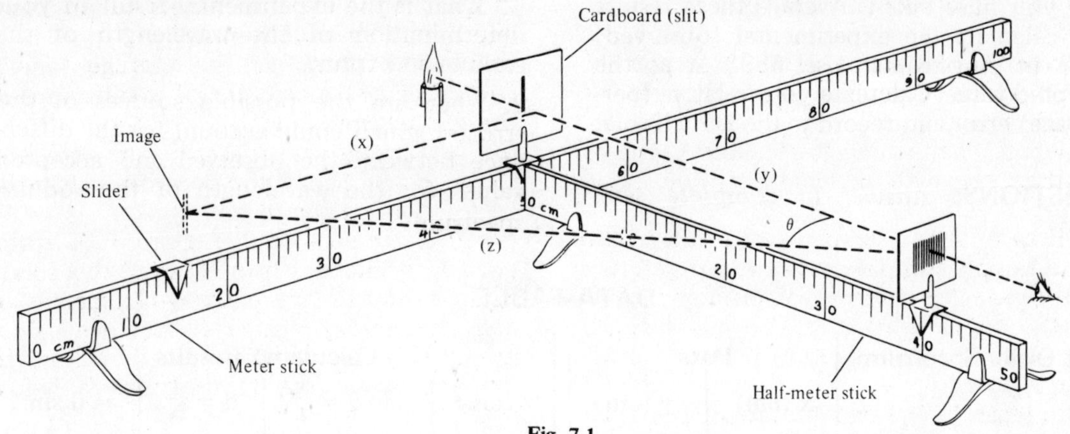

Fig. 7-1

electromagnetic radiation. The ferquency and then the energy can be calculated if the wavelength of the light is measured. The relationship which is used is c (speed of light) = f (frequency) × λ (wavelength).

PROCEDURE: 1. Arrange the apparatus as shown in Fig. 7-1. The screen support with the diffraction grating is placed on the half-meter stick at a distance of approximately 40 cm. The cardboard slit assembly is placed on the 50 cm mark of the meter stick. The meter and half-meter sticks are placed in the meter stick supports. The half-meter stick is placed perpendicular to the meter stick at the 50 cm mark.

2. Light the burner so that a continuous yellow flame is emitted by the asbestos salt-saturated collar. The burner is placed in back of the slit so that the yellow flame is clearly visible through the slit. Look through the center of the diffraction grating along the half-meter stick to locate the yellow line visible through the slit. With the eye close to the grating look to the left of the yellow line to locate first order sodium spectrum (the two merged sodium spectral lines). A second student moves the slider (screen support) along the meter stick until the student looking at the spectrum indicates that the vertical line through the point of the slider coincides with the location of the spectrum.

3. The distances x and y (Fig. 7-1) are measured to the nearest millimeter and recorded in a Data Table like the one on page 22.

4. The procedure is repeated for locating the spectrum to the right of the 50 cm mark on the meter stick. The distances x and y are measured and recorded. Time permitting, the grating distance y is changed and two more readings (left and right spectrum) are made and recorded.

CALCULATIONS: 1. The value of z is computed to the correct number of significant figures by using the Pythagorean formula: $z = \sqrt{x^2 + y^2}$. Record the values for z in the Data Table.

2. The formula to be used in calculating the wave length is $\lambda = d \sin \theta$. The value of sin θ is calculated ($\sin \theta = \frac{x}{y}$) and recorded in the Data Table.

3. The distance between two grooves of the diffraction grating (d) is calculated using the relationship, $d = \frac{2154 \text{ cm}}{13{,}400}$ since the number of grooves per inch for your grating is 13,400. Record the result in the Data Table.

4. Calculate and record the wavelength in Angstroms using the formula $\lambda = d \sin \theta$.

5. Repeat the calculations for other data

that you have taken. Average these results and calculate the experimental (observed) error in Angstroms. Use 5893 Å as the accepted value. Calculate your relative (percentage) error and record in the Data Table.

QUESTIONS: *Answer in complete sentences.*

1. What is the experimental result of your determination of the wavelength of the sodium spectrum?

2. What are the possible sources of the error(s) which could account for the difference between the observed and accepted values for the wavelength of the sodium spectrum?

DATA TABLE

First Order Spectrum	Data		Calculated Results			
	x (cm)	y (cm)	z (cm)	$\sin\theta = \frac{x}{z}$	$d = \frac{1}{N}$	$= d \sin\theta$ (Å)
1. (a) left image						
(b) right image						
2. (a) left image						
(b) right image						

Average value of λ .... Å

Experimental (observed) error .... Å

Percentage (relative) error .... %

Experiment 8 Covalent Molecules

PURPOSE: To construct models of molecules of covalent substances in order to show how their shapes and structure are related to their polarity.

MATERIALS: Sargent Molecular Model Set or Johnglass Student Molecular Models kit.

INTRODUCTION: A covalent bond consists of a pair of shared electrons. Such a pair of electrons is shared equally between identical atoms producing a bond which is pure (non-polar) covalent. The unequal sharing of the electron pair between two different atoms produces a bond which is more or less polar. The polarity of the bond may be described in terms of its percentage of ionic character. This depends on the electronegativity difference between the two bonded atoms. The electronegativity of an atom (element) is a measure of its tendency to attract the electrons forming a bond between it and another atom.

Molecules of covalent substances may be nonpolar or polar. A diatomic molecule of an elementary gas is nonpolar. A diatomic molecule of a compound is linear (straight line) and may be polar. More complex compounds have molecules which may be polar or non-polar depending on the symmetry of the bonds to the central atom and consequently on the symmetry of the molecular structure. A molecular structure, even though its bonds are polar bonds, will be nonpolar if the bonds are arranged evenly about the central atom. When the arrangement of the polar bonds is unsymmetrical, the resultant molecule is polar and is called a dipole. Representative molecules may be bent (nonlinear) or trigonal pyramids. A dipole acts as if it has a positively charged portion and a negatively charged portion equal in magnitude of charge(s) and separated by some distance.

SUGGESTION: Consult tables of (1) electronegativities and (2) electronegativity difference and percentage of ionic character as needed: See MODERN CHEMISTRY, 1974 edition. Check the Table of Contents of your model set (pasted on the inside of the box cover) with the actual contents. At the end of the experiment, reassemble the kit into the pattern shown on the box cover. Use the long(est) set of spring connectors for multiple bonds.

PROCEDURE: Assemble the first set of seven models and have them checked by the teacher. Fill in a Data Table like the following and at the top of the next page. Take these models apart and proceed similarly with the second set.

DATA TABLE

Formula	Electron-dot formula	Bond type (polar or nonpolar)	Shape of molecule (linear, bent, pyramidal, tetrahedral)	Kind of molecule (polar or nonpolar)
Set 1.				
a. H_2				
b. Cl_2				
c. O_2				
d. N_2				

Formula	Electron-dot formula	Bond type (polar or nonpolar)	Shape of molecule (linear, bent, pyramidal, tetrahedral)	Kind of molecule (polar or nonpolar)
e. HCl				
f. BrCl				
g. HBr				
Set 2.				
a. H_2O				
b. CO_2				
c. H_2S				
d. NH_3				
e. CH_4				
f. CCl_4				
g. CH_3Cl				

QUESTIONS

1. Calculate the electronegativity difference and percentage of ionic character for each of the following bonds:

	Electronegativity difference	Percentage of ionic character
a. H—O		
b. H—N		
c. H—Cl		
d. Br—Cl		
e. H—S		
f. H—S		
g. Cl—Cl		
h. C—O		
i. K—Br		
j. Na—O		

2. Classify each of the following as ionic crystal, polar covalent molecule, or nonpolar covalent molecule.

a. Br_2

b. $MgCl_2$

c. CCl_4

d. HI

e. CO_2

f. H_2O

g. N_2

h. $BaBr_2$

3. Both water and carbon dioxide are triatomic molecules. Explain why one of these is polar and the other is nonpolar.

Experiment 9 Determination of Oxygen in Potassium Chlorate

PURPOSE: To determine the mass of oxygen in a sample of potassium chlorate. To gain practice in precision work in the laboratory.

APPARATUS: Asbestos square; balance, platform; balance, sensitive to 0.01 g; beaker, 250 ml; burner and tubing; crucible and cover; forceps; ring, iron; ring stand; tongs; triangle, pipestem; wire gauze.

MATERIAL: Potassium chlorate, C.P.; potassium chloride, C.P.

INTRODUCTION: In this experiment, you will determine the mass of oxygen in potassium. By weighing the potassium chlorate first, then heating it to drive off the oxygen, and then weighing the residue (potassium chloride), you can measure the mass of the oxygen that was in your sample. *Potassium chlorate* melts at 368.4° C and decomposes at 400° C. *Potassium chloride*, the residue, has a melting point of 776° C and sublimes at 1500° C. The method of heating employed in this experiment is based on these properties of the two compounds.

SUGGESTION: Since potassium chlorate tends to adsorb some water vapor from the air, it is suggested that the instructor heat the potassium chlorate overnight in a drying oven at 105° C and cool it in a desiccator before the class assemblies.

By placing the hot crucible on a bright, clean wire gauze without an asbestos center, the time rqeuired for cooling is considerably reduced.

The results of this experiment may also be used to calculate the percentage of oxygen in potassium chlorate. An alternate experiment is Experiment 19(A) Percentage of Water in a Hydrate.

PROCEDURE: 1. Heat a clean, dry procelain crucible and cover on a pipestem triangle supported by a ring stand strongly for 2 minutes. See Fig. F-10. Using clean tongs, transfer the crucible to a clean bright wire gauze, to cool. When cool, weigh the crucible and cover to the nearest 0.01 g.

Record the mass in a Data Table like the one below. *Do not handle the crucible or cover at any time with the fingers.*

DATA TABLE

Mass of empty crucible and cover	g
Mass of crucible, contents, and cover before heating	g
Mass of potassium chlorate used	g
Mass of crucible, contents, and cover after heating to constant weight	g
Mass of potassium chloride produced	g
Mass of oxygen driven off	g
Theoretical mass of oxygen in $KClO_3$	g
Error	g
Percentage error	%

2. Transfer approximately 2 g of potassium chlorate, weighed out on a platform balance on a square of glazed paper, to the weighed crucible. Determine the mass of the crucible, contents, and cover to the nearest 0.01 g and record.

3. Place the crucible on the pipestem triangle, place the cover in position, and heat very *gently* for 2 minutes. Why? At 2-minute intervals gradually increase the temperature until the crucible is heated *strongly*. Keep the crucible covered until near the end of the heating. Reason? After 10 minutes, remove the burner, take off the crucible cover and place it on a clean asbestos square. What is the appearance of the residue? Heat the crucible strongly, without cover, for 2 or 3 minutes longer. Allow the crucible to cool, preferably on the clean wire gauze, and again determine the mass of the crucible, contents, and cover to the nearest 0.01 g.

4. To make sure that all of the oxygen has been removed from the potassium chlorate, the crucible and cover should be heated again for about 3 minutes, cooled, and reweighed. If this weighing agrees within 0.01 g of the previous one, you may assume that all of the oxygen had been driven off. Otherwise, a third heating is necessary. This is called *heating to constant weight*, and is done by chemists in all precise work.

5. After the crucible and cover are cool, place them in a beaker of cold water and apply heat to dissolve the residue remaining in the crucible. What is the name and composition of this residue? Rinse the crucible and cover, and wipe them dry. The solution in the beaker may be discarded.

CALCULATIONS: 1. Calculate the *theoretical* mass of oxygen in your sample of potassium chlorate, expressed to the proper number of significant figures. Show these and subsequent computations in smooth form on a separate paper.

2. Calculate your experimental error and indicate whether your result is low or high by using the correct sign.

3. Calculate your percentage error.

4. The experimental data may also be used to (a) calculate the percentage of oxygen in your sample of potassium chlorate, and (b) to calculate your error after first computing the *theoretical* percentage of oxygen in potassium chlorate.

FURTHER EXPERIMENTATION: Determine the percent of potassium chlorate in a sample of a mixture of potassium chlorate and potassium chloride issued to you by the instructor. Use approximately 2 g of this sample and repeat procedures 1–4. Determine the mass of oxygen driven off. Using the theoretical percentage of oxygen in $KClO_3$, calculate the mass of $KClO_3$ in the mixture. Then calculate the percent of $KClO_3$ in your sample. Report the result to your instructor. Calculate the percentage error based on the data furnished by your instructor.

1. Percentage of $KClO_3$ in sample

2. Percentage error.

QUESTIONS: *Answer in complete sentences.*

1. What is the experimental result of your determination of the mass of oxygen in the potassium chlorate?
2. What is the theoretical result of your computation of the mass of oxygen calculated from the formula?
3. What are the possible sources of error which could account for the difference between the experimental and theoretical calculations?

Experiment 10 Balancing Chemical Equations

PURPOSE: To show that certain chemical equations may be balanced by the construction and manipulation of molecular models of the reactants and products according to the law of conservation of atoms.

APPARATUS: Apparatus for the electrolysis of water with platinum electrodes (several types are available); beaker, 1000 ml; funnel; graduated cylinder; source of direct current, about 6 volts; test tubes.

MATERIAL: Ball-and-stick model kit (Sargent or Johnglass Molecular Model kit); wooden splints; sulfuric acid, concentrated.

INTRODUCTION: In writing formula equations, each formula must be correctly written. The equation must then be balanced according to the law of conservation of atoms. According to this law, the total number of atoms of each element represented in the reactant formulas must be equal to the total number of atoms of the same element represented in the product formulas. Such balancing is performed by using appropriate *coefficients* in front of each formula. A correctly balanced formula equation furnishes quantitative information about the relative proportions of reactants and products in terms of (a) moles; (b) formula weights; (c) any consistent mass units, such as grams; and (d) for gases only, volumes. The demonstration on the electrolysis of water will show observable experimental results which will be correlated with the use of molecular models in balancing the representative formula equation.

It is suggested that this demonstration be performed, with the aid of students, at the lecture table. The models of reactants and products are to be constructed and manipulated by student teams.

The decomposition of a substance by means of electric energy is called electrolysis. By passing a direct electric current through water, it can be decomposed into the two elementary gases, hydrogen and oxygen, which form this compound.

Pure water is a very poor conductor of electricity. In order to make the liquid a better conductor, a small quantity of sulfuric acid is added. We are interested in (a) the fact that water can be decomposed into oxygen and hydrogen, (b) the relative volumes of these gases which are evolved, and (c) the electrodes at which these gases are discharged.

PROCEDURE: 1. Set up an electrolysis apparatus as shown in Fig. 10-1. Connect the apparatus to one of the following sources of direct current: (a) four dry cells connected in series; (b) a lead storage battery of 6 volts, (c) a low voltage rectifier with 6–8 volt d-c terminals, or (d) a 110-volt d-c outlet with an electric lamp connected in series to regulate the current flowing through the electrolysis apparatus.

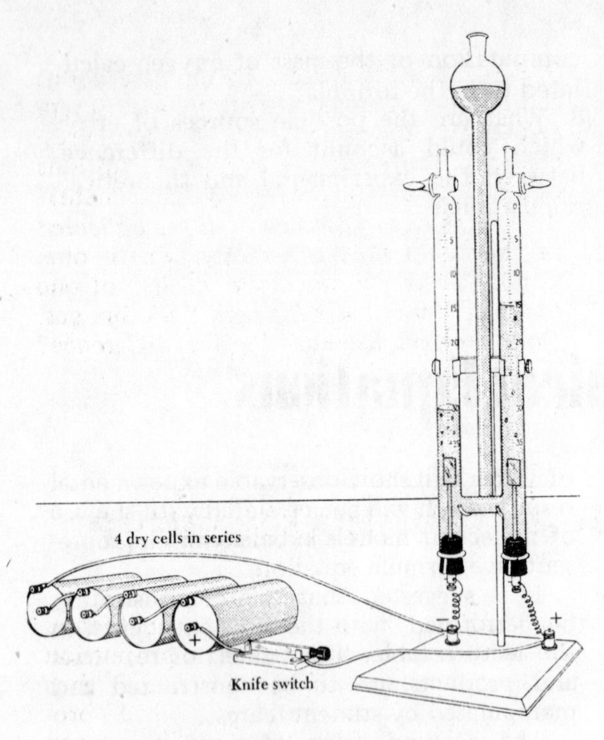

Fig. 10-1

2. Slowly, and with stirring, add 100 ml of concentrated sulfuric acid to 600 ml of water in a 1000-ml beaker. With a small funnel, carefully add the acid-water mixture to the apparatus until the tubes are full and a small excess collects in the reservoir. (Open the stopcocks of the tubes to let the air out as the tubes are filled.)

3. When all is ready, close the switch, and observe the activity at each electrode. After the reaction has been going on for a minute or two, open the switch and observe whether the electrolysis will proceed without an external source of energy. Close the switch again and allow the electrolysis to continue until one of the tubes is about two-thirds full of gas.

4. Collect a test tube full of gas from the tube that has the larger volume of gas in the following manner: (a) hold a test tube inverted above the stopcock, (b) open the stopcock, (c) close the stopcock as the tube again fills with liquid. Hold a *blazing* splint over the test tube of gas to identify it. In the same manner, collect a test tube full of gas from the other tube. Thrust a *glowing* splint into this test tube of gas to identify it.

5. Trace the electric connections to the apparatus to identify the positive and negative electrodes. Which gas collects at the positive electrode? At the negative electrode? Now reverse the electric connections to the apparatus, close the switch, and observe whether the gases collect in the same tubes as before. Result?

6. Write the word equation for the change which the water undergoes.

Using correct formulas for the reactant and the products, write the skeleton formula equation for the change which the water undergoes.

Construct the ball and stick models for the reactant and product molecules represented in the skeleton formula equation. (See directions in Experiment 8 if necessary.) Set the models in the same pattern as the formulas appear in the equation. Then construct as many additional models of reactant and products as are necessary to conform to the law of conservation of atoms. Write the complete balanced formula equation which represents the models arrangement. . . . . . .

7. For each of the skeleton formula equations below construct the necessary number of models of reactants and products and, in each case, in succession, construct enough models and arrange them so that the law of conservation of atoms is followed. Then write in the correct coefficients, corresponding to the number of models appearing in your arrangement, to balance the equation.

$C + O_2 \rightarrow CO_2$

$H_2 + Cl_2 \rightarrow HCl$

$NH_3 \rightarrow N_2 + H_2$

$CH_4 + O_2 \rightarrow CO_2 + H_2O$

$CH_4 + Cl_2 \rightarrow CH_3Cl + HCl$

QUESTIONS

1. Does the reaction, once started, continue after the source of electricity is disconnected? Is electrolysis an exothermic or an endothermic reaction?
2. What relationship do you find between the relative number of molecules represented by the balanced formula equation. (Procedure 6) and the experimentally measured volumes of the gases produced?.
3. What does this seem to indicate about the number of molecules of *any gas* (as represented by the two gaseous products) present in a unit volume at given conditions of temperature and pressure (approximate)?
4. The relative volumes of gases *collected in the tubes* are not exactly two to one, although exactly twice the volume of one gas is *set free* compared with the other gas. How do you account for the difference?

Experiment 11 Mass Relations in a Chemical Change

PURPOSE: To measure the yield of a chemical reaction. To compare the yield with that calculated from the chemical equation.

APPARATUS: Balance, sensitive to 0.01 g; burner and tubing; crucible and cover; ring, iron; ring stand; tongs; triangle, pipestem; bright wire gauze.

MATERIAL: Copper wire, 22-26 gauge; sulfur, powdered.

INTRODUCTION: A chemical equation expresses the relationship between the reactants and products of a chemical reaction in a quantitative sense. By means of a correctly written equation, we may determine, for a particular reaction, the yield that we may expect from a known quantity of reactant.

In this experiment, you will heat a weighed amount of copper with an excess of sulfur to produce a sulfide of copper. The synthesis is carried out in a covered crucible in order to prevent oxygen from combining with the copper. The excess sulfur escapes as a vapor during the heating process. As copper may have an oxidation number of +1 or +2 in combination with sulfur, you will utilize your experimental date to determine the combining proportion of the copper and sulfur atoms and thus the empirical formula of the sulfide produced. This information will enable you to write the chemical equation for the reaction. You may then calculate the theoretical yield of the sulfide from the equation and compare it with the experimental yield of the product.

SUGGESTION: If the laboratory is not equipped with an efficient fume exhaust system, this experiment should be used as a demonstration. The students record the data and make the calculations.

A hot crucible will cool rapidly if removed from the pipestem triangle immediately after removing the flame and placed on a bright, clean wire gauze.

PROCEDURE: 1. Preheat a clean crucible and cover. Recall the technique used in Experiment 9 in this connection. (*See the suggestion above.*) Handle the crucible with clean tongs. Why? When cool, determine the mass of the crucible and cover to the nearest 0.01 g. Record. Wind approximately 2 g of copper wire to form a small compact coil which will fit well down into the crucible (70 cm of 22 gauge wire or 190 cm of

26 gauge wire will do). Find the mass of the copper by the indirect method, that is, by determining the combined mass of the crucible, cover, and copper to the nearest 0.01 g. Record in a Data Table like the one below.

DATA TABLE

Mass of crucible and cover	g
Mass of crucible, cover, and copper	g
Mass of copper used	g
Mass of crucible, cover, and contents after first heating	g
Constant mass of crucible, cover, and contents	g
Mass of product formed (experimental)	g
Mass of combined sulfur	g
Empirical formula (computed)	
Mass of product computed from equation (theoretical)	g
Experimental error	g
Percentage error	%

2. Add just enough powdered sulfur to cover the copper wire and return the covered crucible to the pipestem triangle (tongs). The reactants should be heated under a hood, or the laboratory should be kept well ventilated if a hood is not available. Heat the covered crucible and contents for about 5 minutes. *Do not remove the crucible cover while the crucible is hot.* Reason? Do you observe any blue flames around the rim of the crucible? Explain. If, after 5 minutes of gentle heating, the blue flames persist, continue heating gently until the flame no longer appears. Now increase the heat intensity gradually until the bottom of the crucible is red hot. Play the flame over the sides and top of the crucible to evaporate the last traces of the excess sulfur. Finally heat strongly for 5 minutes. Allow to cool. (Recall the cooling suggestion.)

3. When cool, remove the cover and see if any sulfur remains on the inside surface of the crucible or cover. If all traces of sulfur are gone, determine the mass of the crucible, cover, and contents to the nearest 0.01 g. Record. Replace the crucible on the pipestem trkangle, add about 1 g of powdered sulfur, replace the cover, and apply heat as before. Allow to cool, inspect for traces of sulfur, and reweigh. If it is within 0.01 g of the last weighing, you may assume a constant mass has been attained. If not, add sulfur, heat, cool, and weigh again. By this method, heat to constant mass. Record this final mass. (Do not discard the product until all computations have been made.) Why? Explain the reason for the second addition of sulfur and reheating.

CALCULATIONS: (on separate paper)

1. Determine the empirical formula of the copper sulfide product. The calculations should indicate either a 1:1 or 2:1 atom ratio.
2. Write the equation for the reaction which yields this product. Find the mass of product as indicated by the amount of copper used and the balanced equation. Show the equation, problem setup, and smooth computation on a separate paper. Enter the result in the Data Table.
3. Determine the experimental error and compute the percentage error. Show the smooth computations and enter the results in the Data Table.

QUESTION: *Answer in complete sentences.*

1. How can you account for your experimental error in this experiment?

Experiment 12 Types of Chemical Reactions

PURPOSE: To show that chemical reactions fall into a rather limited variety of types or categories, as preparation for developing skill in equation writing.

APPARATUS: Asbestos square; beaker (100 ml); burner and tubing; clamp, buret; clamp, test tube; dish, evaporating; forceps; funnel; glass plate; graduated cylinder; medicine dropper; ring, iron; ring stand; stirring rod; test tubes; test tube, Pyrex; wire gauze.

MATERIAL: Filter paper; litmus papers; red and blue; sandpaper, fine grit; calcium, turnings; copper foil; copper(II) sulfate pentahydrate, medium crystals; mercury(II) oxide; sodium hydrogen carbonate; sulfur, powd.; zinc strip, 1 cm × 5 cm; ammonia-water solution, dil. (1:4); hydrochloric acid (3.0 *M*); hydrochloric acid (0.1 *M*); sodium hydroxide (0.1 *M*); aluminum chloride (1.0 *M*); chlorine water; copper(II) sulfate (1.0 *M*); lead nitrate (1.0 *M*); sodium bromide (1.0 *M*); soxium chloride (0.5 *M*); sodium iodide (1.0 *M*); sodium sulfite (1.0 *M*); silver nitrate (0.2 *M*).

ADDITIONAL MATERIAL FOR INSTRUCTOR'S EXPERIMENT: Calcium oxide (lump); zinc, powder.

INTRODUCTION: Three factors must be satisfied in writing formula equations: (a) the equation must represent the facts; (b) the equation must include the symbols and formulas of all elements and compounds used as reactants and formed as products; and (c) the law of conservation of atoms must always be satisfied.

It is advantageous to learn to recognize that reactions fall into the main categories: (1) *composition* reactions, (2) *decomposition* reactions, (3) *replacement* reactions, and (4) *ionic* reactions. In *composition* reactions, two or more substances combine to form a more complex substance. They have the general form A + X → AX. In *decomposition* reactions, the reverse of the first type, a complex substance breaks down to form two or more simpler substances. They have the general form AX → A + X. In *replacement* reactions, one substance is displaced from its compound by another substance. They have the general form A + BX → AX + B or Y + BX → BY + X. In *ionic* reactions of the ion-exchange type, ions in solution combine to form a product that leaves the reaction environment. They may have the general form Al (aq) + Y; (aq) → AY. A sample formula equation for this type has the general form AX + BY → AY + BX. In order for this type of reaction to occur, a product must be formed that separates ions from the reaction environment (the solution) as a solid precipitate or an insoluble or slightly soluble gas, or as a new molecular species (generally water).

SUGGESTIONS: Where the length of the laboratory period prevents each student from doing all parts of this experiment, individual students may be assigned to different sets of procedures. Toward the end of the period they may present their findings to the entire class.

Students are to write the equations for the Instructor's Experiments. They are to use a sample of the experimental product of the reaction between calcium oxide and water in Procedure 1.*c*.

PROCEDURE: 1. *a.* Sandpaper a piece of copper foil (1 cm × 5 cm). Holding one end with forceps, hold it in the outer cone of the Bunsen flame for 1-2 minutes. Let it cool and re-examine it. Name the product, describe it briefly, and complete the representative equation a table similar to Data Table 1.

b. Similarly clean a longer piece of copper foil (1 cm × 25 cm). Place 5 g of sulfur powder in a test tube. Holding the test tube with the buret clamp, heat the sulfur to boiling. Holding the copper foil with the forceps, insert the foil into the sulfur vapor. Result? Examine the product and complete the representative equation in your Data Table 1.

DATA TABLE 1

Complete, balanced equation	Name of Product	Brief Identification of product
$Zn + S \rightarrow$		
$Cu + O_2 \rightarrow$		
$Cu + S \rightarrow$		
$CaO + H_2O \rightarrow$		

c. Obtain a one gram sample of the solid product resulting from the Instructor Experiment with calcium oxide and water. Place this in a test tube and add 10 ml of water. Shake the tube for 2 minutes, then filter. Test the filtrate with red and blue litmus papers. Blue litmus paper turns red in the presence of acids and red litmus paper turns blue in the presence of metallic hydroxides. Name the product. Describe the product briefly, and complete the equation in Data Table 1 which pertains to it.

2. In each part of this procedure, 5 grams of the reactant will be placed in separate test tubes, held with the buret clamp, and heated for three minutes. The appearance of the product is to be observed. Certain products may be identified according to specific directions. Use a table like Data Table 2 to write the complete, balanced equation, and to name the products. Describe their appearance or identification procedures.

DATA TABLE 2

Complete, balanced equation	Products	Identification or appearance of products
$HgO \rightarrow$		
$NaHCO_3 \rightarrow$		
$CuSO_4 \cdot 5H_2O \rightarrow$		

a. Heat the sample of mercury(II) oxide. Insert a glowing splint into the upper part of the test tube. Result? Note the appearance of any deposit on the side of the test tube. Record your results.

b. Heat the sample of sodium hydrogen carbonate holding the test tube in a horizontal position. Insert moistened pieces of red and blue litmus paper into the upper part of the test tube. Result? Insert a flaming splint into the upper part of the test tube. Result? Positive results identify carbon dioxide. Note any deposit on the sides of the test tube. Record your results. Retain this test tube and its contents for part 4*e*.

c. Heat the sample of copper(II) sulfate pentahydrate holding the test tube at an angle, mouth downward. What substance appears on the colder portion of the test tube? Note any change in appearance of the solid left in the test tube. Record your results.

3. Follow specific directions for each part of this procedure. Record details in your Data Table 3 as in previous procedures.

a. Add 5 ml of hydrochloric acid to a test

DATA TABLE 3

Complete, balanced equation	Products	Identification or appearance of products
$Zn + HCl \rightarrow$		
$Zn + CuSO_4$		
$Cu + AgNO_3 \rightarrow$		
$NaBr + Cl_2 \rightarrow$		
$Ca + H_2O \rightarrow$		

tube. Drop a cleaned zinc strip into the acid. After one minute, bring a flaming splint to the mouth of the test tube. Result? Fill the test tube with water and pour off the liquid in the test tube.

b. Add 5 ml of the copper(II) sulfate solution to a test tube. Drop a cleaned zinc strip into the solution. Permit the strip to remain in the solution for 10 minutes. Note the substance deposited on the zinc strip and any change in the color of the solution.

c. Repeat procedure (*b*) using 5 ml of silver nitrate solution into which a piece of copper foil is dropped. Make similar observations.

d. Add 5 ml of the sodium bromide solution to a test tube. Add 1 ml of chlorine water to this solution and note any change in the color of the solution. (Elementary bromine in water solution has a red-brown color.)

e. Add 5 ml of water to a test tube. Drop a clean calcium turning into the water. Result? Immediately bring a flaming splint to the test tube mouth. Result? Insert pieces of red and blue litmus paper into the resultant solution. Result?

4. Follow specific directions for each part of this procedure. Record details in your Data Table 4 as in previous procedures.

DATA TABLE 4

Complete, balanced equation	Products	Identification or appearance of products
$AgNO_3 + NaCl \rightarrow$		
$Na_2SO_3 + HCl \rightarrow$		
$AlCl_3 + NH_3 + H_2O \rightarrow$		
$NaOH + HCl \rightarrow$		
$Na_2CO_3 + HCl \rightarrow$		
$2NaI + Pb(NO_3)_2 \rightarrow$		

a. Add 1 ml of silver nitrate solution to 5 ml of sodium chloride solution in a test tube. Use the Table of Solubility of Salts on page 281 of **MODERN CHEMISTRY**, if necessary, to identify the products. Record your results.

b. To 5 ml of sodium sulfite solution add 1 ml of hydrochloric acid. Result? Test for the odor of a product by using the procedure of Fig. F-5. Result? Insert moistened pieces of red and blue litmus paper into the upper part of the test tube. Record your results.

c. To 5 ml of aluminum chloride solution add 1 ml of ammonia-water solution. Result? Refer to the Table of Solubility of Salts in the text, if necessary, to identify the products.

d. Place 5 ml of hydrochloric acid (0.1 *M*) in the beaker. Add 4 ml of sodium hydroxide solution (0.1 *M*) to the acid with stirring. Place one drop of the resultant solution in separate pieces of red and blue litmus paper (on a clean glass plate over white paper). Result? Continue to add the sodium hydroxide solution dropwise to the beaker contents (with stirring) until the test litmus papers undergo no change (red stays red and blue stays blue). Evaporate 5 ml of the fluid (in the beaker) in an evaporating dish over a wire gauze with asbestos center, using a very low flame near the end of the process. When only a few drops of liquid remain, remove the burner and allow the residual heat to evaporate the last few drops. Allow the dish to cool and identify the residue.

e. Add 2 ml of hydrochloric acid to the residue left in the test tube of part 2*b*. Insert moistened pieces of red and blue litmus paper into the upper part of the test tube. Result? Insert a flaming splint into the upper part of the test tube. Result?

f. Add 5 ml of sodium iodide solution to a test tube. Add 5 ml of lead nitrate solution. Result? Use the Table of Solubility of Salts in the text to identify the product(s).

g. Complete Data your Table 4.

INSTRUCTOR EXPERIMENT: 1. Mix 2 g of zinc powder with 4 g of sulfur powder in a mortar. Make a small cone of the mixture on the asbestos square. Holding the Bunsen burner by the base, play the tip of the flame on the tip of the cone of the mixture.

2. Place approximately 50–60 g of fresh lump calcium oxide in a beaker. Add approximately 18 g of water. Have students observe the result. Dispense the powder resultant to the class for procedure 1.*c*.

QUESTIONS: The terms *type of reactant* or *type of product* mean element(s) and/or compound(s).

1. What type(s) of reactant(s) typify composition reactions?
What type(s) of product(s) typify composition reactions?
2. What type(s) of reactant(s) typify decomposition reactions?
What type(s) of product(s) typify decomposition reactions?
3. What type(s) of reactant(s) typify replacement reactions?
What type(s) of product(s) typify replacement reactions?
4. What type(s) of reactant(s) typify ion-exchange reactions?
What type(s) of product(s) typify ion-exchange reactions?

Experiment 13 Gas Laws

PURPOSE: To show how the volume of a fixed mass of a gas (air) varies (*a*) with changes in pressure at constant temperature, and (*b*) with changes in temperature at constant pressure.

APPARATUS: Barometer, mercurial; beaker, 600 ml; burner and tubing capillary tube, 40 cm length (either No. 1303 or No. 1303A, Welch); clamp, buret; Charles law tube, mounted (No. 1674A, Welch). Welch apparatus is recommended but details as to preparation and use of alternate glassware are described in references in the Teacher Edition of the text; (2) hydrometers or graduated cylinders, 500 ml (one polypropylene); meter stick; protractor; ring, iron; ring stand; thermometer; tongs; beaker; wire gauze.

MATERIAL: Mercury.

INTRODUCTION: According to Boyle's law, the volume of a certain amount of dry gas is inversely proportional to the pressure, provided the temperature remains constant. This law may be stated mathematically as $\frac{V}{V'} = \frac{p'}{p}$ where V is the original volume, V' the new volume, p the original pressure, an p' the new pressure. This law may also be stated mathematically as $pV = k$ (a constant) where p and V represent corresponding sets of values for the fixed mass of gas.

According to Charles' law, the volume of a certain amount of dry gas varies directly with the Kelvin temperature, provided the pressure remains constant. This law may be stated mathematically as $\frac{V}{V'} = \frac{T}{T'}$ where V is the original volume, V' the new volume, T the original *Kelvin* temperature, and T' the new *Kelvin* temperature. This law may also be stated mathematically as $\frac{V}{T} = k$ (a constant) where V and T represent corresponding sets of values for the fixed mass of gas.

PROCEDURE: 1. *Volume variation with pressure changes.* Set up the capillary tube containing approximately 20 cm of mercury in the vertical position, Fig. 13-1. Measure the length of the enclosed air column to the nearest millimeter. Now measure the height of the upper and lower levels of the mercury column above the table top. Construct a Data Table like the following. Enter these values in the Data Table for the vertical position, 90 degrees.

Rotate the tube to the horizontal position. Measure the length of the enclosed air column. Record this quantity in the Data Table for the horizontal position where the angle is 0 degrees. In this position, the pressure on the enclosed air column is equal to atmospheric pressure. Read the atmospheric pressure on the lecture table barometer and enter it as the pressure for the horizontal position.

Rotate the capillary tube until it makes an angle of 60 degrees with the horizontal, using the protractor to check the angle. Measure the height of the air column and the upper and lower levels of the mercury column as shown in Fig. 13-2. Record the measurements in the Data Table. Change the position of the tube to a 30 degree angle and repeat the measurements made for the 60 degree position.

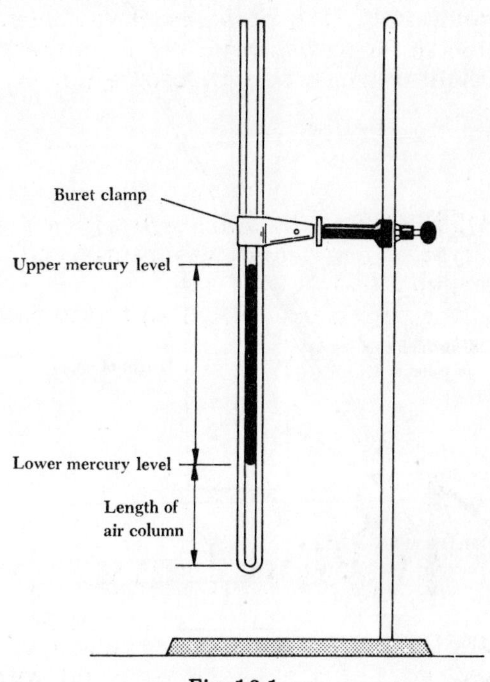

Fig. 13-1

DATA TABLE

Position (angle) of capillary tube	Vertical 90°	60°	30°	Horizontal 0°	Inverted
V (length of air column, mm)					
Height of upper level of mercury, mm					
Height of lower level of mercury, mm					
p (applied pressure, mm of mercury)				Atmospheric = mm Hg	
pV					

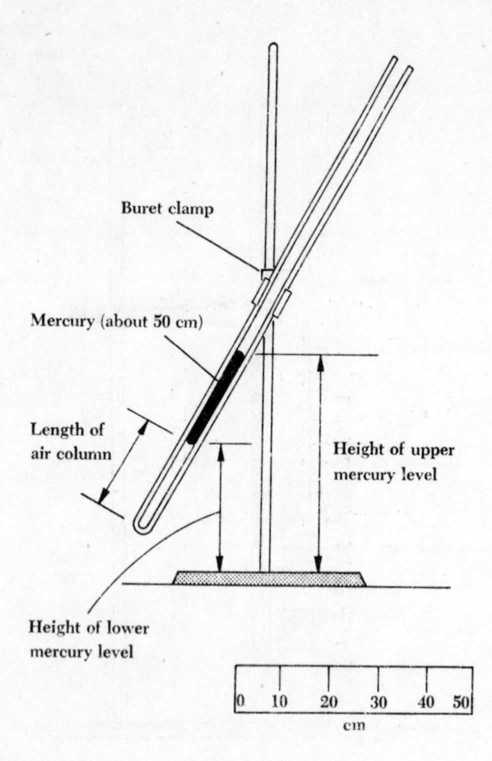

Fig. 13-2

Now place the capillary tube in the inverted position with the open end of the tube facing downward. In this position, the enclosed air is under less than atmospheric pressure, the applied pressure being equal to the *difference* between atmospheric pressure and the height of the mercury column. Measure the height of the air column and the upper and lower levels of the mercury column. Record these quantities in the Data Table.

Calculate the applied pressure for the vertical position (90 degrees) and for the 60 and 30 degree positions respectively by adding the measured height of the mercury column to the atmospheric pressure. Enter these quantities in the Data Table.

Calculate the pV product for each position of the capillary tube and enter the results in the Data Table.

On a piece of graph paper plot a graph of volume versus pressure for the readings obtained. Use the horizontal axis for p values (the applied pressure in mm of mercury) and the vertical axis for V values (the length of the enclosed air column in mm). What is the shape of this graph? What mathematical relationship does such a curve represent?

2. *Volume variation with temperature.* In this part of the experiment you will use the Charles' law tube assembly (Fig. 13-3) which consists of a 40 cm capillary tube containing a column of dry air confined by a short

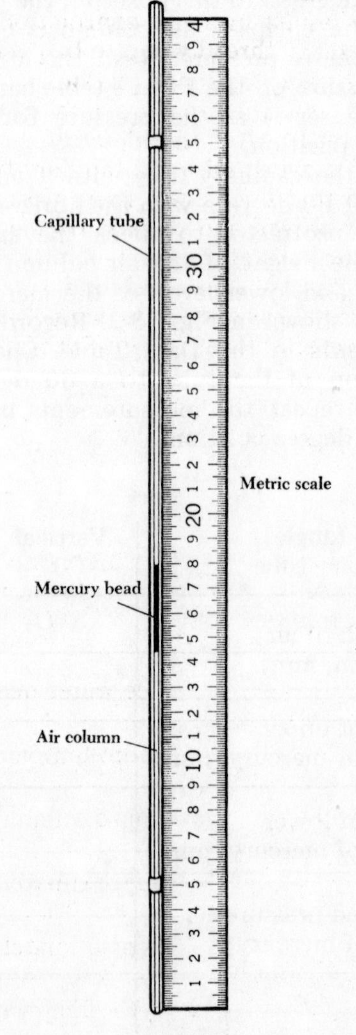

Fig. 13-3

thread of mercury. Set up this tube in a vertical position, clamp it to the ring stand. Measure the length of the enclosed air column and the room temperature. Construct a Data Table like the following. Record these measurements in the Data Table.

Fill a cylinder (hydrometer jar) almost completely with a mixture of ice and water and take the temperature of the mixture to the nearest degree. Now insert the capillary tube assembly as shown in Fig. 13-4. Initially, the bottom of the mercury thread should be at the same level as the top of an ice-water mixture. Cooling the enclosed air column results in some contraction so that the mercury thread will also be pushed downward by the combined pressure of the atmosphere and the pressure due to the mercury thread. After the mercury thread has stopped moving, raise the capillary tube assembly so that once again the bottom of the mercury thread and the top of the ice-water mixture are at the same level. Measure the length of the air column and record this measurement as well as the temperature of the ice-water mixture in the Data Table.

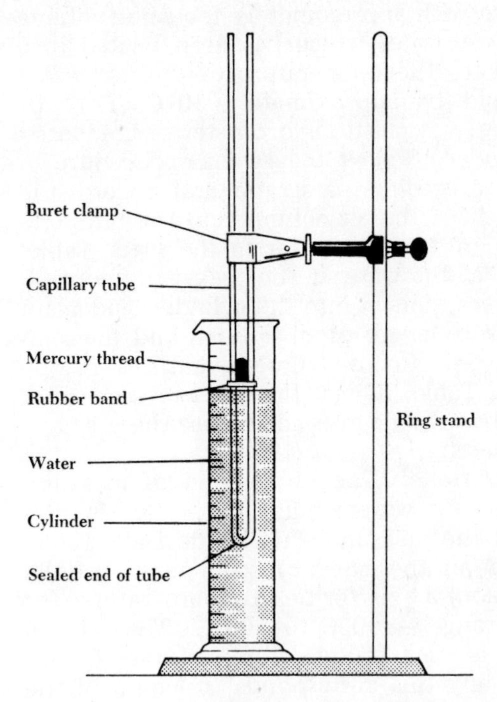

Fig. 13-4

DATA TABLE

Gas Volume, V (length of column, mm)	Thermometer Temperature (°C)	Temperature, T (°K)	$\frac{V}{T}$
	(ice-water mixture)		
	(room temperature)		
	(approximately 40°)		
	(approximately 60°)		
	(approximately 80°)		
	(boiling water)		

Remove the ice-water mixture and replace with approximately the same volume of hot water which has been heated in a beaker. The temperature of the hot water should be approximately 40° C. For hot water, use plastic hydrometer or graduated cylinder. Repeat the general procedure in the preceding paragraph and record the length of the air column and the temperature of the hot water in the Data Table. Reheat the water in the beaker to about 60 degrees, pour it into the cylinder, and again measure length of air column and the temperature. Record these quantities in the Data Table. Reheat the water in the beaker to about 80 degrees and repeat the previous procedure.

(*Optional:* Take a final set of measurements for water boiling in the beaker. Record the measurements in the Data Table.

On another sheet of graph paper, use the horizontal axis for Celsius temperatures for the range −300° C to 100° C. The vertical axis is used for recording volumes of air. Actually this corresponds to length of the air column in millimeters. Use an appropriate scale starting with 0 mm so that the measured volumes (lengths of air column) fit on the graph paper. Plot the values you found on the graph and construct the graph using a solid line for these values. Extend this graph to the left, using a dashed line, until it intersects the temperature axis. At what Celsius temperature would the extrapolated volume of the gas be zero?

Convert the Celsius temperatures in the Data Table to Kelvin temperatures and record in the appropriate column in the Data Table. Calculate values for $\frac{V}{T}$ from the recorded lengths of air column and Kelvin temperatures. Enter these values in the Data Table.

Convert the lowest possible Celsius temperature on your graph to the Kelvin scale. This is the temperature at which the theoretical volume of the gas would be zero. The value for Absolute zero on the Kelvin scale is zero, and on the Celsius scale it is nearly −273° C. What is the difference between your Celsius value for Absolute zero and −273° C? Calculate the experimental and percentage errors for this experiment. Experimental error is the difference between your value and the accepted value (−273° C). Percentage error is the experimental error divided by the accepted value and converted to a percentage.

Substitute the Kelvin temperatures for the Celsius temperatures on your graph. Assuming that your extrapolated Celsius temperature corresponds to Absolute zero, what mathematical relationship does the shape of your graph indicate between V, volume of a gas held at constant pressure and T, Kelvin temperature?

FURTHER EXPERIMENTATION: Additional data for temperature variations may be obtained by using the mercury tube in (a) boiling water or steam, (b) ice-NaCl(s), (c) Dry ice-acetone. An oil drop may be substituted for the mercury for the low-temperature readings since the oil solidifies and makes the measurement easier.

Experiment 14 Percentage of Oxygen in Air

PURPOSE: To find the percentage of oxygen in a sample of air.

APPARATUS: *Phosphorus method:* battery jar; clamp, buret; eudiometer, 50 ml;

metric ruler; ring stand; thermometer. *Pyrogallic acid method:* balance, platform; battery jar; eudiometer, 50 ml; graduated cylinder; rubber stopper, solid No. 0.

MATERIAL: *Phosphorus method:* copper wire, bare, No. 16, 60-cm long; phosphorus, white. *Pyrogallic acid method:* Pyrogallic acid; solution of sodium hydroxide (1.0 *M*).

INTRODUCTION: If a volume of air is measured accurately and then the oxygen removed by chemical means, the percentage of oxygen in the original sample may be computed easily. White phosphorus unites readily with oxygen and forms a white smoke of diphosphorus pentoxide. The white smoke gradually settles and dissolves in the water. The volume of gas remaining, subtracted from the original volume of air, gives the volume of oxygen removed.

An alternate method that gives quicker results is to add a mixture of pyrogallic acid and sodium hydroxide solution to a measured volume of air contained in a stoppered eudiometer. This mixture rapidly unites with the oxygen in the air. The stoppered tube is inverted a few times to mix the chemicals thoroughly with the enclosed air. The stoppered end is then thrust under water in a battery jar. As soon as the stopper is removed, water is forced in to take the place of the removed oxygen. The volume of gas remaining in the tube, subtracted from the volume of air used, gives the volume of oxygen.

PROCEDURE: 1. *Phosphorus method.* Add sufficient water to a 50-ml eudiometer so that 40 to 50 ml of air will be enclosed when the tube is inverted in a battery jar of water. It is a good plan to fill several large vessels with water the day before the experiment, so that the water will be at room temperature. Determine accurately the volume of air enclosed in the eudiometer. Measure the difference in water levels, if any, in millimeters. Record the temperature of the water and also the barometer reading in the room. Compute the volume of dry air enclosed at STP.

Cut a stick of phosphorus *under water* so as to get a piece with freshly cut surfaces the size of a small bean. **CAUTION:** *Do not handle phosphorus with the fingers.* Thrust one end of a flexible, bare, copper wire, about 60 cm long, into the piece of phosphorus *white it is still under water.* Now push the wire, with the phosphorus on the end, up into the eudiometer to within several centimeters of the top. See Fig. 14-1. Observe the reaction which begins at once. Allow at least 24 hours for the reaction to be completed.

INITIAL DATA

Volume of air enclosed in eudiometer	ml
Difference in water levels	mm
Equivalent difference in levels in mm of mercury	mm
Temperature	°C
Barometer reading	mm
Water vapor pressure	mm
Volume of dry air enclosed at STP	ml

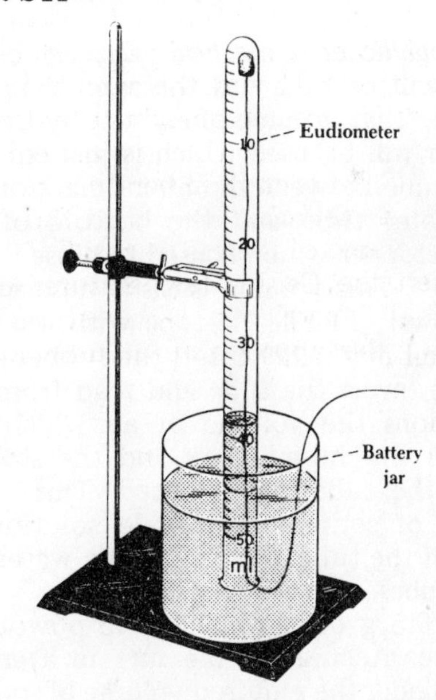

Fig. 14-1

FINAL DATA

Volume of gas remaining	ml
Difference in water levels	mm
Equivalent difference in levels in mm of mercury	mm
Temperature	°C
Barometer reading	mm
Water vapor pressure	mm
Volume of gas remaining at STP	ml
Volume of dry O_2 removed	ml
Percentage of O_2 in sample of air taken	%
Accepted percentage of O_2 in air	%
Percentage error	%

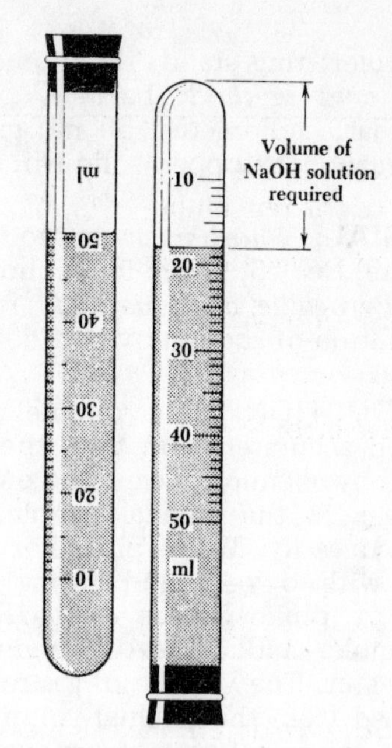

Fig. 14-2

When the white smoke has disappeared, remove the copper wire, measure the difference in levels, and read the volume of the gas remaining. Record the temperature of the water and the barometer reading. Compute the volume of dry gas remaining at STP.

2. *Pyrogallic acid method.* Exactly 50 ml of air will be taken as the sample in this method. That volume of sodium hydroxide solution will be used which is just equal to the volume between the 50-ml mark on the eudiometer tube and the bottom of the rubber stopper which is used to close it. See Fig. 14-2. This volume is easily determined as follows: (1) Fill the tube with water to the 50-ml mark. (2) Insert the rubber stopper. (3) Invert the tube and read from the graduations the volume of air which *was* between the 50-ml mark and the stopper before the tube was inverted. This is the volume of sodium hydroxide solution to use with the tube. (4) Empty the water out of the tube.

Add 0.5 g of pyrogallic acid powder to the tube. Accurately measure in a graduated cylinder the required volume of sodium hydroxide solution and pour it into the tube. Quickly close the tube with the rubber stopper. Invert the tube a few times to mix the contents. Place the stoppered end of the tube under water in a battery jar and then remove the stopper. Note how the water is forced in to replace the oxygen. Allow the tube to cool for a few minutes. Now raise or lower the tube so that the level of water in the tube is the same as that in the battery jar. Read the volume of gas remaining in the tube. It is not necessary to correct the gas to STP in this method because the operations are all done within a few minutes. The volume of gas remaining, subtracted from the original volume of air, 50 ml, gives the volume of oxygen. The volume of oxygen divided by the volume of the sample taken and multiplied by 100% will give the percentage of oxygen in air. Repeat the experiment several times until consistent results are obtained. Construct a Data Table like the following to record your results.

DATA TABLE

	1	2	3
Volume of gas remaining	ml	ml	ml
Volume of oxygen removed	ml	ml	ml
Percentage of oxygen	%	%	%
Accepted percentage of oxygen in air	%	%	%
Percentage error	%	%	%

Experiment 15 Replacement of Hydrogen by a Metal

PURPOSE: To determine the mass of magnesium needed to replace one gram of hydrogen from a compound.

APPARATUS: Balance, analytical; battery jar, 1 qt; clamp, buret; eudiometer, 50 ml; graduated cylinder; ring stand; thermometer.

MATERIAL: Magnesium ribbon, untarnished; thread; hydrochloric acid, concentrated.

SUGGESTIONS: To save time in weighing, the instructor may weigh a bright, untarnished piece of magnesium ribbon a meter or more in length (allow approximately 6 cm per student). An analytical balance should be used and the mass should be determined to the nearest 0.001 g. Assuming the ribbon to be uniform, the length of sections having a mass from 0.040 to 0.045 g may be determined. Such an amount of magnesium will liberate 40 to 45 ml of hydrogen gas.

INTRODUCTION: The law of definite composition holds true for all compounds. Therefore, it is possible to find out how many grams of one element are needed to unite with *one gram* of another element, hydrogen for example. As a rule, metals do not combine readily with hydrogen, but they do displace hydrogen from compounds, such as hydrochloric acid. Magnesium will react with hydrochloric acid to liberate hydrogen gas. In this experiment, we shall undertake to find out just how many grams of magnesium are required to replace one gram of hydrogen from hydrochloric acid.

Time permitting, your instructor will issue a second piece of magnesium whose mass you are to determine from the volume of hydrogen liberated.

PROCEDURE: 1. Half fill a battery jar with water. If possible, use water that has adjusted to room temperature. Roll a length of magnesium ribbon of known mass into a loose coil. Tie it with one end of a piece of thread, approximately 25 cm in length, in such manner that all the loops of the coil are tied together. Pour 5 ml of concentrated hydrochloric acid into the gas measuring tube, or eudiometer. Add enough water to the eudiometer to fill it completely, being careful not to mix the water and the acid. Reason? Lower the magnesium coil into the water in the gas measuring tube to a depth of about five centimeters. Close the tube with your thumb so that the thread is held firmly against the edge of the tube. Taking care that no air enters, invert the eudiometer in the battery jar and allow it to rest against the bottom to hold the thread. It may be clamped in this position on the ring stand, as shown in Fig. 15-1. The acid flows down the tube (why?) and reacts with the magnesium. Is the acid now concentrated or dilute?

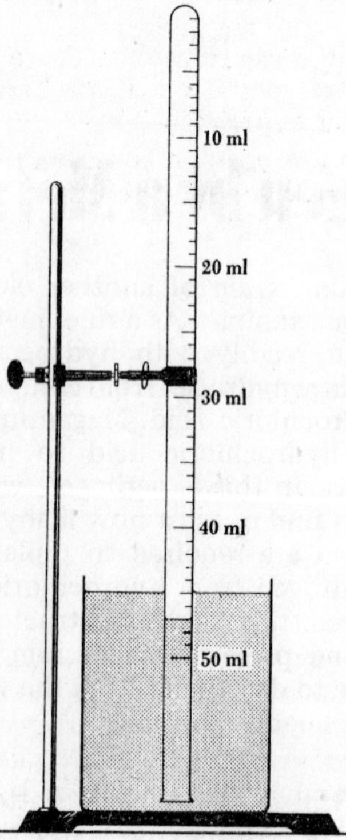

Fig. 15-1

2. When the magnesium has disappeared entirely and the reaction has stopped, adjust the tube until the liquid levels inside and outside are the same. Add water to the battery jar if necessary, using water at room temperature. (If this adjustment is not possible with the apparatus you are using, what computation can you carry out that will yield the same result?) Read as accurately as possible the volume of hydrogen liberated. Take the temperature of the water in the battery jar and assume this to be the temperature of the hydrogen gas collected. Why is this a reasonable assumption? Take a barometer reading from the laboratory barometer. Record these data in a Data Table like the one below.

CALCULATIONS: 1. From the table, Pressure of Water Vapor, in the textbook, determine the correction that must be made in the barometer reading to yield the partial pressure of dry hydrogen gas in the eudiometer. Then calculate the volume of the hydrogen gas under standard conditions of temperature and pressure. Enter the result in the Data Table.

2. Calculate the mass of hydrogen liberated, recognizing that this mass of hydrogen bears the same relationship to the volume of hydrogen collected at STP as the g-mol. wt. of hydrogen bears to the g-mol. vol. of the gas. Enter the result in the Data Table.

DATA TABLE

Mass of Mg used	g
Volume of H_2 collected (at laboratory conditions)	ml
Temperature of H_2 collected	°C
Barometer reading	mm
Vapor pressure of water at observed temperature	mm
Pressure of the dry H_2 collected	mm
Volume of H_2 (corrected to STP)	ml
Mass of H_2 liberated	g
Mass of Mg replacing 1 g of H_2 (experimental)	g
Theoretical mass of Mg replacing 1 g of H_2	g
Experimental error	g
Percentage error	%

3. From the mass of magnesium used and the mass of hydrogen evolved, calculate the mass of magnesium needed to replace 1 g of hydrogen. From the balanced equation for this reaction, determine the mass of magnesium theoretically required to replace 1 g of hydrogen. Compute your percentage error. Enter the results in the Data Table.

FURTHER EXPERIMENTATION: Repeat Procedure 1 using the unweighed sample of magnesium ribbon issued to you by the instructor. From the volume of hydrogen collected at laboratory conditions, calculate the mass of the hydrogen liberated according to the directions appearing under CALCULATIONS 1 and 2. Then calculate the mass of magnesium that would theoretically replace this mass of hydrogen. Report this mass to your instructor. Calculate your percentage error on the basis of the data he furnishes regarding the mass of the magnesium sample issued.

DATA TABLE

Reported mass of Mg	g
True mass of Mg	g
Experimental error	g
Percentage error	%

QUESTIONS: *Answer in complete sentences.*

1. Why is it necessary to make a water-vapor pressure correction of the barometer reading in this experiment?
2. What are the possible sources of the experimental error you have shown?

EQUATION

Mg + HCl →

Experiment 16 Molar Volume of a Gas

PURPOSE: To determine the molar volume of a gas experimentally.

APPARATUS: Balance, sensitive to 0.01 g; beaker, 400 ml; burner and tubing; clamp, buret; flask, Florence, 500 ml; glass bend, 8 × 8 cm; glass tubing, 6 mm; graduated cylinder; pinch clamp; ring stand; rubber connector; rubber tubing, connector; rubber stoppers, 1-hole No. 4, 2-hole No. 5; test tube, Pyrex; thermometer; wing top.

MATERIAL: Manganese dioxide, C.P.; potassium chlorate, C.P.

INTRODUCTION: The gram-molecular volume, or *molar volume*, of a gas is the volume of 1 mole (1 g-mol. wt.) of the gas at standard conditions of temperature and pressure. A mole of any gas will have a volume equal to that of a mole of any other gas measured under the same conditions. You can see that this is true as a consequence of two important principles which you have learned. First, one mole of any molecular substance consists of the same number of molecules as one mole of any other molecular substance. Second, equal volumes of all gases consist of the same number of molecules when measured under the same conditions of temperature and pressure.

In this experiment, you will collect a known mass of oxygen by water displacement under known conditions of temperature and pressure. You will measure the volume of water displaced as an indication of the volume of oxygen collected. The volume of this known mass of oxygen can then be corrected to standard conditions from which the volume of a mole of the gas may be found.

SUGGESTION: Since potassium chlorate tends to adsorb some water vapor from the air, it is suggested that the instructor heat the potassium chlorate overnight in a drying oven at 105° C and cool it in a dessicator before the class assembles.

By placing the hot crucible on a bright, clean wire gauze without an asbestos center, the time required for cooling is considerably reduced.

If balances, sensitive to 0.001 g are available, better results are obtained.

If students are not permitted to use potassium chlorate, the experiment may be used as a demonstration. An alternate to this experiment using Dry Ice is described in *Chemistry*, 43 (1970—Jan), Lab Bench: "*Molar Volume: A Safe Method.*"

PROCEDURE: 1. Heat about 1 g of powdered manganese dioxide in the Pyrex test tube momentarily to drive off moisture. While the test tube is cooling, assemble the two glass tubing-rubber stopper connections as shown in Fig. 16-1. Add about 1.2 g of dry potassium chlorate to the test tube and mix thoroughly with the manganese dioxide. Insert the dry stopper assembly, determine the mass of the tube and contents to the nearest 0.01 g, and record. Clamp the tube on the ring stand with the stoppered end tilted upward at a small angle.

2. Completely fill the 500-ml flask with water and assemble as in Fig. 16-1. Add water to the beaker to a depth of 1 or 2 cm. Open the pinch clamp and blow on the generator end of the rubber connector to force water out of the flask and over into the beaker so as to displace the air in the interconnecting tube. Keeping the end of the glass tube submerged in the water in the beaker, raise the beaker until the two water levels are the same. (The clamp is open during this operation.) How does this affect the pressure inside the flask? Move the beaker up or down so as to bring the level of the water in the flask into the neck but below the end of the short bend. Reset the clamp while the beaker is in this position, empty the beaker, and wipe it dry. Attach the rubber connector to the oxygen generator and release the pinch clamp. If drops of water run out of the rubber tube for no

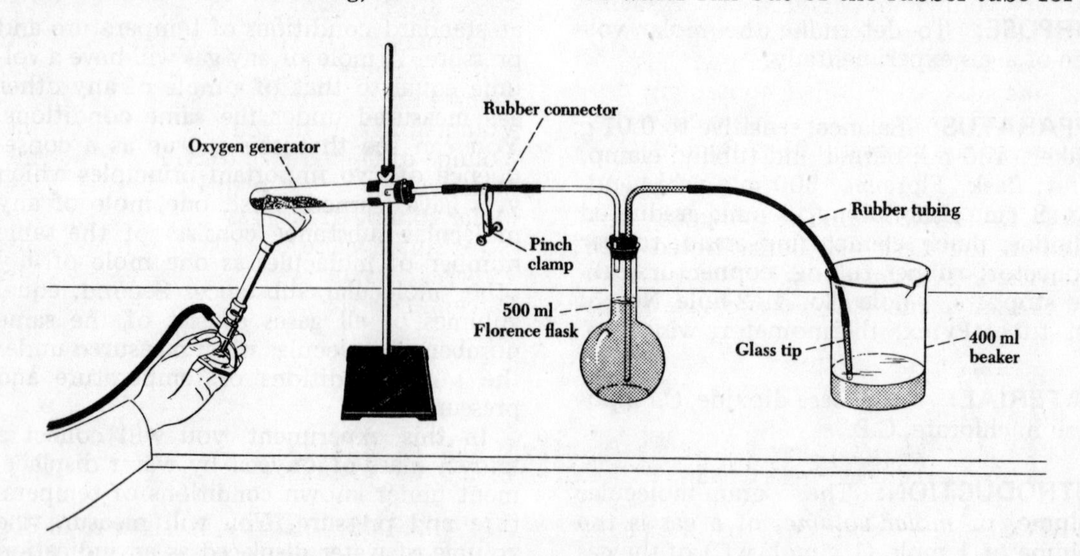

Fig. 16-1

more than a few seconds, the system is airtight. Put the *dry* beaker back in place.
3. With the wing top on the burner and holding the burner base in your hand, heat the potassium chlorate gently (BE SURE THE PINCH CLAMP IS OPEN). Regulate the heating so as to maintain a moderate flow of oxygen. Avoid excessive heating as shown by the formation of a white cloud in the generating tube. *Under no circumstances allow the water level in the flask to drop below the end of the long glass tube.* Discontinue the heating when the beaker is nearly full. Leave the apparatus undisturbed until the generator has cooled to room temperature. Why?
4. While the generator is cooling, obtain the barometer reading. Read the temperature of the water in the beaker. We may assume this to be the temperature of the oxygen. Record.
5. When the generator is at room temperature, make the levels of water in the flask and beaker equal by lowering the beaker. Avoid handling the flask during this manipulation. Why? Be sure that the end of the tube remains below the surface of the water in the beaker. Reset the pinch clamp while the identical levels are maintained, then remove the beaker of water. Carefully measure the volume of water in the beaker. This volume is equal to the volume of oxygen collected in the flask. Record. Disconnect the generator tube containing the residue and weigh, with stopper assembly in place, to the nearest 0.01 g. Record.

CALCULATIONS: 1. The oxygen collected in the flask will be saturated with water vapor as determined by the temperature of the system. Thus the pressure of the gas is due to the partial pressures of the dry oxygen and the water vapor. Determine the partial pressure of the dry oxygen gas produced in the generator and enter in a Data Table like the following.
2. You now have the volume, temperature, and pressure of the known mass of oxygen collected. Determine the volume occupied by this mass of oxygen under standard conditions of temperature and pressure and enter in the Data Table.
3. Since one mole of oxygen is 32 g, the volume occupied by the mass of oxygen at STP will represent the *molar volume* of the gas. Calculate this value, using your known mass of oxygen and its volume at STP. Enter your *experimental* molar volume, in liters, in the Data Table.
4. Taking the accepted molar volume of any gas as 22.4 liters, determine your percentage error and enter the result in the Data Table.

DATA TABLE

Mass of generator before heating	g
Mass of generator after heating	g
Mass of oxygen collected	g
Barometer reading	mm
Water vapor pressure at temperature of O_2	mm
Partial pressure of O_2 collected	mm
Temperature of O_2 collected	°C
Volume of O_2 collected	ml
Volume of O_2 reduced to STP	ml
Molar volume of O_2 (exptl.)	liter
Molar volume of any gas (accepted value)	liter
Experimental error	liter
Percentage error	%

Experiment 17 Molecular Weight of a Gas

PURPOSE: To determine the molecular weight of a common gas experimentally.

APPARATUS: Balance, sensitive to 0.01 g; beaker, 250 ml; bottle, wide mouth; clamp, buret; drying tube; flask, Florence, 250 ml; funnel tube; glass bend, 8 × 8 cm; glass tube, 20 cm; glass tubing, 6 mm; graduated cylinder; ring stand; rubber connector; rubber tubing, connector; rubber stoppers, 1-hole No. 2, 1-hole No. 4, 2-hole No. 6; thermometer.

MATERIAL: Calcium carbonate, marble chips; calcium chloride, anhydrous, 4–8 mesh; cotton; hydrochloric acid, concentrated.

INTRODUCTION: You have learned that 1 mole of any gas occupies 22.4 liters at STP. Thus the mass, in grams, of 22.4 liters of a gas measured at standard conditions is numerically equal to the molecular weight of the gas. In this experiment, you will collect a container of a gas and determine its mass and volume under laboratory conditions. By application of the gas laws, you may determine the volume this mass of gas would occupy at STP. Then by simple arithmetic, the mass of 22.4 liters may be determined.

It is not practical to weigh an *empty* flask, that is, one completely devoid of gas molecules. You may, however, weigh a flask filled with air. Then, knowing the volume of the flask and the density of the air, the mass of air in the flask may be calculated. The difference in masses yields the mass of the *empty* flask.

PROCEDURE: 1. Place 20 g of calcium carbonate (marble chips) in a wide-mouth bottle and just cover with water. Assemble a 2-hole stopper, a glass bend, and a funnel tube to complete the generator. The end of the funnel tube should extend below the surface of the water in the wide-mouth bottle when the stopper assembly is in place. Why? Fill a drying tube with anhydrous calcium chloride, fitting a loose cotton plug in each end. Fit a 1-hole rubber stopper, in which is inserted a short length of glass tubing, into the open end of the drying tube. Clamp the assembled drying tube in a horizontal position on a ring stand and connect one end of the glass bend of the generator as shown in Fig. 17-1.

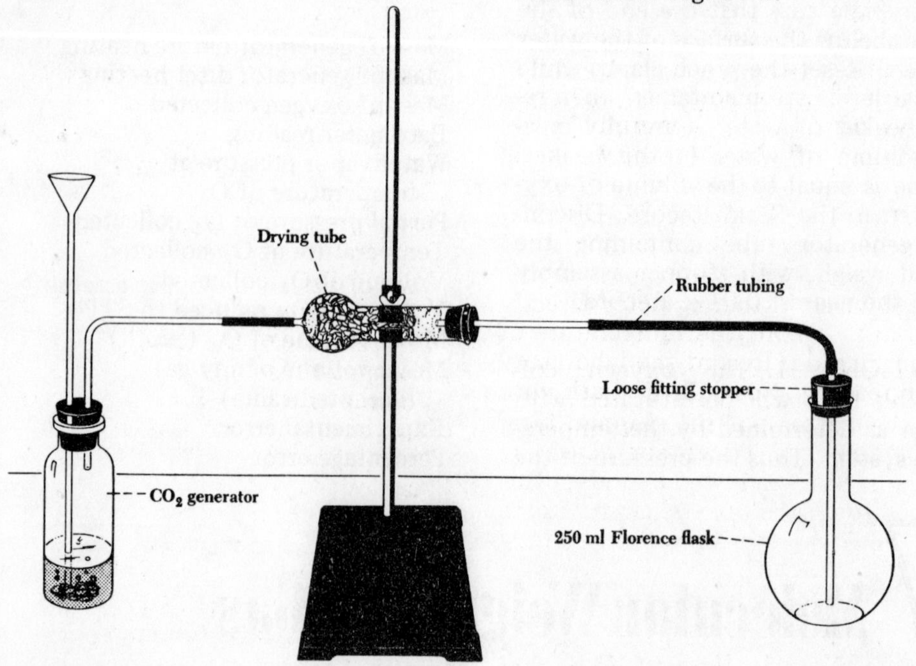

Fig. 17-1

2. Clean and thoroughly dry a 250-ml Florence flask. Select the largest 1-hole stopper which will just fit the flask and insert a glass tube about 20 cm in length so it extends to within 1 cm of the bottom of the flask. Determine the mass of the flask (which contains air at room temperature and pressure) with the stopper assembly in place to the nearest 0.01 g. *From this point on, handle the flask only by the rim.* Why? Record this mass in a Data Table like the following. Place the flask on a sheet of clean paper (why?) and attach it to the drying tube by means of a suitable length of rubber tubing. *The stopper must be placed loosely in the neck of the flask.* It must not seal the flask. Why?

3. With the apparatus assembled as shown in Fig. 17-1 and the stopper loose on the Florence flask, you are ready to commence the generation of carbon dioxide. Add concentrated HCl a little at a time through the funnel tube to maintain a gentle evolution of carbon dioxide. Continue the delivery of CO_2 into the flask for about 20 minutes. You may *momentarily* tighten the stopper on the flask from time to time and observe that the liquid in the generator backs up in the funnel tube. How does this indicate that CO_2 is being delivered to the flask?

4. Detach the rubber hose from the flask, *being careful to handle the flask by the rim only*. Tighten the stopper assembly and weigh the stoppered flask of carbon dioxide gas. Record. Immediately remove the stopper and insert a thermometer directly into the flask. Record the temperature of the carbon dioxide. Record the laboratory barometer reading. Now fill the flask with water to the bottom of the stopper. Measure the volume of water contained by transferring it to a graduated cylinder. This corresponds to the volume of air first contained in the flask, and the volume of CO_2 collected.

CALCULATIONS: 1. *Mass of CO_2 collected.* The density of air may be taken as 1.29 g/liters at STP. To determine the mass of air contained in the flask, first correct the volume of air in the flask at the recorded temperature and pressure to STP. Then calculate the mass of this corrected volume of air. Knowing the mass of the flask containing air and the mass of the contained air, the mass of the "empty" flask may be computed and recorded. Determine the mass of CO_2 collected and record.

2. *Volume of CO_2 at STP.* The volume of CO_2 at STP is the same as the volume of air at STP calculated above. Record.

3. *Molecular weight of CO_2.* Knowing the mass of a given volume of CO_2 gas at STP, you may calculate the mass of the molar volume (22.4 liters at STP) of the gas. This mass in grams is numerically equal to the molecular weight of the CO_2 (experimental). Record.

4. *Experimental error.* Determine the correct molecular weight of carbon dioxide from the formula. The difference between your experimental value and this value represents your experimental error. Calculate your percentage error based on the correct molecular weight of the gas. Record your experimental and percentage error.

DATA TABLE

Mass of flask and stopper assembly, filled with air	g
Mass of flask and stopper assembly, filled with CO_2	g
Temperature of the CO_2	°C
Barometer reading	mm
Volume of the flask	ml
Mass of empty flask and stopper assembly	g
Mass of CO_2 collected	g
Volume of CO_2 at STP	ml
Molecular weight of CO_2 (experimental)	
Molecular weight of CO_2 (from molecular formula)	
Experimental error	
Percentage error	%

Experiment 18 Chemical Properties of Water

PURPOSE: To learn some of the chemical properties of water.

APPARATUS: Balance, platform; beaker, 150 ml; bottle, wide mouth; burner and tubing; clamp, test tube; dish, evaporating; flask, Erlenmeyer; forceps; 2 glass plates; graduated cylinder; spoon, deflagrating; test tube, Pyrex.

MATERIAL: Calcium, metal; calcium oxide, lump; copper(II) sulfate, crystals; phosphorus, red; potassium, metal; sodium aluminum sulfate, powdered; sodium hydrogen carbonate; sodium, metal; asbestos, paper; litmus paper, red and blue; solutions of lead(II) nitrate (0.1 *M*); potassium chromate (0.1 *M*).

INTRODUCTION: Water is a very stable substance that does not decompose easily. It does react, however, with a great many substances. Water is necessary for the formation of some crystals and is present in such crystals as water of hydration. Water promotes many chemical changes as is shown by the reaction which occurs when water is added to baking powder.

SUGGESTION: Use the lump calcium oxide from a newly opened bottle.

In place of sodium, use "dry-Na," containing approximately 8.8% sodium. This sodium-lead alloy (J. T. Baker Chemical Co.) is a convenient and moderately safe source of metallic sodium and is reasonably stable in air (*J. Chem. Educ.*, 48, 278 (1971).

PROCEDURE: 1. Obtain from your instructor a small piece of sodium metal, not larger than half a pea. Carry it to the laboratory desk of a dry glass plate. Always use forceps to handle sodium; never touch it with your fingers! Hold a glass plate in one hand to act as a shield between you and the reaction, and with your other hand drop the sodium into an evaporating dish that is half full of water. CAUTION: *Stand aside! Sometimes a slight explosion scatters particles of sodium which are caustic to the flesh.* Result? After the reaction is complete, dip a stirring rod into the liquid in the evaporating dish and touch it to a piece of red litmus paper on a clean glass plate. What happens? (Solutions of metallic hydroxides turn red litmus blue.)

Repeat the experiment using a small piece of potassium metal. CARE! How does this reaction compare in violence with that of sodium and water? What is the effect of the resulting solution on a strip of red litmus paper?

Drop a small piece of calcium metal into a test tube which is one quarter full of water. Result? Perform the flaming splint test for hydrogen. Dip a stirring rod into the liquid in the test tube and touch it to a piece of red litmus. Result?

2. Place a lump of calcium oxide about the size of a lima bean on a glass plate. Pour not more than 2 ml of water on the calcium oxide, until it becomes quite wet. It may take a minute or two for the reaction to occur. Result? After the reaction is over, transfer some of the residue on a stirring rod or spatula to a piece of moist red litmus paper on a clean glass plate.

3. Prepare the oxide of a nonmetal by igniting a piece of red phosphorus the size of a match head in the asbestos-lined bowl of a deflagrating spoon. Lower the spoon with the burning phosphorus into a wide-mouth bottle. Partly cover the bottle with a glass plate so as to retain as much of the smoke in the bottle as possible. Allow the phosphorus to burn out completely before removing the deflagrating spoon. Now add 30

ml of water to the bottle, and quickly cover the bottle tightly with the glass plate. Shake the bottle vigorously for a minute or two until the smoke disappears. What happens to it? Test the liquid in the bottle with a piece of blue litmus paper. Result? (Acid solutions turn blue litmus red.)

4. Place a crystal of copper(II) sulfate the size of a pea in a dry Pyrex test tube, and heat the test tube gently with a low burner flame. Hold the test tube with the open end inclined slightly downward. As the reaction proceeds, you should be able to tell why this is necessary. What happens to the copper(II) sulfate crystal? Observe the substance which appears near the open end of the test tube. Identify this substance, give its source, and tell why it appeared near the open end of the test tube. After the test tube cools, add a drop of water to the residue in the test tube. Result. Why?

5. Mix 1 g of powdered sodium aluminum sulfate and 2 g of sodium hydrogen carbonate on a square of paper, and then add the mixture to a dry Erlenmeyer flask. Is there any evidence of chemical action? Pour 30 ml of water into the flask. What do you observe? Describe. (These substances are used in some types of baking powders.)

6. Add 5 ml of the lead(II) nitrate solution to 5 ml of the potassium chromate solution. Result? Consult the Table of Solubilities in the text and explain the result.

QUESTIONS: 1. What are the products of the reaction between the very active metals and water?

2. What class of compounds is produced when water reacts with the oxide of a metal?

3. What kind of compound is produced when water reacts with the oxide of a nonmetal?

4. Why do a definite number of molecules of water combine with a definite amount of a compound in forming a hydrate?

5. Why is baking powder always stored in watertight containers?

EQUATIONS: *Write balanced formula equations.*

1. Action of sodium on water.
2. Action of potassium on water.
3. Action of calcium on water.
4. Action of calcium oxide on water.
5. Action of diphosphorus pentoxide (P_4O_{10}) on water forming phosphoric acid (H_3PO_4).
6. Action of heat on copper(II) sulfate crystals.
7. (a) Reaction between solutions of $Pb(NO_3)_2$ and K_2CrO_4.
   (b) The net ionic equation for (a).

Experiment 19 (a) Percentage of Water in a Hydrate (b) Water of Crystallization

PURPOSE: (a) To find the percentage of water in crystallized barium chloride. (b) To determine the formula of the hydrate.

APPARATUS: Asbestos square, or bright wire gauze; balance, sensitive to 0.01 g; burner and tubing; crucible and cover; forceps; ring, iron; ring stand; tongs; triangle, pipestem.

MATERIAL: Barium chloride, C.P., crystals. Clear crystals of magnesium chloride, magnesium sulfate, potassium nitrate, sodium carbontae, sodium sulfate; crystals of copper(II) sulfate, potassium chloride, sodium aluminum sulfate, sodium chloride; calcium chloride, anhydrous, granular.

INTRODUCTION: Many ionic compounds, when crystallized from water solution, take up definite proportions of water as an integral part of their crystal structures. This water of crystallization may be driven off by the application of heat. Since the law of definite composition holds for crystalline hydrates, the number of moles of water of crystallization driven off per mole of the anhydrous compound is some simple number. If the formula of the anhydrous compound is known, you can then determine the formula of the hydrate.

PROCEDURE: 1. Arrange a suitable support for heating a crucible over a burner; use an asbestos square or preferably a clean, bright wire gauze for cooling the crucible. Throughout the experiment, handle the crucible and cover with clean crucible tongs only. Why?

Preheat a clean, dry crucible and cover to redness, cool, then determine their mass to the nearest 0.01 g. Add approximately 5 g of fine barium chloride crystals to the crucible and determine its mass to the nearest 0.01 g by the indirect method. Heat the crucible, contents, and cover gently at first (why?), increasing the temperature gradually, and finally heating strongly for 10 to 15 minutes. Cool and again determine the mass of the crucible, contents, and cover. (Keep a labeled record of each weighing as suggested in Experiment 1.)

2. Heat the covered crucible and contents again to redness for five minutes. When cool, reweigh. If the last two mass determinations differ by no more than 0.01 g, you may assume that the water has all been driven off. Otherwise repeat the process, heating to constant mass. The dehydrated compound left in the crucible should be returned to your instructor, since it can be used in the preparation of solutions.

CALCULATIONS: 1. *The percentage of water in crystallized barium chloride.* Knowing the mass of crystallized barium chloride used and the mass of the anhydrous compound which remained after heating, the mass of water of crystallization lost during the heating becomes evident. This loss of mass (the mass of water of crystallization) may be expressed as a percentage of the mass of the hydrates as follows:

$$\frac{\text{mass of water lost by heating}}{\text{mass of crystallized barium chloride}} \times 100\% =$$

$$\frac{\qquad}{\qquad} \times 100\% = \qquad \%$$

This is your *experimental* result. Now calculate the theoretical percentage of water of crystallization in crystallized barium chloride from the correct formula, $BaCl_2 \cdot 2H_2O$. Do your computations in smooth form and enter the results in a Data Table like the one that follows.

DATA TABLE

Mass of empty crucible and cover	g
Mass of crucible, cover and crystallized barium chloride	g
Mass of crystallized barium chloride	g
Mass of crucible, cover, and anhydrous barium chloride	g
Mass of anhydrous barium chloride	g
Mass of water lost by heating	g
Percentage of water in crystallized barium chloride	%
Theoretical percentage of water in crystallized barium chloride	%
Experimental error	%
Percentage error	%

2. *The formula of crystallized barium chloride.* The *g-formula wt.* of crystallized barium chloride is in the same ratio to the *g-formula wt.* of anhydrous barium chloride as the *actual mass* of crystallized barium chloride used is to the *actual mass* of anhydrous barium chloride recovered. You have the masses of these two substances, and you can compute the g-formula wt. of anhydrous $BaCl_2$ from the atomic weights.

g-formual wt. of crystallized barium chloride ______ g

g-formula wt. of anhydrous barium chloride ______ g

part of the g-formula wt. of the hydrate due to water ______ g

number of moles of water per g-formula wt. of hydrate ...... ______ moles
(calculate to the nearest whole number)

formula of crystallized barium chloride ______

The g-formula wt. of crystallized barium chloride can then be found by means of the following proportion:

$$\frac{\text{g-formula wt. of cryst. barium chloride}}{\text{g-formula wt. of anhyd. barium chloride}} = \frac{\text{g of cryst. barium chloride used}}{\text{g of anhyd. barium chloride left}}$$

3. In *dry* test tubes, heat successively *one* or *two* small crystals of as many of the compounds listed in the table below as your instructor may direct. In most of the cases only moderate heating is required. Note the effects. Tabulate the results in a table similar to the one below.

QUESTION: How does the percentage of water in crystallized barium chloride exemplify the law of definite composition?

FURTHER EXPERIMENTATION: In the table below investigate the specific properties of several familiar crystalline hydrates to determine others which lend themselves to this method of determining percentage hydration.

Collect data on some representative substances and verify their hydrate formulas.

Undertake an explanation of any large deviations from the correct hydrate formulas that your data may yield.

Name of compound	Water of crystallization present?	Description of residue
sodium carbonate		
sodium sulfate		
sodium chloride		
copper(II) sulfate		
sodium aluminum sulfate		
potassium chloride		
magnesium chloride		
potassium nitrate		

Experiment 20 Solution and Molecular Polarity

PURPOSE: To show how the nature of the attractive forces between molecules determines and helps to explain the solution process and the selectivity of solvents.

APPARATUS: Graduated cylinder (10 ml); microspatula (or wooden splint); stoppers, cork; test tubes, Pyrex, small.

ADDITIONAL APPARATUS FOR INSTRUCTOR'S EXPERIMENT: 2 bottles, wide-mouth, drying tube; hydrogen chloride generator.

MATERIAL: Iodine, solid; benzene; carbon tetrachloride; ethanol; ethylene glycol; glycerol.

ADDITIONAL MATERIAL FOR INSTRUCTOR'S EXPERIMENT: calcium chloride; sodium chloride; litmus papers, red and blue; sulfuric acid, concentrated.

SUGGESTION: If students are not permitted to use carbon tetrachloride, tetrachloroethylene (C_2Cl_4, perchloroethylene) may be substituted.

INTRODUCTION: A rough rule which applies to the phenomenon of solubility is: "like dissolves like." In general, the possibility of solution taking place is increased by a similarity in the composition and structure of the substances involved. The forces between molecules which play a role in the solution process include (1) the dispersion interaction forces which are common to all atoms and molecules, both polar and nonpolar, (2) the dipole forces between polar molecules, and (3) the forces related to hydrogen bonding. Consult Sec. 9.4, page 166 for dispersion interaction and Sec. 11.16, page 215 for hydrogen bond in *Modern Chemistry*, 1974. Nonpolar substances dissolve in nonpolar liquids because of dispersion interaction. Polar liquids and substances dissolve in polar liquids because of dipole-dipole interaction and dispersion interactions. Hydrogen bonding may also play a role in the solution of polar substances. Some nonpolar substances do dissolve in polar liquids because of the magnitude of the dispersion interactions. For a particular substance, these three types of forces play an important role in determining its melting point, boiling point (condensation temperature), vapor pressure, and critical temperature. The hydrogen bonding in water is responsible for its unusually high melting and boiling points. Hydrogen bonds also exist in alcohols such as ethanol (C_2H_5OH), ethylene glycol ($C_2H_4(OH)_2$), and glycerol ($C_3H_5(OH)_3$). The molecules of these water-related compounds are also dipoles.

One measure of the polarity of a substance is the measurable property known as the dielectric constant. (You may wish to refer to a physics textbook for a detailed explanation.) The relative magnitudes of the dielectric constants of the liquids used in this experiment are listed in the following table.

Substance	*Dielectric constant (20° C)*
carbon tetrachloride, CCl_4	2.238
benzene, C_6H_6	2.284
hydrogen chloride, HCl (−15° C)	6.35
ethanol, C_2H_5OH	24.30
ethylene glycol, $C_2H_4(OH)_2$	37.
glycerol, $C_3H_5(OH)_3$	42.5
water, H_2O	80.37

As part of this experiment, you will test the solubility of one nonpolar solid, iodine, which exists as a molecular crystal composed of I_2 molecules. The Instructor experiment deals with the solubility of hydrogen chloride, a polar substance.

SUGGESTIONS: Students should measure out the recommended volume of water, generally 5 ml, in the 10 ml graduated cylinder. They should approximate this measured volume by using similar small size test tubes and a dropper. To prevent waste of materials and promote safety, the liquids should be dispensed from stoppered bottles having long-stemmed droppers through the stopper.

CAUTION: During this experiment the following directions *must* be followed because some of the substances used are highly toxic or combustible. All laboratory burners are to be extinguished. Benzene, carbon tetrachloride, and ethylene glycol are *poisonous*. Benzene is *combustible*. Therefore all liquids are to be used in 1 ml quantities. Shaking of mixtures is to be performed only in cork-stoppered test tubes. Iodine must be handled with a microspatula so that the recommended quantity of two tiny crystals is used in each case.

PROCEDURE: 1. *Solubility and the polarity of solvents.* Measure out 5 ml of water with the graduated cylinder and pour into the test tube in the test tube rack. Place 5 ml of ethanol, benzene, and carbon tetrachloride into successive test tubes approximating the volume of water in the first test tube. Add 2 small iodine crystals to each. Stopper and shake vigorously. Report evidence of solubility and the resultant color of solutions, when produced, in a table like Data Table 1.

2. *Comparative polarity of liquids.* Into each of four separate test tubes add 5 ml of benzene. To the first test tube add 5 ml of water, to the second 5 ml of ethanol, to the third 5 ml of ethylene glycol, and to the fourth 5 ml of glycerol. Stopper and shake each test tube. Report the existence of one layer which indicates miscibility or that of two separate layers indicating nonmiscibility. Save the test tube contents for Part 3. Basing your judgment on the results of Part 2, how would you expect a mixture of benzene and carbon tetrachloride to behave when shaken? Make this test, using 1 ml of each liquid, and record its result.

3. Add 5 ml of ethanol to each of the test tubes, saved from Part 2, except the one containing ethanol. Stopper and shake vigorously. Look for the existence of more than one layer and the height of the lower layer compared to that of the upper layer. Where benzene is immiscible, it will float on top of the other liquid(s). Record your results in a table like Data Table 2.

On the basis of the results obtained, list the liquids; glycerol, ethanol, and ethylene glycol in order of increasing polarity.

4. INSTRUCTOR EXPERIMENT: Place the end of the delivery tube from the hydrogen chloride generator one-quarter of an inch above the surface of a one-inch layer

DATA TABLE 1

I_2 in	Soluble or insoluble	Color of solution
water		
ethanol		
benzene		
carbon tetrachloride		

DATA TABLE 2

Addition of ethanol to:	No. of layers at start	No. of layers at finish	Height of lower layer
benzene + water			
benzene + ethylene glycol			
benzene + glycerol			

of water in a gas collecting bottle. Set the generator into operation. Students should note the appearance of apparent convection currents of an oily substance where the hydrogen chloride comes into contact with the water. What does this indicate about the solubility of HCl in water? Add blue litmus to the contents of the bottle. Students should note results and explain evidence of solubility of hydrogen chloride in water. Now permit dry hydrogen chloride [dry by passing through $CaCl_2$ or H_2SO_4 (conc.)] to pass into and through one inch of benzene in a small gas collecting bottle. Have residual hydrogen chloride gas blown out of the top of the bottle with air. Add litmus (blue) to benzene. Now add one inch of water to the bottle, shake vigorously and inspect the litmus paper in the water layer. What is its color? Where did the hydrogen chloride come from? What does this result indicate about the comparative solubility of hydrogen chloride in water as compared with its solubility in benzene? What does this indicate about polarity of HCl? The conductivity apparatus (page 246 in MODERN CHEMISTRY, 1974) may be used to test for electrical conductivity of 1. HCl in benzene, and 2. HCl in benzene + water.

QUESTIONS:

1. Explain why iodine is soluble in benzene and carbon tetrachloride.
2. Explain why iodine dissolves in ethanol but practically not at all in water.
3. Look up and record the dielectric constant of iodine.
4. Ethanol has the formula, C_2H_5OH, ethylene glycol, $C_2H_4(OH)_2$, and glycerol $C_3H_5(OH)_3$. What apparent effect does increasing the number of hydroxyl groups in a compound have on its polarity?
5. Explain the difference in results which occurred when ethanol was shaken with (1) benzene and ethylene glycol and (2) benzene and glycerol.
6. Cite experimental evidence which indicates that nonpolar liquids (substances) are soluble in polar liquids having a wide range in polarity.
7. Cite experimental evidence that a nonpolar liquid may be insoluble with liquids of high polarity.
8. Cite experimental evidence which indicates that "like dissolves like" as it relates to preference of polar liquids for each other rather than for nonpolar liquids.

Experiment

21 The Solid State, Crystals and Crystallization

PURPOSE: To show various processes by which crystals are formed and to study the nature of crystals.

APPARATUS: Balance, platform; beaker; burner and tubing; clamp, test tube; dish, evaporating; funnel; glass plate; graduated cylinder; hand lens; ring, iron; ring stand, spatula; thermometer; watch glass; wire gauze.

ADDITIONAL APPARATUS FOR INSTRUCTOR'S EXPERIMENT: Graduated cylinder; test tube; watch glass.

MATERIAL: Ammonium chloride; ice; iodine; sodium chloride; sulfur, powder; filter paper.

ADDITIONAL MATERIAL FOR INSTRUCTOR'S EXPERIMENT: Sulfur, powder; carbon disulfide.

SUGGESTION: Amorphous solids: To demonstrate or have your students prepare amorphous sulfur refer to Exp. 58, Forms of Sulfur, Procedure 3. An alternate procedure is to have the students heat a piece of glass tubing or a glass rod in the burner flame and permit it to bend under its own weight as the solid softens.

INTRODUCTION: The properties characteristic of the solid state are evident from the study of true solids composed of crystals. In crystalline solids, the particles have a regular arrangement resulting in a definite geometric shape. A specific crystal has a definite number of faces so arranged that the interfacial angles between adjacent faces are definite. The classes of crystals, according to their shape, are isometric (cubic), tetragonal, triclinic, hexagonal, orthorhombic, and monoclinic. The definite shape, definite volume, and incompressibility of solids is due to the forces which hold the particles together in fixed positions. Crystalline solids have definite melting points whose magnitudes indicate the nature of the binding forces which hold the particles together in the crystal lattice. Crystals may be classified according to the types of lattice structure, that is, whether the particles that compose the crystal lattice are ionic, covalent, metallic, or molecular. Perfectly shaped crystals rarely occur in nature. Examination of a laboratory specimen of quartz generally reveals a jumble of imperfectly shaped crystals joined together. The formation of multiple crystals tends to interfere with the development of single perfect crystals. In this experiment, the various processes by which natural forces arrange the particles of substances into crystals will be studied. These are cooling a molten mass, evaporation from solution, cooling a hot saturated solution, and sublimation.

PROCEDURE: 1. *Crystallization. a.* Put 5 grams of powdered roll sulfur into a test tube. Holding the test tube in a clamp, gently heat the contents. Note the color of the sulfur as it melts in contact with the hot glass. Continue to heat gently until all the sulfur liquefies. Avoid over-heating and try to keep the color of the final melt close to that of the initially melted sulfur. If the sulfur darkens due to local over-heating, stop heating for a short time and gently shake the tube contents (shake in a nearly horizontal, not vertical plane). Pour the liquid sulfur into a folded dry filter paper placed in a funnel. When a crust forms over the fold, remove the paper and quickly open the fold. Permit any excess liquid sulfur to run onto a piece of paper rather than onto the table top. Describe the appearance of the crystals that have been formed and state the crystal system to which they belong.

b. Put 3 or 4 small pieces of solid iodine in an evaporating dish using a spatula or wooden splint. Place the dish on the wire gauze and cover the dish with a watch glass (convex side down). Pour 10 ml of water into the watch glass. Heat the evaporating dish with a low flame. See Fig. 21-1. Note the color of the iodine vapor. Continue to heat until most of the solid has vaporized. Permit the apparatus to cool. Remove the watch glass, discard the water, and examine the deposit on the bottom of the watch glass. Note the color and shape of the solid crystals. Scrape off a small portion of the deposit onto a glass plate. Examine under the hand lens. You may be able to detect a crystal which has the characteristic shape of solid iodine. To which crystal system does it belong? Wash off the iodine deposit with hot water. **CAUTION:** *Avoid contact of solid iodine with the skin.*

c. Into 10 ml of water in a test tube pour 5 grams of ammonium chloride. Shake thoroughly. To what extent does it dissolve? If necessary, heat gently until all the ammonium chloride dissolves. Add another 5

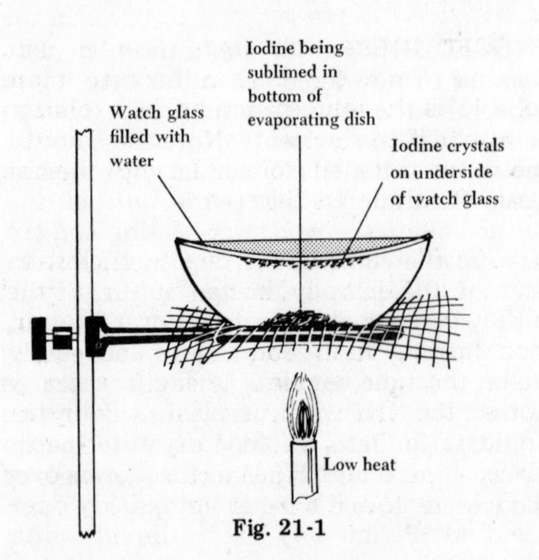

Fig. 21-1

grams of ammonium chloride and continue to heat with shaking until it all dissolves. Now permit cold tap water to run over the outside of the test tube until you note signs of crystallization. Note the appearance of the crystals. Permit the crystals to settle out. Remove some of them with a splint. Place the crystals on a piece of filter paper to remove most of the water. Transfer a portion of the sample to a glass plate and examine under the hand lens. Describe the shape and size of the crystals you see.

d. INSTRUCTOR EXPERIMENT. Use procedure 1 of Exp. 58, Forms of Sulfur, for preparation of rhombic sulfur. Add 2 grams of powdered roll sulfur to 5 ml of carbon disulfide in a test tube. **CAUTION:** *All open flames should be extinguished since the vapors of carbon disulfide are dangerously combustible.* Have students note any evidence of solution, i.e., color of solution. Permit the excess solid sulfur to settle, and pour the clear solution into a watch glass. Place the watch glass under the hood and partially cover with a beaker, one side of which is supported by a match box. Students should explain the effect of this arrangement on the rate of carbon disulfide evaporation and hence the rate of crystal formation. When evaporation is complete, students should examine the watch glass deposit and samples from it under the hand lens. Students should describe and identify the crystal shape, and compare the size of these crystals (produced slowly) with those of ammonium chloride (produced rapidly). The teacher may wish to use the overhead projector in this demonstration or an alternate using a drop of sodium chloride solution on a microscope slide.

2. *Crystal Properties. a.* Examine several grains of sodium chloride under the hand lens. Note the shape of a single crystal. How does the shape of this crystal compare with that of the other crystals that you can also see? You have previously examined two different samples of sulfur crystals. Name the crystal system to which the sodium chloride crystals belong.

b. Put several cubes or chunks of ice into a small beaker and insert a thermometer. Permit the ice to melt and record three readings of the thermometer at 5 minute intervals during the period (some ice must always be present). What property of a crystal is revealed by this procedure?

QUESTIONS: 1. State two characteristics of crystals.

2. Name three crystalline systems of which you observed at least one example in this experiment.

3. Name or briefly describe the four different crystallization processes.

4. *a.* To what state does a solid usually change upon being heated?

b. To what state does a solid go when it undergoes sublimation?

5. Explain the apparent "disappearance" of such solids as Dry Ice and naphthalene moth balls (crystals).

6. What condition determines the size of crystals being produced by crystallization processes?

Experiment 22 Solubility, Rate of Solution, Heat of Solution

PURPOSE: To study some of the factors affecting the solubility and the rate of solution of a solid in water. To observe evidence that the heat of solution of a substance is related to the effect of temperature on its solubility.

APPARATUS: Balance, platform; beaker, 400 ml; burner and tubing; clamp, test tube; 2 flasks, Erlenmeyer, 125 ml; graduated cylinder; mortar and pestle; rubber stoppers, solid, No. 2; spatula; test tubes; thermometer.

ADDITIONAL APPARATUS FOR INSTRUCTOR'S EXPERIMENT: Beaker, 100 ml; burner and tubing; dish, evaporating, large; funnel, large; ring, iron; ring stand; thermometer; wire gauze.

MATERIAL: Ammonium chloride; potassium nitrate; sodium hydroxide (pellets).

ADDITIONAL MATERIAL FOR INSTRUCTOR'S EXPERIMENT: Filter paper (large); sulfuric acid, concentrated.

INTRODUCTION: The three factors that hasten the solution process of a solid in water will be studied in this experiment. You will observe the effect of temperature changes on the quantity of solid that can be dissolved in a given amount of water. You will also observe that some solids dissolve in water with the absorption of heat while others dissolve with the evolution of heat. This indicates that the heat of solution of a particular substance plays a role in the effect of temperature changes on the solubility of the substance. Solutes with positive heats of solution become more soluble as the temperature of their solution is raised. The effect of temperature on saturated solutions of solutes having negative heats of solution is the reverse.

SUGGESTION: Two students may work together, thereby reducing the quantity of KNO_3 solution to be processed by the instructor. A clean container of adequate volume shuold be designated in which to collect the KNO_3 solutions prepared by the students in Parts 2, 3, 4, and 5. The instructor may wish to delegate the task of recovering the KNO_3 in crystalline form

DATA TABLE

Solute	Water temperature °C		Heat of solution of solute (kcal/mole)
	Initial	Final (solution)	
KNO_3			
NH_4Cl			
NaOH			
H_2SO_4			

to one or two interested students as an extra project.

PROCEDURE: 1. *a.* Put 10 ml of water in each of three test tubes. Insert a thermometer into the water in the first test tube and record the temperature. To the water in the first test tube, add 5 g of potassium nitrate. Gently stir the tube contents with the stirring rod. Note the temperature when all 5 g have been dissolved, or almost completely dissolved. Repeat this procedure with the second test tube using 5 g of ammonium chloride. To the third test tube add 5 pellets of sodium hydroxide, transferring them from the bottle to the test tube by using a spatula. **CAUTION:** *Sodium hydroxide is a powerful caustic hydroxide. Do not handle the pellets or permit any of the solution to touch your skin.* Record your results in a Data Table like the one above. Refer to the Heats of Solution Table in Chapter 12 of MODERN CHEMISTRY, 1974, or to a Handbook.

b. INSTRUCTOR'S EXPERIMENT. To 20 ml of water in a beaker add with stirring 5 ml of concentrated sulfuric acid. Have a student read the initial and final temperatures. Students should record this information in the Data Table.

2. Weigh out two 2-g portions of coarse crystals of potassium nitrate. Grind one portion to a fine powder, using a rotary motion of the pestle; *do not pound the crystals.* Have at hand two Erlenmeyer flasks each containing 25 ml of distilled water at room temperature. Add the two portions to the two flasks simultaneously and agitate similarly with swirling motions. Observe the time required for complete solution in each case. Explain the difference in time on the basis of surface area of solute. *Label a clean 400-ml beaker and pour all solutions prepared in Parts 2, 3, 4, and 5 into the beaker.*

3. Repeat the experiment, but pulverize both portions. Swirl one portion as before, but let the other stand without stirring. Compare the rates at which solution occurs. *Pour the solutions into the labeled beaker.*

4. Repeat, using two 2-g portions of large crystals. Compare the rate of solution in one case using 25 ml of distilled water at room temperature, and in the other case 25 ml of distilled water heated to near the boiling point. Stir both solutions similarly. Pour the solutions into the labeled beaker.

5. Grind 5 g of potassium nitrate to a powder. **CAUTION.** To 10 ml of distilled water (at room temperature) in a test tube, add the powdered KNO_3 gradually, a little at a time. Stopper the test tube and shake it after each addition of solute. After all the KNO_3 has been added and the solution is saturated at room temperature (how do you know it is saturated?), warm *gently* over a low burner flame. *The stopper must be removed.* Move the test tube in and out

of the flame carefully to avoid sudden, violent boiling. When the liquid appears to be near the boiling point, remove the test tube from the flame and examine the solution. Has all the KNO_3 dissolved at the higher temperature? Is the solution *saturated* or *unsaturated*? Justify your decision. Drop in a small crystal of KNO_3 to see if it dissolves. If not, warm the solution carefully again until all of the potassium nitrate is in solution. What do you conclude about the solubility of potassium nitrate in hot water, as compared with its solubility in cold water? (Refer to the solubility curves in Chapter 12 of MODERN CHEMISTRY, 1974.) Now allow the solution to cool. Devise a means of hastening the cooling process. Result? Reheat the solution to dissolve the crystals which formed and transfer all accumulated KNO_3 solution to a container designated by the instructor. Carefully summarize your observations concerning the influence of the temperature of the water on the solubility of the potassium nitrate.

6. INSTRUCTOR'S EXPERIMENT. Filter the solutions of potassium nitrate collected from the students into a large evaporating dish. Evaporate to approximately one-half volume and, when cool, pour off the mother liquor and dry the crystals between sheets of filter paper. The process may be repeated, and a second or even a third crop of crystals may be obtained. When dry, return the crystals to a properly labeled stock bottle for future use.

QUESTIONS: 1. Explain why pulverizing a solid solute increases the rate of solution.
2. Why does stirring increase the rate at which most solids dissolve?
3. Why does increasing the temperature, other conditions being kept constant, increase the rate of solution of potassium nitrate?
4. What effect would you expect increased temperature to have on the solubility of ammonium chloride? Why?
5. The heat of solution of lithium carbonate is −3.06 kcal/mole solute in 200 moles of H_2O. What effect would you expect increased temperature to have on the concentration of Li_2CO_3 in its saturated solution? Explain.

FURTHER EXPERIMENTATION: Two other chemicals which may be used in experiments on the heat of solution are ammonium nitrate and calcium chloride. These are used in instant cold and hot packs as first aids devices. Consult the article, "Thermochemistry and First Aid," by Smith, W. L. *Chemistry*, 45, 18 (1972 – Sept.).

Experiment 23 A Solubility Curve

PURPOSE: To show how the solubility of a salt such as ammonium chloride varies with the temperature and how to plot its solubility curve on the basis of observed data.

APPARATUS: Balance, sensitive to 0.01 g; beaker, 400 ml; burner and tubing; pipet, 10 ml; ring, iron; ring stand; test tubes, Pyrex; thermometer; wire gauze.

MATERIAL: Ammonium chloride; graph paper.

INTRODUCTION: The solubility of a solute is the amount of solute dissolved in a given amount of a certain solvent at equilibrium, under specified conditions. The usual units used on solubility graphs are grams of solute per 100 ml of water at specified Celsius temperatures. Increasing the temperature usually increases the solubility of solids in liquids. Decreasing the temperature usually decreases the solubility. In this experiment we will determine the solubility of ammonium chloride at various temperatures by allowing a hot solution of the compound to cool and observing the temperature at which the solid begins to crystallize.

PROCEDURE: 1. Weigh out 4.00-g, 5.00-g, 6.00-g, and 7.00-g samples of ammonium chloride. Put each sample in a properly labeled test tube. Using a pipette, measure 10.0 ml of water into each test tube. Fill the beaker half full of water, put the test tubes containing the 4.00-g and 5.00-g samples in the water, and bring the water to a boil. Meanwhile, heat the test tube containing the 7.00-g sample gently with the burner, stirring continuously until all the solute dissolves. Do not bring the test tube contents to a boil. With the thermometer in the solution, allow the contents to cool while stirring gently. Construct a Data Table like the one shown. Record the temperature at which the solid begins to crystallize (when the first crystals appear). Heat the solution in the test tube again to dissolve the crystals, allow it to cool, and recheck the temperature at which crystallization occurs. Repeat this procedure with the test tube containing the 6.00-g sample. Repeat with the 5.00-g and 4.00-g samples using the hot water bath as a source of heat, rather than the burner. A cold water bath is needed to hasten the crystallization of the 4.00-g sample.

2. Plot the solubility curve for ammonium chloride from the results listed in your Data Table. Along the horizontal axis on the graph paper, write the temperature scale 0°C to 100°C using 10 degree intervals. Along the vertical axis, write the solubility in g/10 ml H_2O from 0 to 10.00 g intervals. Place dots corresponding to the four masses you used at the places corresponding to the observed temperatures. Draw a small circle around each of these points and construct a smooth curve for the observed data. Extrapolate this curve to the temperature limits by using a dashed (----) line to indicate extrapolation.

DATA TABLE

Solubility (g/10.0 ml H_2O)	Temperature
4.00 g	°C
5.00 g	°C
6.00 g	°C
7.00 g	°C

QUESTIONS: 1. From your solubility curve determine the solubility of ammonium chloride in g/100 ml H_2O at 60°C.
2. Consult a Handbook and record the accepted value for the solubility of ammonium chloride at 60°C.
3. Calculate your percentage error from the answers to Questions 1 and 2. Percentage error.

FURTHER EXPERIMENTATION: Repeat the procedure using other compounds. For $NaNO_3$ try samples starting with 8.00 g and going up by successive increments to 14.00 g. For KNO_3, try samples starting with 4.00 g and going up by increments of 3.00 g to 13.00 g. Evaluate the changes in solubilities of NH_4Cl, $NaNO_3$, and KNO_3. Construct solubility curves using molalities instead of grams per 100 ml of water.

Solubility Data for NH_4Cl in grams per 100 ml H_2O

30°C	41.4 g
50°C	50.4 g
70°C	60.2 g
90°C	71.3 g

Experiment

24 (a) Preparation and Properties of Acids

PURPOSE: To prepare some acids from their anhydrides. To study some common properties of acids.

APPARATUS: Balance, platform; beaker, 400 ml; 3 bottles, wide-mouth; burner and tubing; clamp, buret; clamp, test tube; flask, Florence; funnel, separatory; 4 glass plates; graduated cylinder; medicine dropper; ring stand; rubber stoppers, 1-hole No. 4, 2-hole No. 4; spoon, deflagrating; test tubes; 2 test tubes, hand glass; trough.

MATERIAL: Charcoal, wood, lumps; copper wire, 22-30 gauge; phosphorus, red; sodium peroxide; sulfur, roll; zinc, sheet, 1 cm^2 pieces; asbestos paper; litmus papers, red and blue; sandpaper; nitric acid, concentrated; acetic acid, dilute (1:4); hydrochloric acid, (1:3); phosphoric acid, dilute (1:14); sulfuric acid, dilute (1:11); solutions of methyl orange, phenolphthalein.

SUGGESTION: If a separatory funnel is not available, a suitable dropping funnel may be improvised from a short-stemmed funnel, iron ring, pinch clamp, rubber connector, and glass tubing.

Satisfactory results may be obtained by burning the substances in bottles of air if time does not permit the use of the oxygen generator. A small candle in a deflagrating spoon may be substituted for charcoal in the production of carbon dioxide in the bottle of air.

INTRODUCTION: Except for fluorine, oxygen is the most highly electronegative element. We would naturally expect many elements, both metals and nonmetals, to combine readily with oxygen. Some of the chemical properties of the oxides, notably their reactions with water, enable us to recognize the correlation between the elements and their positions in the Periodic Table. In general, oxides in reaction with water form oxygen-hydrogen groups. The character of the product may depend on the character of the associated element. Elements near the central region of the Periodic Table may show amphiprotic properties. Thus $Zn(OH)_2$ is the proper formula for zinc hydroxide in the presence of a strong acid. However, H_2ZnO_2 is more suitable when the same compound is in the presence of a strong hydroxide. In a general sense, oxides of the highly electropositive elements react with water to form solutions which are distinctly basic. These elements are located to the left of the central region of the Periodic Table. Oxides of the highly electronegative elements react with water to form solutions which are distinctly acidic. These elements are located to the right of the central region of the Periodic Table. Such nonmetallic oxides are known as acid anhydrides. In this experiment, you will prepare some typical acid anhydrides and observe some of the common properties of their water solutions.

It is true, of course, that some acids do not contain oxygen. Binary acids, such as hydrochloric and hydrosulfuric, will be studied in later experiments.

PROCEDURE: 1. Assemble an oxygen generator as shown in Fig. 24-1. The flask (Pyrex) to be used as the generator must

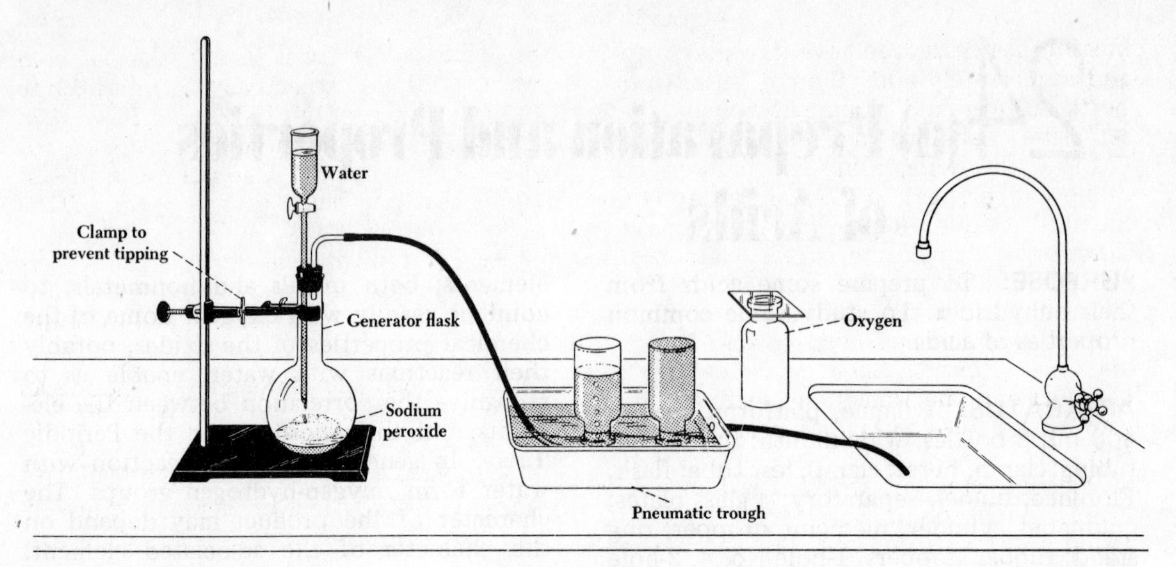

Fig. 24-1

be clean and *thoroughly* dry. **CAUTION:** *Sodium peroxide is a vigorous oxidizing agent and reacts with a limited supply of water to produce oxygen, releasing much heat in the process.* Weigh out 10 g of Na_2O_2 on a dry weighing paper and transfer it to the *dry* generator flask. Wet the weighing paper thoroughly with water before discarding. Why? Prepare three wide-mouth bottles to collect the O_2 by water displacement. When ready, ask your instructor to inspect the apparatus.

Close the stopcock of the funnel and partially fill it with water. Place a collecting bottle in position and open the stopcock just enough to allow water to enter the generator dropwise. Regulate the addition of water to provide a moderate evolution of oxygen. Discard the first bottle of oxygen collected. Why? Refill the bottle with water and return it to the trough. As the water in each bottle is displaced, cover the mouth with a glass square and place it mouth upward on the desk (covered). Feel the sides of the generator. Result? How would you describe the reaction in the generator? Continue the addition of water to the generator until the reaction is completed.

2. Clear away the oxygen-generating apparatus *after* the reaction has ceased. Select a 1-hole stopper to fit a hard glass test tube and insert the short leg of an 8 × 20 cm glass bend. Place a small coil of copper wire in the Pyrex test tubes Add 10 ml of distilled water to a second hand glass test tube. Cover the copper with 1 ml of water and add 4 ml of concentrated nitric acid. Immediately insert the stopper assembly and pass the evolved gas into the distilled water. The gaseous product is nitrogen dioxide, NO_2. **CAUTION:** *NO_2 is poisonous and must not be inhaled.* Describe it. What do you think is its source? After the evolution of the gas has subsided, heat the solution of NO_2, using a test tube clamp and a low flame. **CAUTION:** *Hold the test tube in a slanting position with the mouth of the tube turned away.* Move the tube over the flame to heat the solution uniformly and allow to boil quietly for about 1 minute. Set aside to cool for later use.

3. Clean a deflagrating spoon, line it with asbestos paper, and heat it strongly for a moment in the burner flame. When cool, add a small lump of sulfur (no larger than a pea) and ignite over the burner. Quickly insert the burning sulfur well down into a bottle of oxygen. Keep the bottle covered as completely as possible with the glass plate. What is the product? When the combustion has ceased, remove the spoon (hot) and immediately add 10 ml of water to the bottle. Cover and shake vigorously; then set aside. Label to avoid confusion later.

Clean the deflagrating spoon as before; reline and preheat to burn away any combustible residue. Repeat the above procedure, using a small lump of red phosphorus (½ pea size) and another bottle of oxygen. Result? What is the combustion product? Does it appear to be soluble in water? Label and save. Repeat, using a small piece of charcoal and the remaining bottle of oxygen. What is this combustion product? Label and save.

4. Place several test strips of red and blue litmus papers on a clean dry glass plate. Using a clean stirring rod, test each of the four solutions just prepared by dipping the stirring rod in the solution and then touching both red and blue test strips. *Rinse the rod in distilled water and wipe dry between tests.* Results? What action between water and nonmetallic oxides is indicated?

Divide each of the four solutions equally between 2 test tubes. Label all 8 test tubes to avoid confusion. To one test tube of each solution, add a drop of phenolphthalein indicator. To the remaining test tube of each solution, add 1 drop of methyl orange indicator. Shake each to mix uniformly. Observe the colors by looking lengthwise through the tubes against a white background. Results? Construct a suitable table and record your observations for Part 4. If the tests on the solutions containing CO_2 are indecisive, suggest a possible reason.

5. Place 4 test tubes in a beaker of cold water and add respectively 5 ml of dilute (approximately 3 *N*) H_2SO_4, H_3PO_4, HCl, and $HC_2H_3O_2$. Brighten 1-cm^2 pieces of sheet zinc and drop 1 square in each test tube. List the acids in the order of the activity observed.

Repeat this procedure with the 4 test tubes placed in a beaker of hot water. How does the action compare? Explain the difference observed.

QUESTIONS: 1. How can you define an acid anhydride?

2. What general class of elements reacts with oxygen to form acic anhydrides?

3. What is the effect of increased temperature on the chemical activity of acids?

FURTHER EXPERIMENTATION: Use a conductivity apparatus setup like the one shown on page 246 of MODERN CHEMISTRY, 1974 to test conductivity of glacial acetic acid. (Test with litmus paper and Hydrion paper.) To one sample of glacial acetic acid add an equal volume of benzene and stir the mixture. Test for conductivity. Repeat tests with litmus and Hydrion paper. Repeat with another sample of glacial acetic diluted with an equal volume of water and again test with litmus and Hydrion. Test a benzene solution of hydrogen chloride with litmus paper (dried in disiccator) and with Hydrion paper similarly dried. Test its conductivity. To this solution add an equal volume of water. Stopper and shake vigorously. Repeat the tests with litmus paper, Hydrion paper, and conductivity apparatus.

EQUATIONS

1. Reaction between sodium peroxide and water
2. Reaction between sulfur dioxide and water
3. Reaction between diphosphorus pentoxide and water
4. Reaction between carbon dioxide and water
5. Reaction between nitrogen dioxide and water (nitrogen monoxide is one of the products).
6. Reaction between zinc and sulfuric acid
7. Ionization of acetic acid in water
8. Ionization of hydrogen chloride in water

Experiment

24 (b) Preparation and Properties of Hydroxides

PURPOSE: To prepare some hydroxides and to study the properties of the metallic hydroxides.

APPARATUS: Beaker, 250 ml; burner and tubing; clamp, buret; dish, evaporating; froceps; funnel; glass plates; graduated cylinder; ring, iron; ring stand; test tubes; watch glass; wire gauze.

MATERIAL: Barium hydroxide; calcium; calcium oxide; sodium; Hydrion paper D (pH:11-13); litmus papers, red and blue; filter paper; ammonia-water solution, concentrated; ammonia-water solution, dilute (1:4); hydrochloric acid, dilute (1:4); solutions of aluminum sulfate (0.03 *M*), iron(III) chloride (0.07 *M*); magnesium hydroxide (suspension); methyl orange; phenolphthalein; sodium hydroxide (2 *M*).

INTRODUCTION: A solution of a metallic hydroxide has basic properties due to the presence of hydroxide, OH^-, ions. Some very active metals, such as sodium and potassium, replace part of the hydrogen from water at ordinary temperatures to form solutions containing hydroxide ions. Such metallic oxides as calcium oxide, CaO, react directly with water to form basic solutions. Some insoluble hydroxides are formed by ionic reactions.

In the modern sense, a base is a proton acceptor. Thus many particles are basic. In general chemistry the most common base is the hydroxide, OH^-, ion. Soluble metallic hydroxides form our most common basic solutions.

CAUTION: *Do not handle sodium with the fingers.* Large pieces of sodium produce *dangerous explosions when placed on water.* Secure from your instructor a small piece of metallic sodium at the time you are ready to use. it. You may use your forceps, or have the sodium placed on a piece of filter paper. Step back a few feet after you have added the sodium to water, since a slight explosion could occur near the end of the reaction.

PROCEDURE: 1. Read the *caution* before you begin. Drop a small piece of sodium, not larger than one quarter of a *small pea*, into an evaporating dish half-filled with water. Cover immediately with a glass plate. When the action is complete, test the solution with red and blue litmus papers. To make this test, place the test strips on a clean, dry glass plate. Then dip a clean stirring rod into the solution and touch the test strips. Result? Test the solution with Hydrion paper in the same manner as that used with the litmus papers and record the pH.

Transfer 2 ml of the solution to a test tube and add to it a drop of phenolphthalein solution. Result? Repeat with a second 2-ml portion and a drop of methyl orange solution. Result? To what particles in the solution do you attribute these color changes? Evaporate 3 ml of the solution to dryness on a watch glass over boiling water. Name the solid residue. *It is caustic and burns the flesh.*

Drop a small calcium turning into a test tube half-filled with water. After the reaction is complete, test the contents with red and blue litmus paper by dipping a stirring rod into the solution and applying to the litmus papers. Note how the test tube contents differ in appearance from the results obtained from the racetion of sodium with water. Test the solution with Hydrion paper, using the same technique as that used with litmus paper. Record the pH of the solution.

2. Test dry calcium oxide with litmus. Result? To one gram of *fresh* calcium oxide in a test tube, add 10 ml of water. Describe the action. What is this process called? Shake the tube for 2 or 3 minutes, then filter. Test the filtrate with litmus papers and Hydrion paper in the manner described in Part 1. Record the pH of the solution. Add a drop of phenolphthalein to one portion of the filtrate. Explain the result. Add a drop of methyl orange to another portion. Result? Name the responsible particles in this solution. How would you describe the solubility of the product?

3. Test dry barium hydroxide with litmus. Result? To 0.5 g of barium hydroxide in a test tube, add 10 ml of water. Shake for 2 or 3 minutes, filter, and then test the filtrate with litmus papers, Hydrion paper, phenolphthalein, and with methyl orange as before. Record the pH. How do you interpret the results of these tests?

CAUTION: *Barium hydroxide is poisonous.*

4. To 5 ml of magnesium hydroxide (suspension) in a test tube, add 10 ml of water. Shake for 2 or 3 minutes, filter, and then test the filtrate with litmus papers. Hydrion paper, phenolphthalein, and with methyl orange as before. Record the pH. How do you interpret the results of these tests?

5. Add a few drops of concentrated ammonia-water solution to 10 ml of water in a test tube. Test this solution with litmus papers, Hydrion paper, phenolphthalein, and methyl orange. Result? Explain. Clamp the test tube in an inclined position and heat about 5 ml of the solution to boiling. Hold a piece of moist red litmus paper in the vapor escaping from the mouth of the tube, taking care that it does not touch the sides of the tube. Result? After the liquid has been boiled for a few minutes, test it again with red litmus (stirring rod technique). Result? Explain.

6. Fill a test tube one-fourth full of a solution of iron(III) chloride, and add to it 2 or 3 ml of dilute ammonia-water solution. Shake the test tube to mix its contents. Name and describe the precipitate.

7. Fill a test tube one-fourth full of a solution of aluminum sulfate, and add to it 2 or 3 ml of dilute ammonia-water solution. Shake. Name and describe the gelatinous precipitate formed. This precipitate does not settle readily and may be regarded as a suspension. Transfer one-half of the suspension to another test tube and add dilute hydrochloric acid with mixing until an excess is present. (How can you tell when this condition exists?) Result? Write the formula for the gelatinous precipitate (suspension) which is suitable to this behavior. To the portion of the suspension still in the original test tube, add a solution of sodium hydroxide, a few milliliters at a time, until an excess is present. Mixing may be necessary. Result? Explain. Can you write the formula of the original gelatinous precipitate in a form more suitable to show its behavior in the presence of a strong hydroxide solution? What name is used to describe this property in such substances?

QUESTIONS: 1. What are two general methods of preparing soluble hydroxides?

2. Given an unknown solution, how would you test to determine whether it is acidic or basic?

3. What particle do the solutions of the soluble metallic hydroxides have in common?

4. Based on the results obtained by use of the Hydrion paper and the color code for the corresponding pH, list the four soluble hydroxides in order of *decreasing* hydroxide

5. How does the strength of the hydroxide of Na (Group I) compare with that of the hydroxides of Ba, Ca, Mg (Group II)?

6. Based on your pH observations how does the strength of the hydroxides of Group II metals vary with the ionic size?

7. Based on your pH observations, which metallic hydroxide is approximately as basic as the diluted ammonia-water?

FURTHER EXPERIMENTATION: Test the solutions of NaOH, $Ba(OH)_2$, $Ca(OH)_2$, and $Mg(OH)_2$ with the conductivity apparatus, using a 60-watt bulb. For the one(s) which does (do) not light this bulb, try a 25-watt bulb.

Test the solution of NH_3 in benzene with litmus papers and Hydrion paper indicators. Also test conductivity again. Repeat after shaking the benzene solution with an equal volume of distilled water.

EQUATIONS: Write in ionic form.

1. Reaction between sodium and water
2. Reaction between calcium and water
3. Reaction between calcium oxide and water
4. Reaction between ammonia and water
5. Reaction between iron(III) chloride solution and ammonia-water solution
6. Reaction between aluminum sulfate solution and ammonia-water solution
7. Reaction between aluminum hydroxide and hydrochloric acid solution
8. Reaction between aluminum hydroxide and sodium hydroxide solution

Experiment 25 Hydronium Ion Concentration, pH

PURPOSE: To determine the pH of various solutions of comparable concentration, and to study the effect of dilution on the pH of acids and a metallic hydroxide.

APPARATUS: Beaker, 250 ml; graduated cylinders, 10 ml, 50 ml; test tubes.

MATERIAL: pH papers, wide range, i.e. A & B, narrow range, i.e. D, Hydrion papers or equivalent pH papers; solutions of acetic acid (0.10*M*); ammonia water (0.10*M*); ammonium acetate (0.10*M*); hydrochloric acid (0.10*M*); phosphoric acid (0.033 *M*); sodium carbonate (0.050 *M*); sodium chloride (0.10 *M*); sodium hydrogen carbonate (0.10 *M*); sodium hydroxide (0.10 *M*).

INTRODUCTION: The concentration of hydronium ion is usually represented by the expression $[H_3O^+]$ which means the hydronium ion concentration in moles (gram-ions) per liter of solution. A one molar (1.0-*M*) solution of hydronium ions contains 1 mole, 19 g, of hydronium ion per liter of solution.

Pure water is slightly ionized and contains 0.0000001 mole of hydronium ion per liter. Its hydronium ion concentration, $[H_3O^+]$ is therefore represented as 1.0×10^{-7} *M* or 10^{-7} *M*. Since pure water is neutral, its hydroxide ion concentration is also 1.0×10^{-7} *M* or 10^{-7} *M*. In any water solution, the product of the hydronium and hydroxide ion concentrations is known as the ion-product of water and is equal to 1.0×10^{-14}. This equilibrium is represented by the equation:

$$H_2O + H_2O \rightleftharpoons H_3O^+ + OH^-$$

For neutral water, (25° C)

$$K_w = 10^{-14} = [H_3O^+] \times 10^{-6}$$
$$= (1 \times 10^{-7})(1 \times 10^{-7}) = 1 \times 10^{-14}$$

The pH of a solution is defined as the common logarithm of the reciprocal of the hydronium ion concentration. For neutral water,

$$pH = \log \frac{1}{0.0000001} = \log \frac{1}{10^{-7}}$$

Therefore: $pH = \log 10^7$, and $pH = 7$.

If the hydronium ion concentration is greater than that of pure water, the pH of the solution is numerically less than 7. Thus, for a solution which is acid such as 0.000001-*M* (1×10^{-6}-*M*) HCl (completely ionized), the pH is 6. For acidic solutions, therefore, the pH is *smaller* than 7. The smaller the pH the larger the hydronium ion concentration. If the solution is basic, its hydronium ion concentration is less than 10^{-7} *M* and its pH is *larger* than 7. For a 1×10^{-6}-*M* solution of NaOH (completely dissociated), the hydroxide ion concentration is 1×10^{-6}. Its hydronium ion concentration therefore is 1×10^{-8}, and its pH is 8.

$K_w = 10^{-14} = [H_3O^+] \times 10^{-6}$
$[H_3O^+] = 10^{-8}$; the pH being 8

SUGGESTIONS: The teacher may wish to demonstrate the use of a pH meter to complement the use of the indicator and to obtain more exact pH readings.

PROCEDURE: 1. Test for the pH of each of the solutions by dipping a stirring rod into each of the solutions and applying first to the wide range pH papers (A and B) and if necessary, to the narrow (short) range paper (D). Record your observations and complete a Data Table like Data Table 1.
2. *Effect of dilution on pH of acids and hydroxides.* Start with 5.0 ml of stock (0.1-*M*) solutions and dilute to 50 ml. Save 5 ml of the diluted solution in a properly labeled test tube and use another 5.0 ml for the next dilution to 50 ml. Repeat the dilution process 4 times for each stock 0.1-*M* solution, in each case saving the 5.0 ml sample for testing with the pH papers as in Part 1. Record your results in a Data Table like Data Table 2.

QUESTIONS: 1. Which of the substances among those having a definite acidic reaction is (a) the strongest acid, (b) the weakest acid?
2. Why is a 0.1-*M* solution of NaOH a much stronger base than a 0.1-*M* solution of NH_3-aq?
3. What effect does dilution have on the pH of (a) an acid, (b) a base?

DATA TABLE 1

0.1 *N* Solutions	Indicator color	Numerical pH	Strength as acid or base
HCl			
$HC_2H_3O_2$			
H_3PO_4			
NaOH			
NH_3			
NaCl			
Na_2CO_3			
$NaHCO_3$			
$NH_4C_2H_3O_2$			

DATA TABLE 2

HCl	Calculated pH	Indicator color	Observed pH
1. 0.1 *M*			
2. 0.01 *M*			
3. 0.001 *M*			
4. 0.0001 *M*			
5. 0.00001 *M*			

NaOH	Calculated pH	Indicator color	Observed pH
1. 0.1 *M*			
2. 0.01 *M*			
3. 0.001 *M*			
4. 0.0001 *M*			
5. 0.00001 *M*			

$HC_2H_3O_2$	Indicator color	Observed pH
1. 0.1 *M*		
2. 0.01 *M*		
3. 0.001 *M*		
4. 0.0001 *M*		
5. 0.00001 *M*		

Experiment 26 Brønsted Acids and Bases, Indicator

PURPOSE: To show the existence of conjugate acid-base pairs in protolytic reactions involving a weak acid or a weak base, and to show how the relative strength of an acid or base causes indicator reactions.

APPARATUS: Burner and tubing; clamp, test tube; graduated cylinder; test tubes.

MATERIAL: Acetic acid, glacial; ammonium chloride, crystals; sodium acetate, pellets; litmus papers, red and blue; acetic acid (1.0 *M*); ammonia-water solutions (conc., 1.0 *M*); hydrochloric acid (1.0 *M*); sulfuric acid (1.5 *M*); solutions of ammonium chloride (1.0 *M*); sodium acetate (1.0 *M*); sodium carbonate (0.05 *M*); sodium chloride (1.0 *M*); sodium hydroxide (6 *M*, 0.1 *M*); ammonia, household, bromthymol blue; lemon juice; vinegar.

INTRODUCTION: According to the Brønsted concepts, an acid is a proton donor and a base is a proton acceptor. When an acid gives up a proton, the remainder of the acid particle becomes itself capable of accepting a proton. This remainder is called the conjugate base of the acid. Together they constitute a conjugate acid-base pair. This pair consists of two particles differing from each other by a proton. If HB represents a Brønsted acid, the following shows the relationships of the conjugate acid-base pair: A_1 and B_1

$$\underset{A_1}{HB} + H_2O \rightleftarrows H_3O^+ + \underset{B_1}{B^-}$$

The protolytic reaction contains a second conjugate-acid base pair: A_2 and B_2

$$HB + \underset{B_2}{H_2O} \rightleftarrows \underset{A_2}{H_3O^+} + B^-$$

For a weak acid, this reaction proceeds to the right to a limited extent only. An indicator is a colored substance, generally a dye, which changes color in the presence of an acid or a base. It may be regarded as a weak acid, represented by the formula HIn. In a water solution of the indicator at equilibrium, the situation may be represented by the equation

$$HIn + H_2O \rightleftarrows H_3O^+ + In^-$$

A simpler version of this is

$$HIn \rightleftharpoons H^+ + In^-$$

The molecular species, HIn, has one color and the anion, In^-, has a different color. At equilibrium, the characteristic color is that resulting from the proportions of these two species, HIn and In^-, mixed in the solution. Since the indicator is a weak acid, its ionization is slight. The equilibrium color in neutral water depends on the relative concentrations of HIn and In^-. The ionization constant for the indicator, K_a like that of other weak acids (refer to Chapter 20, MODERN CHEMISTRY, 1974 for detailed discussion) is represented by the expression:

$$K_a = K_{HIn} = \frac{[H^+][In^-]}{[HIn]}$$

Increasing the hydronium ion concentration, represented simply as $[H^+]$, by the addition of acid causes the formation of more of the molecular species, HIn, thereby decreasing the concentration of the In^- ion. Decreasing the hydronium ion concentration, for example by the addition of OH^- ion, results in an increase in the concentration of the In^- ion and consequent decrease in the concentration of HIn. Thus the ratio $[In^-]/[HIn]$ is inversely proportional to the hydronium ion concentration. The indicator end point is the hydronium ion concentration (pH) at which a perceptible change in indicator color occurs. The definite range of pH values, over which the color of the indicator changes, is called the transition interval. (Consult Table of Indicator Colors, Chapter 15, and the color plates, in MODERN CHEMISTRY, 1974.)

PROCEDURES: 1. Remove the stopper from a bottle of glacial acetic acid and carefully test for the odor of acetic acid using the wafting technique, Fig. F-5. Place one drop of the glacial acetic acid on a piece of blue litmus paper. Result? Place this litmus paper into 2 ml of water in a test tube. Result? What ion is present in the solution? Complete the equation for this ionization in a Data Table like Data Table 1. Add 6 pellets of sodium acetate to 2 ml of water in a test tube. Test for its odor. Sodium acetate is a salt. Show the ions present in its solution by completing the equation in Data Table 1. To six pellets of solid sodium acetate add 2 ml of 1.5-*M* H_2SO_4. Heat gently. Identify the odor of one of the products. Complete the representative net ionic equation in the Data Table.

Remove the stopper from the bottle of concentrated ammonia-water solution. Carefully test for the odor of ammonia using the wafting technique, Fig. F-5. Place a drop of the solution on a piece of red litmus paper. Result? What ion is present in the solution? Complete the equation for this ionization in the Data Table. Dissolve 6 crystals of ammonium chloride in 2 ml of water and test for its odor. Ammonium chloride is a salt. Show the ions present in its solution by completing the representative equation in the Data Table. Add 2 ml of 6-*M* sodium hydroxide solution, gently heat the test tube, and test for odor using the wafting technique. Complete the representative net ionic equation for the reaction.

DATA TABLE 1

	Acetic acid (glacial)	Ammonia-water solution
Odor		
Litmus reaction		
a. H_2O added		
b. Ion identified		
c. Ionization equation	$HC_2H_3O_2 + \quad H_2O \rightleftarrows$	$NH_3 + \quad H_2O \rightleftarrows$
	Sodium acetate	**Ammonium chloride**
Odor		
Dissociation equation	$NaC_2H_3O_2(s) \rightarrow$	$NH_4Cl(s) \rightarrow \quad (aq)$ $+ \quad (aq)$
and H_2SO_4		and NaOH
a. Odor		
b. Net ionic equation		

2. Add 5 drops of bromthymol blue to 2.0-ml samples of the solutions listed. Compare indicator colors by looking through the tube lengthwise against a white (paper) background. Report the indicator colors in a Data Table like Data Table 2. Save solutions *a* and *b*. Mix them and note the resultant color.

DATA TABLE 2

Solutions	Color of indicator
0.1-*M* HCl *(a)*	
0.1-*M* NaOH *(b)*	
0.1-*M* NaCl	
vinegar	
lemon juice	
ammonia (household)	
0.05-*M* Na_2CO_3	
(a) and *(b)* mixed	

3. In this part of the experiment you will determine the comparative strengths of the weak acids: acetic acid, the molecular form of bromthymol blue represented by HBtB, and ammonium ion. The equations for the conjugate acid-base pairs in water solution are:

$$\begin{array}{ccccc} A_1 & & B_2 & & A_2 & & B_1 \\ HC_2H_3O_2 & + & H_2O & \leftrightharpoons & H_3O^+ & + & C_2H_3O_2^- \\ H_2O & + & NH_3 & \leftrightharpoons & NH_4^+ & + & OH^- \\ HBtb & & H_2O & \leftrightharpoons & H_3O^+ & + & Btb^- \end{array}$$

(a) In a test tube mix 2 ml of 1.0-*M acetic* acid with 2 ml of 1.0-*M* sodium acetate. This solution has equal concentrations of acetic acid and its conjugate base, the acetate ion. What is the concentration of each of these in the mixture? Add 5 drops of bromthymol blue to the mixture. Result? In which of its colored forms is the indicator in this mixture? Complete the equation in a Data Table like Data Table 3 to show how this result took place. Which is the stronger acid, acetic acid or bromthymol blue indicator?

(b) Mix 2 ml of 1.0-*M* NH_3-aq with 2 ml of 1.0-*M* NH_4Cl. This solution contains equal concentrations of NH_3 and its conjugate acid, NH_4^+. What is the concentration of each of these in the mixture? Add 5 drops of bromthymol blue to the mixture. Result? In which of its forms is the indicator present? Complete the equation in Data Table 3 to show how this result took place. Complate Data Table 3 below.

QUESTIONS: 1. Of the three acid species being evaluated, which is (a) the strongest acid?
2. Of the conjugate bases, which is (a) the strongest base? (b) the weakest base?

DATA TABLE 3

	$HC_2H_3O_2$	NH_3-aq
Concentrations of conjugate acid-base pair		
Color after indicator addition		
Form of indicator present		
Equations		

Experiment

27 Relative Strengths of Acids and Bases

PURPOSE: To develop a table of the comparative strengths of a series of weak acids and, conversely, a table of the strengths of their conjugate bases.

APPARATUS: Graduated cylinder; test tubes.

MATERIAL: Acetic acid (0.1 *M*); boric acid (0.1 *M*); carbonic acid (sat. CO_2 sol'n); hydrochloric acid (0.1 *M*); hydrosulfuric acid (sat. sol'n of H_2S); oxalic acid (0.1*M*); solutions of aluminum chloride (0.1 *M*); ammonium chloride (0.1 *M*); calcium nitrate (0.05 *M*); sodium hydrogen carbonate (0.1 *M*); sodium hydrogen sulfate (0.1 *M*); sodium oxalate (0.05 *M*); indicators: bromthymol blue; litmus; methyl orange; phenolphthalein.

INTRODUCTION: All strong acids have approximately the same acid strength in water solution since they are highly ionized. Their protolytic reaction with water is practically complete even in concentrated solutions. Hydrochloric acid is used as a representative strong acid. In aqueous solutions of weak acids the concentration of the hydronium ion is quite low even in dilute solutions. The weak acid does not compete very successfully with hydronium ions to donate protons to a base. Conversely, the water molecules do not compete very successfully with the conjugate base of the weak acid to accept protons. Thus, in the reversible situation, the reaction toward the weaker acid and base predominates. The situation is represented by the generalized equation:

$$\underset{\text{acid}}{\overset{\text{weaker}}{HB}} + \underset{\text{base}}{\overset{\text{weaker}}{H_2O}} \rightleftarrows \underset{\text{acid}}{\overset{\text{stronger}}{H_3O^+}} + \underset{\text{base}}{\overset{\text{stronger}}{B^-}}$$

PROCEDURE: 1. Add one drop of each indicator to a separate 2-ml sample of each of the solutions listed in the Data Table. Estimate each color by looking through the vertical test tube against a white background. Record each color and the estimated pH of the solution in a Data Table like the one shown. Save the first set with HCl for color comparison purposes. Wash out the test tubes thoroughly with distilled water before proceeding to the next set.

Arrange the solutions in order of *decreasing* acid strength. Next to each of the acids, write the formula for its conjugate base. Treat each polyprotic species as if it relinquishes one proton only.

Repeat the indicator tests with 2-ml samples of 0.1-*M* boric acid (H_3BO_3). Results?

TABLE OF INDICATOR COLORS

Indicator	Notation	Color			Transition interval (pH)
		Acid	Transition	Alkaline	
Methyl orange	HM	red	orange	yellow	3.2-4.4
Bromthymol blue	HBtb	yellow	green	blue	6.0-7.6
Litmus	HL	red	pink	blue	5.5-8.0
Phenolphthalein	HP	colorless	pink	red	8.2-10.0

DATA TABLE

0.1-*M* solutions	Methyl orange	Bromthymol blue	Litmus	Phenolphthalein	Estimated pH
HCL					
HSO_4-($NaHSO_4$)					
H_2CO_3 (sat. soln.)					
$H_2C_2O_4$					
H_2S (sat. soln.)					
$Al(H_2O)_6^{+3}$ ($AlCl_3$)					
$HC_2H_3O_2$					
HCO_3-($NaHCO_3$)					
NH_4^+(NH_4Cl)					

What is the approximate pH of its solution? Where does boric acid fit into your table? For which of the indicators is its acid (molecular) form a stronger acid than boric acid?

2. To 5 ml of 0.05-*M* calcium nitrate solution add 5 ml of 0.05-*M* sodium oxalate solution. Result? Complete the representative formula equation below. Divide the test tube contents into two equal portions. To one portion add 5 ml of 0.1-*M* HCl. Result? To the second portion add 5 ml of 0.1-*M* $HC_2H_3O_2$. Result? What do these results show about the relative strength of the three acids: hydrochloric, acetic, and oxalic?

$Ca(NO_3) + Na_2C_2O_4 \rightarrow$ . . . .

RELATIVE STRENGTHS OF ACIDS AND BASES

Acid formula	Conjugate base formula
HCl	Cl^-

← Decreasing Acid Strength (downward)

Decreasing Base Strength → (upward)

Experiment

28 Titration of an Acid and a Hydroxide, Heat of Neutralization

PURPOSE: To determine the concentration of a basic solution expressed in normality, and the heat of neutralization.

APPARATUS: Two beakers, 150 ml; 2 burets; calorimeter, plastic cups; clamp, double buret; flask, Erlenmeyer; graduated cylinder, 50 ml; ringstand; thermometer; wash bottle.

MATERIAL: Solutions of hydrochloric acid (3.0*M*, standard solution about 0.1 *N*); solutions of sodium hydroxide (3.0 *M*, ? *N*); phenolphthalein.

INTRODUCTION: Titration is a process by which the concentration of a solution is determined by its reaction with a standard solution, the concentration of which is precisely known. The process consists of the gradual addition of the standard solution to a measured quantity of the solution of unknown concentration until the same number of gram-equivalent weights (equivalents) of each solute has been used. The point in the titration at which equal equivalents are present is known as the end point. An indicator is used to detect the end point in the process.

An indicator which undergoes a color change in the pH region of the end point of the reactants should be selected. In this experiment, the end point will be reached at a pH about 7. Litmus is a suitable indicator. Where the precision is not too exacting, little difference will be noticed if phenolphthalein is chosen instead of litmus. Phenolphthalein is a somewhat more suitable indicator for beginning students.

The concentration of solutions in titration is commonly expressed in *normality*. The advantage of normality over molarity (formality) or molarity is that equal volumes of solutions of the same normality are always chemically equivalent. If solution No. 1 has a higher normality than solution No. 2, a smaller volume of No. 1 will be required to reach an end point with a given volume of No. 2. *That is, the relative volumes are inversely proportional to the normalities of the solutions when equal equivalents of both have reacted:*

$$\frac{N_1}{N_2} = \frac{V_2}{V_1}$$

The normality of the standard solution and the volumes of both solutions are known when the end point of the titration is reached. Therefore, the normality of the solution of unknown normality can be found:

$$N_2 = \frac{N_1 V_1}{V_2}$$

Neutralization is the reaction between hydronium ions and hydroxide ions to form water. In a broader sense, acid-base neutralization is the reaction that occurs when equivalent quantities of an acid and a base are mixed. The meat of neutralization in kilocalories per mole (kcal/mole) is the heat liberated when one mole of water is formed by the reaction between one mole of hydronium ions and one mole of hydroxide ions. This may be expressed by a thermochemical equation (See Chap. 20, Modern Chemistry, 1974): $H_3O^+ (aq) + OH^- (aq) \rightarrow 2\,H_2O(l)$ + heat of neutralization, or ,more simply as $H^+(aq) \rightarrow OH^-(aq) \rightarrow H_2O(l)$ + heat of neutralization.

SUGGESTIONS: Reagent grade chemicals should be used in preparing the solutions.

A fresh bottle of hydrochloric acid should be used and preferably one which shows the actual assay of HCl rather than the average assay. If one laboratory session is to be allowed for this experiment, the standard acid solution and the basic solution of unknown normality should be prepared in advance by the instructor. If two sessions are available, the first could be used profitably by allowing the students to prepare their own standard solutions. The assay (in % HCl) and the specific gravity of the acid should be given to the students. Small volumetric flasks should be issued for this work.

The concentration of the sodium hydroxide solution should be roughly the same as that of the standard acid and should be precisely known by the instructor as a check against the preparation of the standard solutions by the students.

PROCEDURE: 1. Set up apparatus as shown in Fig. 28-1. Take approximately 100 ml each of hydrochloric acid and sodium hydroxide separately in clean, dry, labeled 150-ml beakers. Pour directly from the beaker into one buret a 10-ml portion of sodium hydroxide solution. Rinse the walls of the buret thoroughly with this solution, allow it to drain through the stopcock, and discard it. Rinse the buret two more times in similar fashion using a new 10-ml portion of sodium hydroxide each time. Discard all rinsings. Then fill the buret with sodium hydroxide solution above the zero mark. Withdraw enough solution to remove the air from the jet tip and bring the liquid level into the graduated region of the buret. In similar fashion rinse and fill the acid buret. Construct a Table like Data Table 1.

2. Record the initial reading of each buret,

DATA TABLE 1

	First trial	Second trial	Third trial
Initial reading, acid buret	ml	ml	ml
Final reading, acid buret	ml	ml	ml
Volume of acid used	ml	ml	ml
Initial reading, hydroxide buret	ml	ml	ml
Final reading, hydroxide buret	ml	ml	ml
Volume of hydroxide used	ml	ml	ml
Normality of standard acid	*N*	*N*	*N*
Normality of base (computed)	*N*	*N*	*N*
	Average value		*N*
Equivalents of NaOH in $10\bar{0}$ ml of basic solution			/$10\bar{0}$ ml
Mass of NaOH in $10\bar{0}$ ml of basic solution			g/$10\bar{0}$ ml

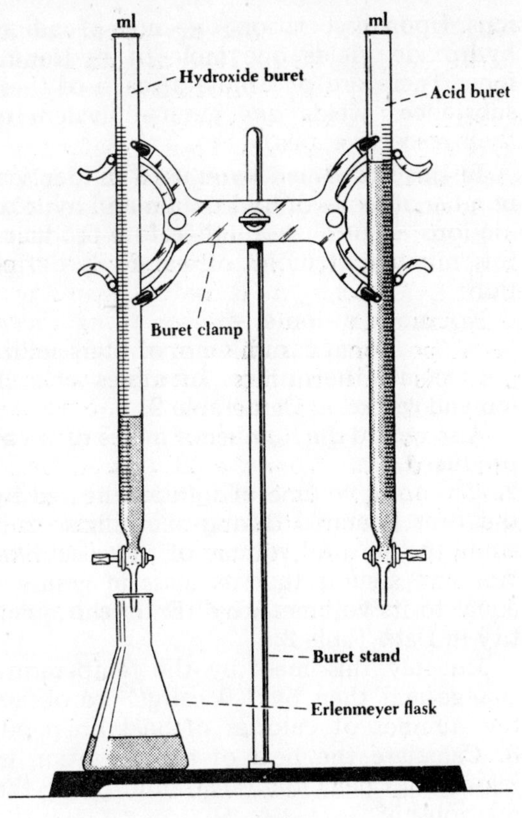

Fig. 28-1

estimating to the nearest 0.01 ml, in the Data Table 1. Then draw off about 15 ml of the hydroxide into an Erlenmeyer flask and add approximately 25 ml of distilled water to give volume to the solution. Add one or two drops of phenolphthalein solution as an indicator. Now run in the acid solution *slowly*, stopping occasionally to mix, using a swirling motion. See Fig. F-13. Wash down the inside surface of the flask frequently with a little distilled water, using your wash bottle. Why may distilled water be added without disturbing the titration procedure? When the pink color of the solution begins to disappear at the point of contact with the acid, add the acid *drop by drop*, swirling the flask gently after each addition, until the last drop added causes the color to disappear. A sheet of white paper under the flask makes it easier to detect the color change. Now add the basic solution dropwise to just return the color. Go back and forth over the end point several times until one drop of the basic solution just brings out a faint pink color. Wash down the inside surface of the flask and make dropwise additions if necessary to re-establish the faint pink end-point color. Read the burets, estimating to the nearest 0.01 ml, and record in your Data Table 1.

Repeat the titration for a second trial, and if time permits, a third trial.

3. Measure out 50̄ ml of 3.0-*M* HCl and pour into the calorimeter. Take the temperature of this solution. Measure out 50̄ ml of 3.0-*M* NaOH and pour into a beaker. Clean and dry the thermometer and take the temperature of the sodium hydroxide solution. Ideally, these solutions should have the same temperature. If they do not, permit them to stand until they do reach the same temperature, carefully cleaning and drying the thermometer each time it is used. Record this temperature in a Data Table like Data Table 2.

Pour the sodium hydroxide solution into the hydrochloric acid solution in the calorimeter. Replace the calorimeter cover, insert the thermometer and use it to gently stir the contents of the calorimeter. Record the maximum temperature reached while the neutralization is taking place.

DATA TABLE 2

Volume (3.0-*M* HCl)	ml
Volume (3.0-*M* NaOH)	ml
Temperature (3.0-*M* HCl)	°C
Temperature (3.0-*M* NaOH)	°C
Maximum temperature (during neutralization)	°C
Change in temperature	C°
Mass of solution heated	g
Moles H_3O^+	mole
Moles OH^-	mole
Moles H_2O formed	mole
Heat liberated	cal
Heat liberated	kcal
Heat of neutralization	$\frac{\text{kcal}}{\text{mole}}$

CALCULATIONS: Titration 1. The volumes of acid and hydroxide solutions used in each trial and the normality of the standard acid solution are known. Solve the inverse proportion as given in the Introduction to find the normality of the basic solution for each trial. Determine the *average value* of the normalities from the different trials and record each result in Data Table 1.

2. By definition:

$$\text{normality} = \frac{\text{no. equivalents solute}}{\text{no. liters solution}}$$

and

$$\text{no. equivs. solute} = \text{normality} \times \text{no. liters sol'n}$$

Knowing the normality (average value) of the sodium hydroxide solution, determine the number of equivalents of NaOH in $10\bar{0}$ ml of solution.

3. Express the no. equivs/$10\bar{0}$ ml (as found above) in no. g NaOH/100-ml of solution, using the following relationship:

$$\frac{\text{no. equivs.}}{10\bar{0}\text{ ml}} \times \frac{\text{g NaOH}}{\text{equiv}} = \text{no. g NaOH}/10\bar{0}\text{ ml of solution}$$

CALCULATIONS: Heat of Neutralization.

1. Upon ionization one mole of hydrochloric acid yields one mole of hydronium ions. Upon dissociation, one mole of sodium hydroxide yields one mole of hydroxide ions. Therefore *one* mole of each of these substances yields *one* gram-equivalent of their respective ions.

In this experiment, you used an identical number of moles of hydronium and hydroxide ions. Neutralization therefore produced this number of moles of water. By definition:

$$\text{No. moles of ion(s)} = \text{molarity} \times \text{no. of liters sol'n.}$$

Calculate the number of moles of each ion and record in Data Table 2.

Also record the number of moles of water produced.

2. The total volume of solution heated by the heat liberated during neutralization is equal to the *total* volume of the reactants. We may assume that its mass in grams is equal to its volume. Why? Enter this quantity in Data Table 2.

Multiply this mass by the temperature change and then by 1.0 cal/gC° to obtain the number of calories of heat liberated.

3. Calculate the heat of neutralization in kilocalories per mole (kcal/mole) using the relationship:

$$\text{Heat of neutralization (kcal/mole)} = \frac{\text{kilocalories liberated}}{\text{no. moles of water formed}}$$

Record the calculated heat of neutralization in Data Table 2.

Experiment 29 Percentage of Acetic Acid in Vinegar

PURPOSE: To determine the acidity of vinegar, using the titration technique.

APPARATUS: Two beakers, 150 ml; 2 burets; clamp, double buret; flask, Erlenmeyer; ring stand; wash bottle.

MATERIAL: Vinegar; standard solution of sodium hydroxide (approximately 0.5 *N*); solution of phenolphthalein indicator.

INTRODUCTION: The quantity of acid in a sample of vinegar may be found by titrating the sample against a standard basic solution. Most vinegars on sale have a mass percentage of between 4.0% and 5.5% acetic acid. By determining the volume of sodium hydroxide solution of known normality necessary to neutralize a measured quantity of the vinegar, the normality of the vinegar can be calculated. From the normality, the mass percentage of acid present can then be calculated. Interesting results are obtained if the students bring samples of vinegar from home.

SUGGESTION: Review the discussion of titration technique and determination of the normality of the unknown solution presented in the Introduction of Experiment 28. Also review the computation methods carried out in the same experiment.

To remove color from a sample of cider vinegar, the instructor may filter it through boneblack before the class assemblies. This makes it easier to detect the end point of the titration.

As an alternate procedure the experiment may be performed by part or all of the glass using molarities instead of normalities. Change using molarities instead of normalities in the Data Table to molarities and the N(s) to M(s). Use Calculation 4 (optional) instead of Calculations 1-3.

PROCEDURE: **1.** Transfer approximately 100 ml each of vinegar and sodium hydroxide solution to separate clean, dry, labeled 150-ml beakers. Pour directly from the beaker into one buret a 10-ml portion of the vinegar. Rinse the walls of the buret thoroughly with the vinegar, allow it to drain through the stopcock, and discard it. Rinse the buret two more times in similar fashion using a new 10-ml portion of vinegar each time. Discard all rinsings. Then fill the buret with vinegar above the zero mark. Withdraw enough solution to remove the air from the jet tip and bring the liquid level into the graduated region of the buret. In similar fashion rinse and fill the other buret with sodium hydroxide solution. Construct a Data Table like the one shown. Record the initial readings of both burets, estimating to the nearest 0.01 ml.

2. Withdraw about 15 ml of the vinegar into an Erlenmeyer flask. Add 50 ml of distilled water to the flask to add volume and to dilute any color present, thus making it easier to determine the color change when the end point is reached. Add one or two drops of phenolphthalein solution to serve as an indicator. Then titrate the vinegar with the standard solution of sodium hydroxide, swirling and washing down the flask frequently. Add the hydroxide solution drop by drop near the end of the operation, until the last drop (after swirling) just turns the solution a pink color. Now add successive quantities of both solutions dropwise, going back and forth over the end point, until the end point is clearly established. This is indicated by the slightest suggestion of pink coloration in the flask. The end point is most satisfactorily determined with the flask resting on a sheet of white paper and with a beaker of distilled water alongside for comparison purposes. Record the final buret readings of both solutions, estimating to the nearest 0.01 ml.

3. Discard the liquid in the flask, rinse thoroughly with distilled water, and run a second titration, proceeding as before. A third titration should also be made if time permits. Chemists like to have three consistent determinations before they feel confident that their titrations are reliable. Enter the buret readings for each successive trial in the Data Table. A normality calculation will be made for each trial, and the average of these will be considered to be the normality of the vinegar.

CALCULATIONS: **1.** *Normality of vinegar.* The volumes of vinegar and sodium hydroxide solutions used in each trial and the normality of the standard hydroxide solution are known. Solve the *inverse* proportion (see Introduction section of Experiment 28) to find the normality of the vinegar for each trial. Determine the average *value* of the normalities from the different trials. Record each result in the Data Table.

2. *Equivalents of acetic acid in 100 ml of vinegar.* The formula of acetic acid may be

DATA TABLE

	First Trial	Second Trial	Third Trial
Initial reading, acid buret	ml	ml	ml
Final reading, acid buret	ml	ml	ml
Volume of acid used	ml	ml	ml
Initial reading, hydroxide buret	ml	ml	ml
Final reading, hydroxide buret	ml	ml	ml
Volume of hydroxide used	ml	ml	ml
Normality of standard hydroxide	*N*	*N*	*N*
Normality of vinegar (computed)	*N*	*N*	*N*
	Average value		*N*
Percentage of acetic acid in vinegar			%

written as $HC_2H_3O_2$ to show that it is a *monoprotic* acid. What is the g-eq. wt. of acetic acid? A normal solution, by definition, contains the g-eq. wt. (1 equivalent) of solute per liter of solution. Thus,

$$\text{normality} = \frac{\text{no. equivalents solute}}{\text{no. liters solution}}$$

and

$$\text{no. equivs solute} = \text{normality} \times \text{no. liters sol'n}$$

Knowing the normality (average value) of the vinegar, determine the number of equivalents of $HC_2H_3O_2$ in $10\bar{0}$ ml of the vinegar. Show computations in smooth form on a separate sheet of paper.

3. *Percentage of acetic acid in vinegar.* Find the number of grams of acetic acid in $10\bar{0}$ ml of vinegar. This is determined from the number of equivalents of acetic acid per $10\bar{0}$ ml of vinegar and the number of grams of acetic acid per equivalent (g.-eq. wt.):

$$\text{no. g } HC_2H_3O_2\text{/100-ml vinegar} = \frac{\text{no. equivs}}{10\bar{0}\text{ ml}} \times \frac{\text{g } HC_2H_3O_2}{\text{equiv}}$$

The mass percentage of solute in a solution may be expressed on the basis of grams of solute per $10\bar{0}$ grams of solution. By neglecting the slight difference in density between water and vinegar, we may assume $10\bar{0}$ ml of vinegar to weigh $10\bar{0}$ g. Thus, when the mass of acetic acid in $10\bar{0}$ grams of vinegar is known, the mass-percentage composition may be expressed:

$$\%\ HC_2H_3O_2 = \frac{\text{g } HC_2H_3O_2}{10\bar{0}\text{ g vinegar}} \times 100\%$$

Show your computations in smooth form and record the percentage of acetic acid in vinegar in the Data Table.

4. *(Optional).* This experiment may also be carried out by using molarities. The standard sodium hydroxide solution is approximately 0.5-*M*. The empirical equation is

$$HC_2H_3O_2 + NaOH \rightarrow H_2O + NaC_2H_3O_2$$

The number of moles of sodium hydroxide is calculated from its known molarity and the volume used. Thus

$$\text{molarity} = \frac{\text{no. moles solute}}{\text{no. liters solution}}$$

and

$$\text{moles solute} = \text{molarity} \times \text{no. liters sol'n}$$

The balanced equation shows that 1 *mole* of NaOH is used for 1 *mole* of $HC_2H_3O_2$; NaOH and $HC_2H_3O_2$ are chemically equivalent, mole for mole. Therefore the number of moles of $HC_2H_3O_2$ used in the titration is equal to the number of moles of sodium hydroxide. Calculate the molarity (average value) of the vinegar. Calculate the number of moles of $HC_2H_3O_2$ in $10\bar{0}$ ml of the vinegar. Determine the number of grams of acetic acid in $10\bar{0}$ ml of vinegar:

no. g $HC_2H_3O_2$ /$10\bar{0}$ ml vinegar =

$$\frac{\text{no. moles}}{10\bar{0}\text{ ml}} \times \frac{\text{g } HC_2H_3O_2}{\text{mole}}$$

The mass percentage of solute in a solution may be expressed on the basis of grams of solute per 100 grams of solution. By neglecting the slight difference in density between water and vinegar, we may assume $10\bar{0}$ ml of vinegar to weigh $10\bar{0}$ g. Thus when the mass of acetic acid in $10\bar{0}$ grams of vinegar is known, the mass-percentage composition may be expressed:

$$5\ HC_2H_3O_2 = \frac{\text{g } HC_2H_3O_2}{10\bar{0}\text{ g vinegar}} \times 100\%$$

Record the percentage of acetic acid in vinegar in the Data Table.

Experiment 30 Adsorption

PURPOSE: To determine the amounts of dissolved substance adsorbed at different solution concentrations.

APPARATUS: Balance, sensitive to 0.01 g; beakers; 2 burets, 50 ml; clamp, double buret; 4 corks; 5 flasks, Erlenmeyer; flask, volumetric, 250 ml; funnel; graduated cylinder; medicine dropper; pipet, 10 ml; ring, iron; ring stand; wash bottle.

ADDITIONAL APPARATUS for INSTRUCTOR'S EXPERIMENT: ammonia generator (see Exp. 57); beaker, 100 ml; burner and tubing; cork; flask, Erlenmeyer; funnel; ring, iron; ring stand; wire gauze.

MATERIAL: Charcoal, activated; filter paper; standard solutions of acetic acid (approximately 0.4 *M*), sodium hydroxide (approximately 0.1 *M*); succinic or benzoic acid, A. R. grade.

ADDITIONAL MATERIAL for INSTRUCTOR'S EXPERIMENT: ammonium chloride; calcium hydroxide; charcoal, activated. litmus paper, pink; solutions of copper(II) sulfate (1 *M*); methylene blue (1 g in 20 ml water).

INTRODUCTION: Adsorption is defined as the concentration of a gas, liquid, or solid on the surface of a solid or liquid. The substance adsorbed is known as the *adsorbate*, and the substance upon whose surface adsorption occurs is known as the *adsorbent*. Adsorption is selective. A given *adsorbent* will preferentially adsorb more of one substance than of another present in the same environment.

In this experiment, we shall prepare several solutions of acetic acid having equal volumes but different concentrations. Equal quantities of activated charcoal will be introduced into each solution. The amount of acetic acid adsorbed on the charcoal in each solution may then be determined by titrating each against a standard solution of sodium hydroxide.

As the molarity of the standard acetic acid solution from which the test solutions are made is known, and the number of milliliters in each test solution is known, the quantity of acetic acid in each test solution may be expressed in *millimoles* of $HC_2H_3O_2$. Similarly, after adsorption, the quantity of NaOH required to neutralize the remaining $HC_2H_3O_2$ may be expressed in *millimoles* of NaOH. The millimoles of NaOH used in each titration is, of course, equal to the millimoles of $HC_2H_3O_2$ remaining in the test solution. These computations are made as follows:

1. ml of $HC_2H_3O_2$ × Molarity of $HC_2H_3O_2$ = millimoles of $HC_2H_3O_2$ in sample.
2. ml of NaOH × Molarity of NaOH = millimoles of NaOH used.
3. Millimoles of NaOH used = millimoles of $HC_2H_3O_2$ remaining in sample.
4. Millimoles of $HC_2H_3O_2$ − millimoles of $HC_2H_3O_2$ remaining = millimoles of $HC_2H_3O_2$ adsorbed.

SUGGESTION: If two laboratory periods are available for this experiment, the instructor may supply the standard NaOH solution and allow each student to prepare his own $HC_2H_3O_2$ solution and standardize it by titrating against the NaOH solution, using phenolphthalein as an indicator. The first laboratory period should be devoted to the preparation of the test solutions and the addition of the activated charcoal to each.

INSTRUCTOR EXPERIMENT: Add 5 g of activated charcoal to 20 ml of methylene blue solution in a 100-ml beaker. Stir, heat gently, and filter. Repeat with solution of copper(II) sulfate. What does this show about the nature of adsorption?

Add 5 g of activated charcoal to an Erlenmeyer flask previously filled with ammonia. Stopper and shake the flask vigorously. Test for the odor of ammonia. Try moist red litmus paper. Remove the stopper and heat the flask. Repeat the odor and litmus tests. What does this show about adsorption?

STANDARD SOLUTIONS: 1. *NaOH solution.* Prepare an approximately 0.1-*M* NaOH solution by dissolving about 4 g of A.R. grade NaOH pellets in distilled water and dilute to one liter. Standardize with A.R. grade succinic or benzoic acid (0.2–0.3-g samples), using phenolphthalein as the indicator. Determine the molarity and label the flask accordingly.

2. *$HC_2H_3O_2$ solution* (Student quantity). Prepare an approximately 0.4-*M* $HC_2H_3O_2$ solution by dissolving about 6 ml of glacial acetic acid in distilled water and diluting to 250 ml (mix thoroughly). Standardize by titrating 10-ml samples against the standard sodium hydroxide solution, using phenolphthalein. Calculate the molarity and record in a Data Table like the one shown.

PROCEDURE: 1. All apparatus must be thoroughly clean and dry. Fit each of four 125-ml Erlenmeyer flasks with a cork stopper and number in sequence. Label the $HC_2H_3O_2$ buret to avoid confusion and rinse it with a few milliliters of the $HC_2H_3O_2$ solution. Place it in the clamp, fill, and adjust the level on the scale.

Run 40.0 ml of the $HC_2H_3O_2$ solution into the No. 4 flask. Refill and adjust the buret and then run 20.0 ml into the No. 3 flask, 10.0 ml into No. 2, and 5.0 ml into No. 1. Add 20.0 ml of distilled water to the No. 3 flask, 30.0 ml of distilled water to the No. 2 flask, and 35.0 ml to the No. 1 flask.

2. Weigh out to the nearest 0.01 g four 5-g samples of activated charcoal and add one sample to each of the four flasks. Record the precise mass of each sample in the appropriate place in the Data Table. Shake the four flasks for about 10 minutes. If two laboratory periods are to be used, the stoppered flasks should be set aside and the experiment completed the next day.

3. Set up the NaOH buret as in Part 1 and adjust for titrating. Using a 10-ml pipet, withdraw 20.0 ml of the clear solution from No. 4 flask (filter if necessary) and transfer to a clean Erlenmeyer flask. Add 25 ml of distilled water to provide volume and titrate with the standard NaOH solution, using phenolphthalein as the indicator. Multiply the milliliters of NaOH solution used by 2 (Why?) and record in the Data Table. In a similar manner, titrate a 20.0-ml sample of each of the remaining test solutions. Remember to record twice the number of milliliters of NaOH solution used in each titration. Make the necessary compu-

tations on a separate sheet of paper. Complete the Data Table, referring to the Introduction as necessary.

4. (*Optional*). Construct a graph, plotting *millimoles of $HC_2H_3O_2$ adsorbed per gram of charcoal* as ordinate against *millimoles of $HC_2H_3O_2$ remaining* as abscissa. This is a *smooth curve* and ideally gives a sweeping parabola. Ask your instructor for suggestions in regard to the proper construction of your graph.

QUESTIONS: 1. What relationship exists between the concentration of adsorbate and the amount of adsorption?

2. Recognizing that the molecular concentration of water was greater than that of acetic acid in each test solution, how do you account for the adsorption of acetic acid?

DATA TABLE

Molarity of standard NaOH solution .... *M*

Molarity of standard $HC_2H_3O_2$ solution .... *M*

Volume of each test solution .... ml

Test solution	ml $HC_2H_3O_2$ added	millimoles $HC_2H_3O_2$ present	g charcoal added	ml NaOH required	millimoles $HC_2H_3O_2$ remaining	millimoles $HC_2H_3O_2$ adsorbed	millimoles $HC_2H_3O_2$ adsorbed per g charcoal
1							
2							
3							
4							

Experiment 31 Carbon

PURPOSE: To study the occurrence, methods of preparation, and some of the properties of the various forms of carbon.

APPARATUS: Balance, platform; beaker, 250 ml; burner and tubing; clamp, buret; clamp, test tube; crucible; crucible cover; flask, Erlenmeyer; forceps; funnel; graduated cylinder; molecular model kit (Sargent); rubber stoppers, sold No. 2 (3), solid No. 4; ring, iron; ring stand; test tubes; triangle, pipestem.

MATERIAL: Alcohol, denatured; boneblack, powd.; charcoal, activated, pellets; charcoal, wood, powd.; charcoal, wood, splinters; copper(II) oxide, powd.; detergent, granular; graphite, powd.; lampblack; sugar; filter papers; splints, wooden; hydrochloric acid, dilute (1:4); nitric acid, dilute

(1:5); solutions of dark-brown sugar; hydrogen sulfide (very dilute); lead acetate (1.0 *M*); limewater; sodium hydroxide (1.0 *M*). Instructions for preparing the special dark-brown sugar solution and the very dilute hydrogen sulfide solution are given in TEACHERS' EDITION TO EXERCISES AND EXPERIMENTS IN CHEMISTRY.

INTRODUCTION: Carbon exhibits allotropy, the existence of an element in two or more forms in the same physical state. Its two crystalline allotropic forms are diamond and graphite. Black residues obtained by heating substances which contain combined carbon are sometimes called amorphous carbon. Examples of amorphous carbon include charcoal, coke, boneblack, and lampblack. Carbon atoms form covalent bonds with other elements and link with each other in different ways to produce the diamond and graphite structures. The diamond structure is the result of sp^3 hybridization while the resonant graphite structure probably involves a different type of hybridization known as sp^2. The amorphous forms are produced by a variety of procedures including destructive distillation and incomplete combustion. Carbon is an important reducing agent. The uses of its different varieties are related to particular properties including combustibility and adsorption.

PROCEDURE: **1.** Each student team is to use two molecular model sets, each of which contains 20 black carbon spheres. Using the short stick connectors, construct a model of the diamond. See Fig. 31-1. Start the construction of the model of graphite by constructing two hexagons using only the short connectors. Recall that the distances between the centers of adjacent carbon atoms in a layer of graphite are identical, 1.42 Å. Using Fig. 31-2 as a model, connect the two hexagons, using the longer stick connectors to represent the distance between centers in adjacent layers (3.40 Å). Use the remaining carbon spheres to build up each layer. Two carbons in the existent hexagons (those first constructed) are to be common to the newly constructed hexagons. Use long connectors, as needed, between the rest of the constructed layers. To how many carbons in a layer in graphite is each carbon bonded? What is the nature of the bonding between layers in graphite? **2.** Ignite a wood splint in the burner flame. Note how it burns. Then break several splints and place the pieces in the bottom of a test tube, clamped so its mouth is slightly downward. Place a piece of paper on the table under the mouth of this test tube and heat the contents strongly (until no more volatile matter is released). CAUTION: *Do not breathe the vapor or get any*

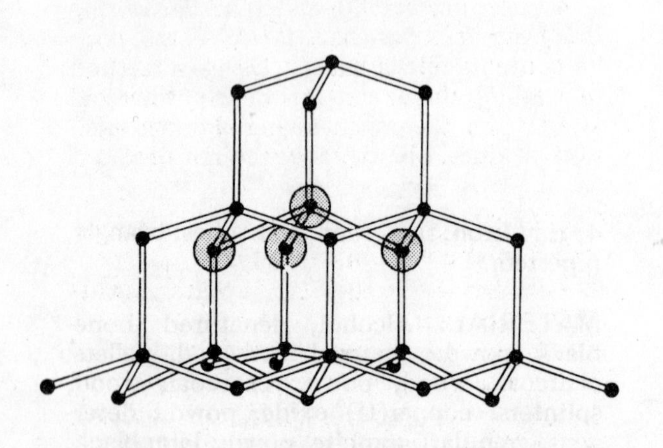

Fig. 31-1

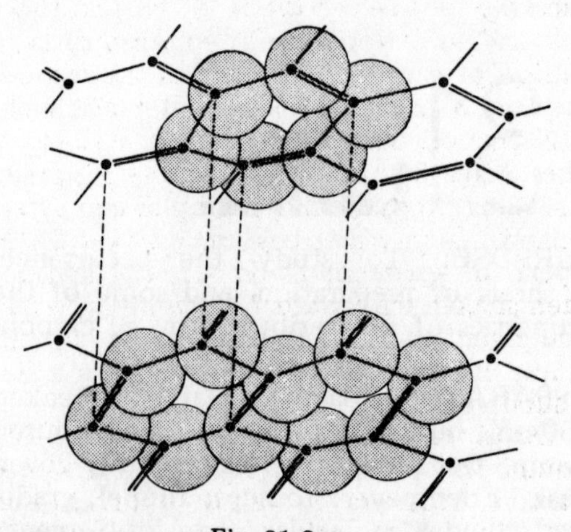

Fig. 31-2

of the liquid on your hands. Remove the residue from the test tube carefully. Describe its appearance. Ignite one piece in the burner and observe how it burns. Pour one inch of limewater into a small test tube. Ignite another piece of the solid residue (hold with forceps) and insert the ignited end in the test tube, holding it above the limewater. If nothing happens to the limewater, repeat with another ignited piece. What happens to the limewater? What does this indicate about the nature of the residue? What name is given to the process employed in heating the wood in the test tube?

Devise and conduct an experiment to show that sugar may be decomposed into carbon and water vapor. Use 2 g of sugar in a porcelain crucible set in a pipestem triangle.

Hold a test tube horizontally with its closed end in the *yellow* burner flame. What form of carbon is produced? Change to the standard blue flame and hold the test tube so that the deposit is in the hottest part of the flame. Note the results.

3. Put 15 ml of water in each of three test tubes. Into the first, add 2 g of powdered graphite. Into the second, add 2 g of powdered wood charcoal. Into the third, add 2 g of lampblack. Shake each sample vigorously and then pour out half the contents of each tube into a second set of test tubes. Place the first set of tubes in the test tube rack and look for signs of solution or suspension of carbon. Into each of the second set place 3 grains of a solid detergent such as Naccanol. Stopper and shake each test tube. After 5 minutes record any instance of settling. Reshake these samples and filter each. Which mixtures pass through the filter paper? In what condition was the carbon when shaken with water? When mixed with a detergent (wetting agent)? Which carbon sample is apparently in the smallest state of subdivision?

4. Devise and conduct experiments to determine the activity and solubility of wood charcoal splinters in dilute hydrochloric acid, dilute nitric acid, water, alcohol, and sodium hydroxide solution. Describe your experiments and indicate their results. Discard the liquids into the sink, but be sure that any pieces of charcoal which remain are placed in the waste jar and *not in the sink.*

5. Pour 50 ml of dark-brown sugar solution into an Erlenmeyer flask. Add to it 1 g of powdered boneblack and stopper the flask. Shake the mixture vigorously for a minute. Filter. Pour the filtrate through the funnel a second time, and even a third time if necessary to remove the color from the sugar solution. Finally, compare the color of the filtrate with that of the original brown-sugar solution.

6. Fill a test tube one-half full of very dilute hydrogen sulfide solution. Cautiously note its odor using the method shown in Fig. F-5. **CAUTION:** *Hydrogen sulfide is very poisonous.* As a chemical test for its presence add 3 drops of the solution to 2 ml of a solution of lead acetate. Result? Add 5 pellets of activated charcoal to the test tube and shake vigorously at intervals for several minutes. Decant and note the odor of the decantage. Drop 3 drops of the decantate into 2 ml of lead acetate solution. Result?

7. Mix 5 g of powdered copper(II) oxide with an equal bulk of powdered wood charcoal. Heat this mixture strongly for 4 or 5 minutes in a test tube. You should observe a reaction occurring in the test tube during this heating. After the test tube cools, pour its contents into a beaker. Devise a method of washing the excess low density charcoal away from the much higher density reaction product. Identify the reaction product.

QUESTIONS: 1. How active an element is carbon at room temperature?

2. Of what use is charcoal in water purification processes?

3. What is the nature of the reaction between hot copper(II) oxide and carbon?

4. What would you predict is the reaction between hot iron(III) oxide and carbon?

5. Carry out the reaction in Question 4 to verify your prediction. Result?

6. What is adsorption? Why are certain forms of charcoal good adsorbing agents?

EQUATIONS

1. Reaction between hydrogen sulfide and lead acetate
2. Reaction in Part 7

Experiment 32 Carbon Dioxide

PURPOSE: To prepare carbon dioxide by a variety of methods and to study its properties.

APPARATUS: Balance, platform; beaker, 250 ml; bottles, wide mouth; burner and tubing; clamp, buret; flask, Erlenmeyer; forceps; funnel tube; glass bends, right angle (2); glass bend, right angle, long arm; glass plates; graduated cylinder; ring stand; rubber stoppers, 1-hole No. 2, 2-hole No. 6; rubber tubing, small diameter; test tubes; trough; wing top.

ADDITIONAL APPARATUS for INSTRUCTOR'S EXPERIMENT: bottle, gallon with delivery tube assembly; bottle, wide mouth.

MATERIAL: Copper(II) carbonate; magnesium ribbon; marble chips; sodium aluminum sulfate; sodium carbonate, anhydrous; sodium hydrogen carbonate; candle; wooden splints; hydrochloric acid, conc.; hydrochloric acid, dilute (1:4); sulfuric acid, dilute (1:6); limewater; litmus solution.

ADDITIONAL MATERIAL for TEACHER'S EXPERIMENT; mineral oil; molasses; yeast; solution of limewater.

INTRODUCTION: Carbon dioxide may be prepared by a variety of methods including heating certain carbonates, combustion of ordinary fuels, and fermentation of sugar. The usual laboratory method consists of adding an acid, such as hydrochloric acid, to a carbonate. Carbonic acid, H_2CO_3, is first produced, but it is unstable and decomposes readily into carbon dioxide and water. Carbon dioxide is moderately soluble in water, but it can be collected by water displacement if the gas is evolved rather rapidly.

PROCEDURE: 1. Thrust a blazing wooden splint into a bottle and keep it there until it is extinguished. Pour limewater to a depth of about 1 cm into the bottle, cover with a glass plate and shake. Result?

Put 2 grams of copper(II) carbonate in a test tube. Insert a one-hole rubber stopper with a long-arm glass-bend delivery tube in the mouth of the test tube. Clamp to a ring stand. Pour limewater to a depth of 2.5 cm into a second test tube and insert the long arm of the delivery tube in the limewater. Heat the test tube containing the copper(II) carbonate vigorously until you see a permanent change in color. What happens to the limewater? Repeat this procedure first with a sample of anhydrous solid sodium carbonate (representing the carbonates of Group I) and then with a sample of sodium hydrogen carbonate. Results?

Repeat Part 5, Experiment 18, which deals with the addition of water to the typical ingredients of a baking powder. Result?

Put about 1 g of sodium hydrogen carbonate, 1 g of sodium hydrogen carbonate, and several marble chips in separate test tubes. To each add 3 ml of dilute hydrochloric acid. Results? Into the upper part of each test tube thrust a blazing splint when the reactions have subsided. Results? Repeat this procedure with separate solid samples, using dilute sulfuric acid instead of hydrochloric acid. Results? What conclusions do you reach?

INSTRUCTOR EXPERIMENT: Mix a cake of compressed yeast or a packet of dried yeast with 100 ml of warm water to form a milky suspension. Add this to a fallon bottle containing 500 ml of molasses diluted with warm water to make 3 liters of solution. Insert a delivery tube assembly in the mouth of the bottle and have the delivery end extend well into a wide-mouth bottle containing limewater over which a thin film of mineral oil has been poured. Put in a warm place and after a day have students observe the action in the limewater bottle. What fermentation product does this indicate?

2. Set up an apparatus for generating a gas by the action of a solution on a solid and for collecting the gas by water displacement. Put 50 g of marble chips in the generator and cover it with water. Why? Using an appropriate technique, add concentrated hydrochloric acid, a little at a time, to produce a constant evolution of gas. Collect two bottles of gas. What physical properties of carbon dioxide do you observe?

3. Into one bottle of carbon dioxide, thrust a blazing wooden splint. Then, with forceps, thrust a 5-cm piece of burning magnesium ribbon into the same bottle. Are the reactions similar? Explain. Note the two different solid reaction products formed from magnesium and carbon dioxide.

4. Place a short piece of candle, not over 2 cm long, in a 250-ml beaker and light it. Rapidly pour the carbon dioxide from the second bottle you collected into the beaker, just as if you were pouring water. What physical and chemical properties of carbon dioxide are demonstrated?

5. Bubble carbon dioxide from the generator through a test tube one-half full of limewater. Observe the results. This is a test for carbon dioxide.

6. Using a glass tube, blow your breath through a test tube one-third full of limewater for at least 2 minutes. Result? What conclusion can you draw from this experiment?

7. Bubble carbon dioxide from the generator for a few minutes through a test tube one-third full of neutral litmus solution. Result? Why?

QUESTIONS: 1. Carbon dioxide may be collected by water displacement or by upward displacement of air. Give an advantage and disadvantage of each method.

2. In Part 3, what evidence is there that the carbon dioxide was decomposed?

3. What use for carbon dioxide is suggested in Part 4?

FURTHER EXPERIMENTATION: Using the Sargent molecular model kit, construct a model of one of the resonance hybrids of carbon dioxide.

Bubble carbon dioxide through limewater until the precipitate formed redissolves. Heat a sample of this solution to boiling.

Heat a marble chip on the grid of a Fisher burner for 15 minutes. Permit the residue to cool. Put it in a small beaker and add 5 ml of water. Test the material produced with red and blue litmus papers.

Perform the limewater test on the gas given off by carbonated beverages.

EQUATIONS

1. Complete combustion of carbon.
2. Decomposition of copper(II) carbonate (heat).
3. Decomposition of sodium hydrogen carbonate (heat).
4. Preparation of carbon dioxide (laboratory method).
5. Fermentation of glucose ($C_6H_{12}O_6$) (molasses).
6. Carbon dioxide and burning magnesium.
7. Reaction in Part 5.
8. Carbon dioxide and water.
9. Two equations representing the successive steps in the ionization of carbonic acid in water.

Experiment

33 Hydrocarbons

PURPOSE: To construct models of representative members of various hydrocarbon series. To prepare and collect methane and ethyne and to study some of their properties.

APPARATUS: Balance, platform: bottles, wide-mouth (5); burner and tubing; clamp, buret; flask, Florence; funnel; glass bends (2); glass plates (4); glass tube; graduated cylinder; molecular model kit, Sargent; mortar and pestle; pinch clamp; ring, iron; ring stand; rubber connector; rubber stopper, solid, No. 2; rubber stopper, 1-hole No. 4; rubber stopper, 2-hole No. 6; test tube, large, Pyrex; test tubes; trough; tubing, delivery; wing top.

MATERIAL: calcium carbide, lump; soda lime; sodium acetate, anhydrous, powdered; solutions of bromine water; bromine in carbon tetrachloride; limewater; splints, wooden.

INTRODUCTION: The hydrocarbons exist in various series. Their structural formulas may be better visualized through the constructions of ball-and-stick models. The shapes of many of the hydrocarbons are accurately reproduced by such models although the role of various *p* orbitals and hybridized orbitals is not necessarily evident. The saturated hydrocarbons react slowly with reagents such as bromine (water solution or carbon tetrachloride solution) by the process of substitution. The unsaturated hydrocarbons react much more rapidly by the process of addition. Practically all hydrocarbons will burn more-or-less completely in air.

SUGGESTION: Review Chapters 6 and 17 of MODERN CHEMISTRY, 1974, particularly those parts dealing with hybridized orbitals and the role of the *p* orbitals in determining the shapes of molecules. Perchloroethylene (C_2Cl_4) may be used instead of CCl_4.

PROCEDURE: 1. General directions: Assemble ball and stick models of the various hydrocarbon series using the Sargent molecular model kit. The short rods are used to connect the hydrogen spheres to the carbon spheres. The long rods are used to connect carbon spheres to each other. The springs are used for multiple bonds between carbon spheres. Before starting, check your kit for completeness using the color code attached to the inside of the box cover. After a number of models have been constructed, and their conformity with structural formulas checked by writing the structural formulas, they will have to be disassembled so that the next successive models may be constructed. Construct Data Table 1. Under each name write the molecular formula. In the space at the right place the structural formula.

By what group do the formulas for successive alkanes differ from the preceding one? Identify the types of bonds in ethane: the carbon-carbon bond, and the carbon-hydrogen bonds.

By what group do the formulas for the successive alkenes differ from the preceding one? What is the shape of the ethene molecule? Of the ethyne molecule? What two types of bonds constitute the double bond in ethyne? What types of bonds constitute the triple bond in ethyne? What is the shape of the two 2*p* orbitals which overlap? How do the carbon-to-carbon distances vary in the series: ethane, ethene, ethyne? Construct Data Tables 2 and 3.

What is the shape of the benzene molecule?

DATA TABLE 1

Alkanes

methane	ethane	propane
methyl group	ethyl group	propyl group
n-butane	isobutane other name	
n-pentane	isopentane other name	neopentane other name . . . . .

DATA TABLE 2

Alkenes

ethene	propene
other name	

Alkynes

ethyne	propyne
other name	

DATA TABLE 3

Alkadienes

1,3 butadiene	isoprene (2-methyl-1,3-butadiene)

DATA TABLE 4

Aromatic: Construct the more complex models on the benzene structure.

benzene	toluene other name	phenyl group
ethyl benzene	naphthalene	styrene

What is believed to be the nature of the carbon-carbon bonding in benzene? What is the size of the carbon-hydrogen bond angles in benzene? Briefly describe the role of the *p* orbitals in each carbon atom in the benzene structure. Complete Data Table 4.

2. *Methane*. Grind 8 g of powdered sodium acetate with 14 g of soda lime in a mortar. Add the mixture to a large Pyrex test tube and incorporate the test tube in an apparatus for generating a gas by heating a mixture of solids and collecting the gas by water displacement. Distribute the mixture evenly at the back of the test tube with an air space above. Why? Heat the test tube, gently at first, and then more strongly. Collect one-half bottle of gas and discard it. Why? Then collect one full test tube of methane and stopper it. Collect two full bottles of methane and complete the filling with methane of a bottle 9/10 full of air and 1/10 full of water. Remove the end of the delivery tube from the water in the trough. Remove the flame from under the generator. What physical properties of methane have you observed? CAUTION: *Do not collect methane or ethyne in any bottle that holds more than 250 ml.* Why?

Ignite a bottle full of methane. Note the color of the flame. Observe the appearance of the walls of the bottle while the methane is burning. Test for the other product of combustion by pouring 5 ml of limewater into the wide-mouth bottle, covering it with a glass plate, and shaking the bottle. Result?

Place the bottle containing 1/10 methane and 9/10 air mouth upward on the laboratory table. Remove the glass plate and *cautiously* at arm's length bring a lighted splint to the mouth of the bottle. Result? Why does this mixture of methane and air produce such a result?

To the methane in another wide-mouth bottle, add 5 ml of bromine water, cover with a glass plate, and shake without inverting the bottle. Result?

To the methane in the test tube add 1 ml of bromine in CCl_4 and quickly restopper the test tube. Shake the contents and observe the color change, if any, of the bromine solution.

3. *Ethyne.* Add 8 g of calcium carbide lumps to a *dry* Florence flask fitted with funnel, rubber connector, pinch clamp, glass tube, glass bend, stopper, and delivery tubing as shown in Fig. 33-1. *Have your instructor approve the apparatus. Wrap a towel around the generator.* With the pinch clamp closed, nearly fill the funnel with water. By opening the pinch clamp slightly, allow the

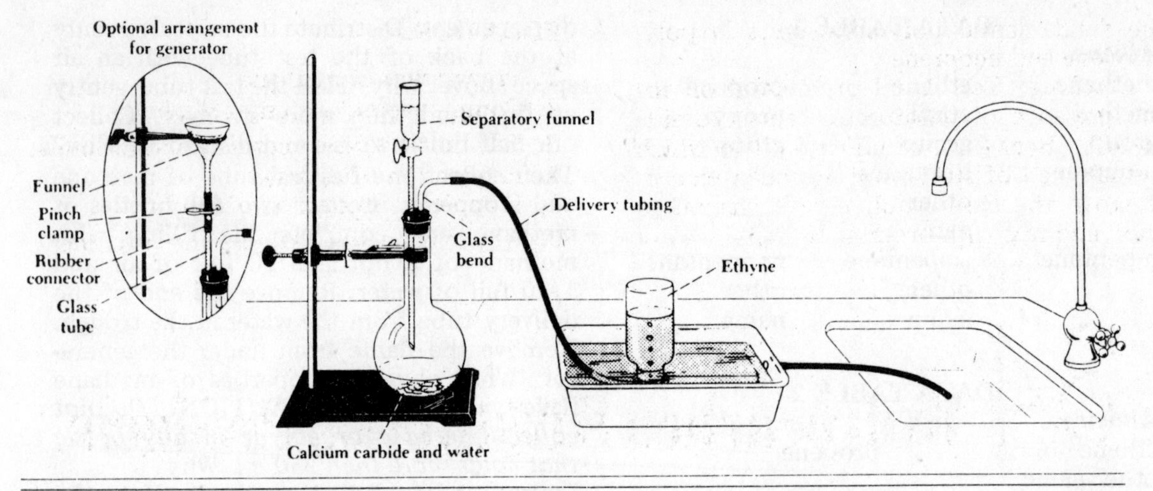

Fig. 33-1

water to flow dropwise on the calcium carbide. When vigorous action starts, close the pinch clamp. Collect a bottle of gas by water displacement and discard it. If action in the generator slows, open the pinch clamp to admit more water. Then collect three bottles of the gas. Finally complete the filling with gas of a bottle which contains 14/15 air and 1/15 water. **CAUTION:** *Before lighting your burner*, dismantle the generator under the hood, and dispose of calcium carbide as directed by your instructor. What physical properties of ethyne have you observed?

Cautiously at arm's length, bring a lighted splint to the uncovered mouth of the bottle containing the ethyne-air mixture as it rests mouth upward on the laboratory table. Result?

Ignite a full bottle of ethyne. Note the color of the flame and one of the products of combustion. Blow hard across the mouth of the bottle. Result? Add 5 ml of limewater to the bottle and shake. Result?

To another bottle of ethyne, add 5 ml of bromine water. Cover with a glass plate and shake without inverting the bottle. Result?

To the last bottle of ethyne add 1 ml of bromine in CCl_4. Cover with glass plate, shake vigorously without inverting the bottle and note the color of the bromine solution.

QUESTIONS: 1. What is one cause of explosions in coal mines that you have learned from this experiment?

2. What is necessary in order for ethyne to burn with a clean flame?

3. Hydrogen is odorless. Yet sometimes a peculiar odor is given off when dilute sulfuric acid is added to scrap iron. How can this odor be accounted for?

4. Name the compounds formed when (a) one bromine atom substitutes for one hydrogen atom in methane, (b) two bromine atoms add to ethene, (c) four bromine atoms add to ethyne.

FURTHER EXPERIMENTATION: Use your models of methane, ethane, ethene, and ethyne to construct the models of products resulting from the reaction of these hydrocarbons with bromine.

To 3-ml samples of the following liquids in test tubes, add 1 ml of bromine in CCl_4, stopper, and shake vigorously to test for unsaturates; kerosene, gasoline (white), mineral oil, benzene, toluene. Also test a small piece of paraffin and naphthalene in the same manner. Collect a bottle of the fuel gas supplied to the laboratory by water displacement and test it this same way.

Try samples (above) with potassium permanganate solution (0.3%).

Use the molecular model kit to construct

the fundamental polymeric units in polyethylene and neoprene.

Cracking: Test 1 ml of mineral oil for the presence of unsaturates using bromine in CCl_4. Heat 2 ml of mineral oil in which a small wad of steel wool has been placed. Remove the steel wool, permit the oil to cool, and test with bromine in CCl_4.

EQUATIONS

1. Preparation of methane
2. Complete combustion of methane.
3. Reaction between methane and bromine.
4. Preparation of ethyne.
5. Complete combustion of ethyne.
6. Reaction between ethyne and bromine.

Experiment 34 Hydrocarbon Substitution Products

PURPOSE: To construct models of representative hydrocarbon substitution products. To show some of the characteristic reactions of certain hydrocarbon substitution products.

APPARATUS: Balance, platform; burner and tubing; clamp, test tube; cork handle; dish, evaporating; graduated cylinder; medicine dropper; molecular model kit, Sargent; ring, iron; ring stand; test tubes; test tube, large, Pyrex; thermometer; wire gauze.

MATERIAL: Acetic acid, glacial; amyl alcohol; copper wire spiral, 25 cm No. 18 gauge; cottonseed oil; ethanol; glycerol; kerosene; magnesium turnings; methanol; olive oil; salicylic acid; litmus papers, red and blue; ammonia-water solution, dilute (1:4); hydrochloric acid, dilute (1:4); sulfuric acid, conc., solutions of: aniline hydrochloride, sat'd; Fehling's A & B; formaldehyde (40% soln. formalin); silver nitrate (0.1 *M*); sodium hydroxide (10 *M*).

INTRODUCTION: Most of the important classes of organic compounds may be regarded as hydrocarbon substitution products. Their properties, for the most part, depend on the nature of the substitution group. For example, alcohols characteristically contain the hydroxyl group. However their water solutions give no evidence of the hydroxide ion. On the other hand, organic acids, which contain the carboxyl group, generally act as weak acids in water solution. The construction of representative models helps in the study of the nature of the bonding in these substituted groups.

PROCEDURE: 1. *Model construction,* general directions: Assemble ball and stick models of the substances whose formulas are given in Data Tables 1 and 2. Use spring connectors for all types of multiple bonds. Where carbon spheres are joined to other carbons by single bonds, use the long rods. Use the short rods for other single bonds. Before starting, check your kit for completeness and identification using the color code attached to the inside of the box cover. After a number of models have been constructed and their conformity with structural formulas checked, disassemble them so their components may be used with subsequent models. Construct Data Tables 1 and 2. Under each formula write the name of the substance. In the space provided, draw the representative structural formula.

2. *Organic Reactions*

A. Alcohols.

a. Test 5 ml of ethanol in a test tube with

DATA TABLE 1

Alkyl halogenides		
CH_3Cl	$CHCl_3$	CCl_4
Alcohols		
CH_3OH	C_2H_5OH	$C_2H_4(OH)_2$
C_3H_7OH	$CH_3CHOHCH_3$	$C_3H_5(OH)_3$

DATA TABLE 2

Ethers	
$C_2H_5OC_2H_5$	$C_2H_5OCH_3$
Aldehydes	
$HCHO$	CH_3CHO
Ketones	
CH_3COCH_3	$C_2H_5COCH_3$
Carboxylic acids	
$HCOOH$	CH_3COOH
Esters	
CH_3COOCH_3	$CH_3COOC_2H_5$

red and blue litmus papers. Results? Add 5 ml of water to the ethanol. Shake. Result? Test this mixture with red and blue litmus papers.

b. Repeat with a 5-ml sample of glycerol and then with amyl alcohol. Results?

c. Place 1 ml of methanol in a test tube. Heat a spiral of copper wire to red heat holding it by a cork which serves as a handle. Plunge the heated spiral into the methanol. Repeat several times. Test the odor of the product using the procedure in Fig. F-5. Note the color changes undergone by the spiral when it is heated and then when it is dipped into the methanol. What substance is produced by this oxidation of methanol?

B. Carboxylic acids

Test 2 ml of glacial acetic acid in a test tube with red and blue litmus papers. Add 5 ml of water to the acid sample and stir. Repeat the litmus paper tests. Results? Add a few magnesium turnings to 5 ml of dilute hydrochloric acid and a similar amount of turnings to 5 ml of the diluted acetic acid. Results?

C. Esters

a. To 5 ml of acetic acid, CH_3COOH, in test tube, add 5 to 6 drops of concentrated sulfuric acid and 3 ml of ethanol, C_2H_5OH. Warm gently and note the odor of the product. Of what fruit flavor does it remind you? Name the product.

b. Put about 1 g of salicylic acid, $C_6H_4OHCOOH$, in an evaporating dish and add to it 1 ml of methanol, CH_3OH. Next, add 3 drops of concentrated sulfuric acid and warm gently. You should be able to identify the odor. Name the product.

c. To $1\bar{0}$ ml of acetic acid in a test tube, add 5 ml of amyl alcohol, $C_5H_{11}OH$, and 2 ml of concentrated sulfuric acid. Warm gently and observe the odor, which is similar to that of a common tropical fruit. Name the product.

D. Aldehydes.

a. To 5 ml of mixed Fehling's solutions add 3 drops of formalin (formaldehyde solution). Result? Heat to boiling. Result?

b. To 5 ml of silver nitrate solution in a well-cleaned test tube add dilute ammonia-water until a precipitate forms. Then add ammonia-water dropwise with stirring until this precipitate just dissolves. Add $1\bar{0}$ drops of formalin and heat the contents until a silver mirror forms. **CAUTION:** The mirror must be destroyed by adding nitric acid since it cannot be safely stored.

E. Aniline ($C_6H_5NH_2$): *Condensation polymerization.*

Pour $1\bar{0}$ ml of aniline hydrochloride into a large test tube. Insert a thermometer. Add 10 ml of formalin with stirring. Note the temperature change. Results?

F. Saponification.

a. Mix 4 ml of cottonseed oil or olive oil with 5 ml of ethanol in an evaporating dish. Stir in 3 ml of sodium hydroxide solution and heat over a low flame, stirring constantly, until the mixture has the consistency of mayonnaise. Remove the flame and allow the contents of the evaporating dish to cool. Do you think the reaction would occur without the application of heat? What has happened to the alcohol during the process?

b. Shake vigorously in a test tube a mixture of 1 ml of kerosene and 10 ml of distilled water. Describe the result. What are such mixtures called? Now transfer a small portion of the soap you prepared to the test tube and again shake the contents vigorously. Add more soap if necessary. Result? Compare with the initial result. State concisely the action of the soap.

QUESTIONS: 1. Give the name and write the structure representative of the characteristic (functional) groups in the following types of compounds: alcohol, aldehyde, ketone, ether, carboxylic acid.
2. Write general formulas for the following: alcohol, aldehyde, ketone, ether, carboxylic acid, ester.

FURTHER EXPERIMENTATION: Try the reaction of a small piece of dry sodium (half the size of a small pea), obtained from your instructor, on ethanol and test for hydrogen production.

Try the Beilstein test for the presence of halogens in organic compounds by plunging the heated copper spiral used in Part 2 into a small sample of CCl_4 (representing an alkyl halogenide). **CAUTION:** *Do not inhale the vapors of carbon tetrachloride since they are poisonous.* Reheating the copper spiral produces a characteristic green color in the burner flame. Try testing the CCl_4 for the presence of chloride ion by reacting it with a small quantity of 0.1-*M* $AgNO_3$ (aq) solution.

Try producing Nylon (reference, Morgan, P. W., and Kwolek, S. L., J. Chem. Educ., 36, 182 (1959), *The Nylon Rope Trick.*

Try the polymerization (addition or vinyl type) of styrene by mixing 5 ml of styrene with a small amount of catalyst (paste benzoyl peroxide) and carefully heating the small test tube in a water bath. **CAUTION:** *Dry benzoyl peroxide should not be used because of its explosive nature. Styrene should not be heated with an open flame because of its volatility and combustibility.*

EQUATIONS

1. First step in direct halogenation of methane.
2. Oxidation of methanol (hot copper(II) oxide).
3. Ionization of acetic acid in water.
4. Ethyl acetate by esterification.
5. Aldehyde reaction (Fehling's solution).
6. Saponification of a fat (sodium hydroxide).

Experiment 35 Rate of Chemical Reaction

PURPOSE: To show how the rate of a particular chemical reaction, the decomposition of sodium hypochlorite, may be measured To study the effects of changing the conditions of concentration and temperature on the rate of this reaction.

APPARATUS: Beaker, 600 ml; burner and tubing; clamp, buret; clamp, pinch; cylinders, graduated, 10 ml, 50 ml, 250 ml; flask, Erlenmeyer, 250 ml; flask, Florence, 500 ml; glass bends, 8 cm × 8 cm (2), 8 cm × 20 cm; glass tubing, 5 cm; ring, iron; ring stands (2); rubber connector; rubber tubing, small diameter; stoppers, rubber, 1-hole No. 6, 2-hole No. 6; test tube, small (litmus paper vial will do); thermometer; watch with second hand; wire gauze.

MATERIAL: Ice; graph paper; solutions of cobalt(II) nitrate (0.17 *M*); sodium hypochlorite (5%) (commercial bleach such as Clorox.)

INTRODUCTION: A solution of sodium hypochlorite decomposes in the presence of a catalyst according to the net equation:

$$2OCl^- \rightarrow 2\,Cl^- + O_2\uparrow$$

Its rate of decomposition is measured in terms of the volumes of oxygen liberated during regular time intervals. Such volumes will be measured by the volumes of water displaced by the liberated oxygen. A catalyst is necessary to speed up the normal, very slow decomposition rate. It is thought to be cobalt(III) oxide, Co_2O_3, which is presumably produced from the standardized amount of cobalt(II) nitrate solution. A negligible quantity of the hypochlorite solution is consumed in the production of the catalyst according to the equation:

$$2Co^{++} + OCl^- + 6H_2O \rightarrow 4H_3O^+ + Cl^- + Co_2O_3$$

The effects of changing the temperature and concentration of the reactant will be determined and the observed results will be tabulated. Graphs will be constructed from the observed, tabulated data.

SUGGESTION: Students should work in pairs. One student times and records results, the other observes the volume of displaced water.

PROCEDURE

1. *General.* The assembled apparatus is shown in Fig. 35-1. Prepare a hot water bath as in Fig. F-6, omitting the watch glass, for Part 3. In general, procedures will parallel Part 2 in dealing with changes in temperatures and concentration. Construct a Data Table similar to the one shown in this experiment. Record all your observations in the proper columns and spaces in the Data Table.

2. *Rate of reaction at room temperature.* Using the 50-ml graduated cylinder, transfer 25 ml of sodium hypochlorite solution

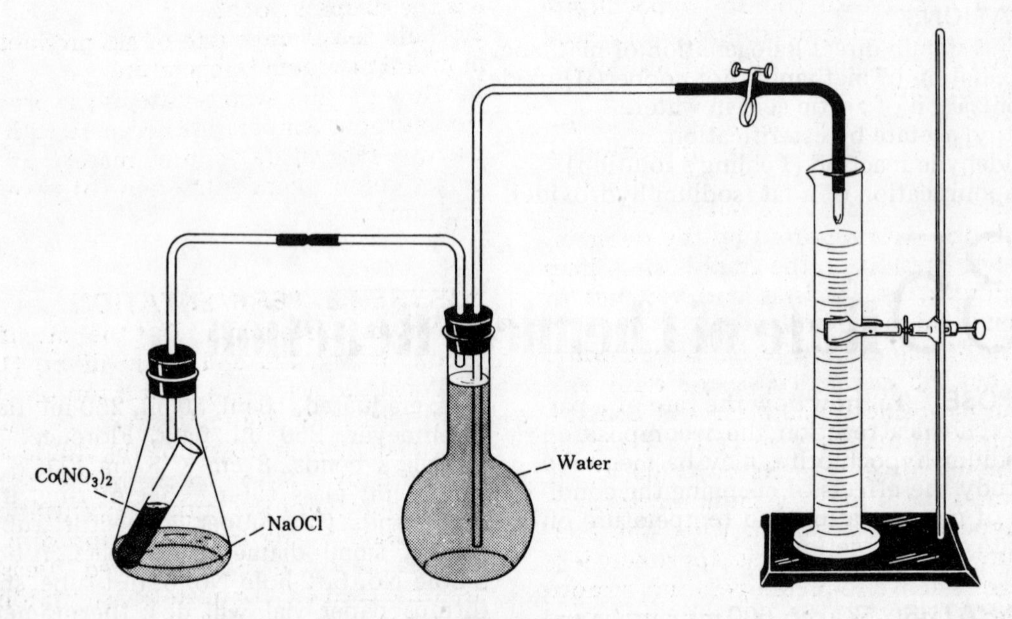

Fig. 35-1

to the Erlenmeyer flask. Take and record the solution temperature. Transfer 5 ml of cobalt(II) nitrate solution to the small test tube. Insert this test tube in the Erlenmeyer flask without spilling. Fill the 500-ml Florence flask with water. Insert the two-hole stopper containing an 8 cm × 8 cm and an 8 cm × 20 cm glass bend in the Florence glask and attach the rubber tubing, pinch clamp, and short glass tube as shown in Fig. 35-1. Open the pinch clamp and blow into the short right-angle bend to fill the delivery tube leading to the graduated cylinder with water. Close the pinch clamp. Insert the second short right-angle bend in the one-hole stopper, and place this stopper in the Erlenmeyer flask. Complete the assembly of the apparatus by connecting the short right-angle bends with a rubber connector. Make sure all stoppers and connections are tight. Remove the pinch clamp. Only a few drops of water will flow into the graduated cylinder if the apparatus is air-tight. Discard this water.

The observer notes the time as the other team member quickly tips over the Erlenmeyer flask so that the cobalt(II) nitrate solution mixes with sodium hypochlorite solution. Hold Erlenmeyer flask at its neck and shake it constantly with a gentle swinging motion throughout the experiment. Observe and record the volume of water displaced every 30 seconds until approximately 200 ml of water (total volume) has been displaced. The timer calls out the time and records the data reported by the observer.

Plot the results on the graph, using times (in minutes) as abscissas and volumes of oxygen in ml as the ordinates.

3. *Rate of reaction at a higher temperature.* Wash out the reaction flask and refill with sodium hypochlorite and test tube containing cobalt(II) nitrate as in Part 2. Place the Erlenmeyer flask with its contents in the hot water bath. Insert a thermometer into the hypochlorite solution. When the temperature of the contents is approximately 10 degrees above room temperature, remove the flask from the bath, reconnect the apparatus, and proceed as in Part 2. Record the results in the Data Table.

4. *Rate of reaction at a temperature below room temperature.* Repeat Part 2 but cool the reaction flask and contents by placing in a beaker of ice water. Take the temperature of the sodium hypochlorite solution, and remove the flask from the ice water bath when the temperature is about 10 degrees below room temperature. Record your results in the Data Table.

5. *Rate of reaction at two-fold dilution.* Wash out the reaction flask and fill as for Part 2. Add 3$\bar{0}$ ml of distilled water to the sodium hypochlorite solution. Note that when 55 ml of diluted sodium hypochlorite solution is mixed with 5 ml of cobalt(II) nitrate solution, the total volume will be 60 ml instead of the original 3$\bar{0}$ ml. Repeat Part 2 and record the results.

6. Graph the data obtained for Parts 2-5 and label each of the four curves by the number of the Part which each graph represents.

QUESTIONS: 1. Which numbered curve has the steepest slope?

2. State the average rate of gas production in ml/min at room temperature.

3. How did the average rate of gas production at room temperature compare with the average rate at (a) approximately 10 C° below room temperature and (b) two-fold dilution?

FURTHER EXPERIMENTATION:

(a) Nature of reactants: Test the rate of reaction of Mg, Zn, and Cu in dilute (1:3) hydrochloric acid. (b) Concentration: Use equal masses of Mg in 10 ml of the dilute HCl, and then in 10 ml of the dilute acid produced by dilution to one-half and then to one-quarter of the initial concentrations. The masses of Mg may be wrapped in Cu wire to keep the Mg submerged. Measure the time used for complete consumption of the Mg at the various dilutions.

DATA TABLE

Time interval (minutes)	Volume of Oxygen produced (ml)			
	Room temp. .... °C	Above room temp. .... °C	Below room temp. .... °C	Room temp. and two-fold dilution
0.5				
1.0				
1.5				
2.0				
2.5				
3.0				
3.5				
4.0				
4.5				
5.0				
5.5				
6.0				

Experiment 36 Course of a Chemical Reactions: Catalysis

PURPOSE: To investigate the decomposition of hydrogen peroxide: (a) the decomposition products; (b) the thermal nature of the reaction; (c) the course of the catalyzed and uncatalyzed reaction.

APPARATUS: Beaker, (2) 400 ml; burner with tubing; clamp, buret; glass tube bend; ring, iron; ringstand; stoppers, rubber, solid No. 2, and a 1-hole No. 2; test tubes, thermometer mounted in stopper; tubing, rubber; wire gauze.

MATERIALS: Hydrogen peroxide solution, manganese dioxide, powder.

INTRODUCTION: Based on the results of the following procedures, you are to attempt to find answers to the problems indicated in the purpose of this experiment and to draw graphs representative of your experimental findings.

PROCEDURE: 1. Add 10 ml of hydrogen peroxide solution to a test tube. Insert the thermometer and record the temperature of the solution. Add about 0.5 gram of manganese dioxide to this solution. Result? Insert the thermometer into the test tube contents and record the temperature after one minute has elapsed. Remove the thermometer and insert a glowing splint into the upper part of the test tube. Result? Explain. Is the decomposition of hydrogen peroxide an endothermic or exothermic reaction. Write a thermochemical equation for the reaction.

a. Initial temperature
b. Temperature during the reaction
c. What is the thermal nature of this reaction?

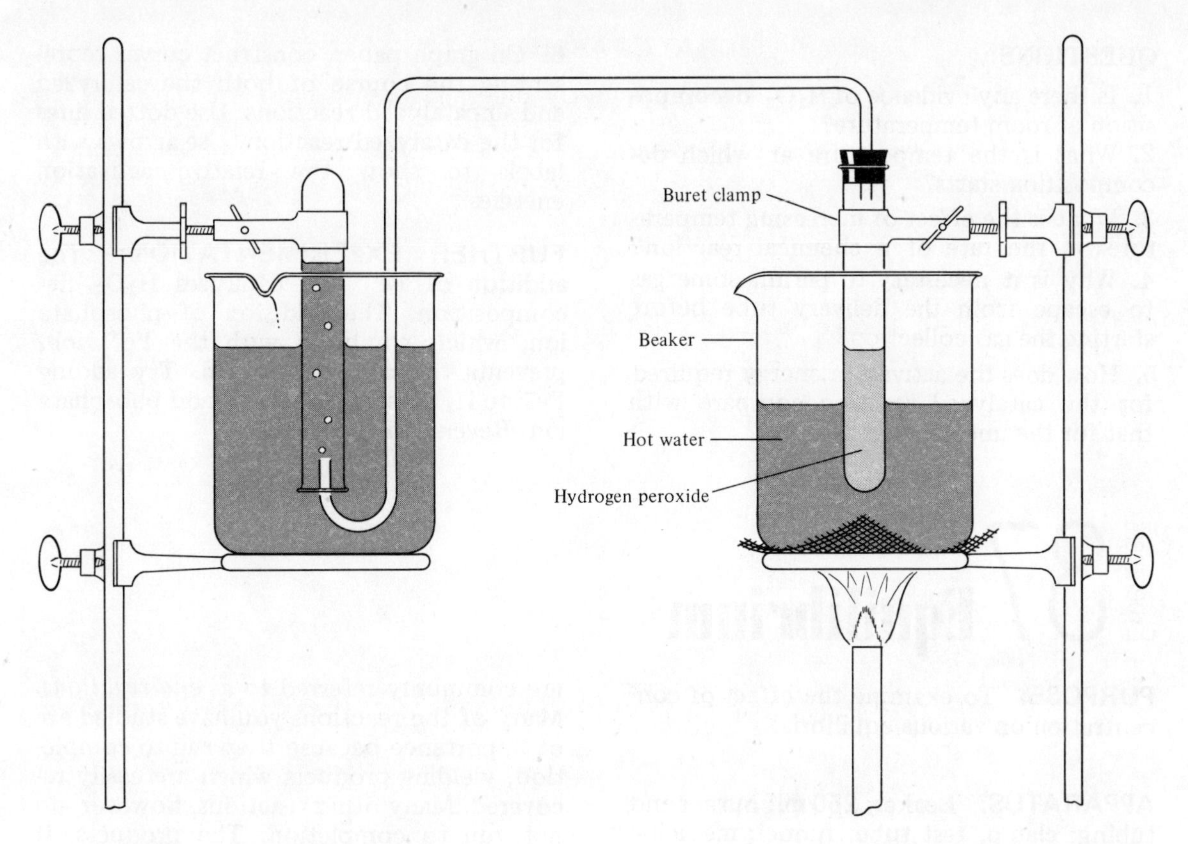

d. Name one product of this reaction that you have identified.
e. What is the other reaction product?
f. Thermochemical equation for the reaction.

2. a. Preheat 200 ml of water in the beaker to approximately 50° C.
b. Fill a test tube with water, stopper it, and place it mouth downward into the second beaker which contains 200 ml of cold water. Remove the stopper under water so that the test tube is ready for gas collection by displacement of water.
c. Place 20 ml of hydrogen peroxide solution into the generator test tube. Is there any evidence of hydrogen peroxide decomposition at room temperature? Insert the delivery tube assembly into the generator test tube. Place the generator test tube into the hot water and place the end of the delivery tube below the water in the beaker having the collector test tube. Heat the hot water and note the temperature at which gas bubbles start to escape from the hydrogen peroxide. What effect does increasing the temperature have on the rate of chemical reactions? Continue heating the hot water to the temperature range 70–80° C. Do not heat above 80° C. After the first 30 bubbles of gas have escaped, insert the delivery tube into the mouth of the collecting test tube. See Fig. 36-1. Note the time necessary to collect a full test tube of the gas being produced. Remove the test tube, open it, and test the contents with a glowing splint. Result? How does the activation energy of this uncatalyzed reaction compare with that for the catalyzed reaction?

QUESTIONS:

1. Is there any evidence of H_2O_2 decomposition at room temperature?
2. What is the temperature at which decomposition starts?
3. What is the effect of increasing temperature on the rate of a chemical reaction?
4. Why is it necessary to permit some gas to escape from the delivery tube before starting the gas collection?
5. How does the activation energy required for the catalyzed reaction compare with that for the uncatalyzed reaction?
6. On graph paper, construct curves representing the course of both the catalyzed and uncatalyzed reactions. Use dotted lines for the catalyzed reaction. Use arrows with labels to show the relative activation energies.

FURTHER EXPERIMENTATION: The addition of Fe^{+++} ion catalyzes H_2O_2 decomposition. The addition of phosphate ion, which combines with the Fe^{+++} ion, prevents the catalytic action. Try adding Fe^{+++} to H_2O_2 solution. Then add phosphate ion. Reverse the procedure.

Experiment 37 Equilibrium

PURPOSE: To examine the effect of concentration on various equilibria.

APPARATUS: Beaker, 250 ml; burner and tubing; clamp, test tube; funnel; medicine dropper; stirring rod, glass; ring, iron; ring stand; rubber stopper, solid No. 2; test tubes.

MATERIAL: Ammonium chloride; ammonium thiocyanate; iron(III) chloride; iron (III) nitrate; silver acetate; silver nitrate; sodium acetate; sodium chloride; sodium nitrate; filter paper; pH paper (Hydrion A and B); acetic acid, dil. (1.0*M*); hydrochloric acid (12*M*); solutions of barium chloride (0.5*M*); calcium chloride(0.5*M*); iron(III) chloride (1*M*); potassium thiocyanate (1*M*); silver acetate (saturated); sodium sulfate (1*M*).

INTRODUCTION: Chemical reactions in which a product is essentially un-ionized, is given off as a gas, or is precipitated, may be thought of as running to completion and are commonly referred to as *end reactions*. Many of the reactions you have studied are of importance because they run to completion, yielding products which are easily recovered. Many other reactions, however, do not run to completion. The products, if formed at all, do not leave the fields of action but remain in contact and react to re-form the original reactants. Under suitable conditions, both reactions may proceed at the same speed. An equilibrium is thus established. Both the forward and the reverse actions continue with no net change in the quantities of either reactants or products.

An equilibrium exists in a saturated solution between undissolved particles and particles in solution. An ionic equilibrium may be established between un-ionized molecules of a molecular solute and the ions of the solution, or between undissociated ions of an ionic solute and the ions in solution. An equilibrium is affected by both concentration and temperature. By the principle of Le Chatelier, we know that a system in equilibrium tends to shift so as to relieve the stress placed upon it by a change in concentration or temperature.

PROCEDURE: 1. Solution equilibrium. Add Rapidly 10 ml of calcium chloride solution to 5 ml of sodium sulfate solution in a Pyrex test tube. Shake. Result? Write the equation for this reaction in ionic form. Use the Table of Solubility of Salts in the Appendix, if necessary, to identify the precipitate. Now add dropwise 5 ml more of the calcium chloride solution, observing closely to see whether the precipitate continues to form. From the quantities of the two solutions used and their molarities, which ions have been added to the mixture in excess? Heat the tube just to boiling and set it aside to allow the precipitate to settle. This should require approximately 30 minutes; in the meantime, proceed with Parts 2 and 3.

After the precipitate has settled, add a drop of calcium chloride solution to the clear supernatant liquid, using a clean, dry medicine dropper. If no precipitate forms where the drop contacts the liquid, you may be sure that calcium chloride is present in excess in the solution. Decant this clear liquid into a second test tube. (if the mixture is still turbid, it may be filtered.) To the filtrate (or decanted liquid), add 3 or 4 ml of barium chloride solution. Result? Refer to the equation you balanced after the initial precipitation. Which ion, when paired with the barium ion just added, will yield a precipitate? The initial precipitate must have separated from a solution that was saturated with respect to *which* pair of ions? Write the equation for the equilibrium between this saturated solution and the *initial* precipitate.

2. *Common-ion affect.* Add a very small amount of solid silver acetate to 15 ml of saturated silver acetate solution. Stopper the test tube and shake vigorously for about one minute. If the solid portion dissolves, add more and repeat until satisfied that your solution is saturated, which will be indicated when the solid silver acetate fails to dissolve. Write the equation for the solution equilibrium now assured. Filter and divide equally among 3 dry test tubes. Add to these three samples, respectively, 0.5 g solid silver nitrate, 0.5 g solid sodium acetate, and 0.5 g solid sodium nitrate. Shake each. Result? To which tubes have ions been added that are common to an ion already present? Refer to the equilibrium equation you have just written and explain the result observed in each tube.

3. *Le Chatelier's principle:* Set up 4 test tubes each containing 5 ml of 1.0-*M* acetic acid. Keep test tube No. 1 as the control. To test tube No. 2 add 1 g of solid sodium acetate. Stir the contents thoroughly. To test tube No. 3 add 1 ml of 12 *M* HCl and mix thoroughly. To test tube No. 4 add 1 g of solid NaCl and mix thoroughly. Place strips of pH paper on a clean dry glass plate. Using a clean stirring rod, first test the contests of test tube No. 1 by dipping the stirring rod in the solution and touching to the pH paper until you have determined the pH of the 1.0-*M* acetic acid. Repeat this operation for the contents of each of the other three test tubes. Construct a Data Table like the one shown. Report the pH in the Data Table. Complete the rest of the Data Table by indicating how the results affect the molar concentrations of each of the species present in the original solution of acetic acid. Use the terms: *increases, decreases, remains the same*. In which test tubes was a stress applied to the equilibrium system? How would you identify this type of stress?

4. *Complex-ion equilibrium.* Mix approximately 1 ml each of the solutions of iron(III) chloride and potassium thiocyanate in a 250-ml beaker. Result? The Fe^{+++} ion and the CNS^{-} ion form the complex $FeCNS^{++}$ ion which shows a deep-red color. Assuming the $FeCNS^{++}$ ion to be only slightly ionized at this concentration to form Fe^{+++} ions and CNS^{-} ions, write the equation for the ionic equilibrium. Now dilute with water (100 ml or more) to give a color of light red to orange-yellow. Half fill 4 test tubes and add, respectively, 0.5 g of the following solid reagents: iron(III) nitrate, iron(III) chloride, ammonium thiocyanate, and ammonium chloride. Results? Explain your observations

DATA TABLE

	pH	$HC_2H_3O_2$	H_3O^+	$C_2H_3O_2^+$
#1 1.0-*M* $HC_2H_3O_2$		xxxxxx	xxxxxx	xxxxxx
#2 plus solid $NaC_2H_3O_2$				
#3 plus 12-*M* HCl				
#4 plus solid NaCl				

in terms of shifts in the equilibrium using the equation you have written.

FURTHER EXPERIMENTATION: Prepare a saturated solution of sodium chloride and filter it. To 5 ml portions of the filtrate add separately: 1 ml of concentrated HCl; 1 ml of saturated NaOH solution; two pellets of solid sodium hydroxide; 1 ml of saturated solutions of sodium nitrate, calcium chloride, and potassium nitrate. Look for evidences of the production of a precipitate in each case, and explain the results in terms of the effect of ions on a solution equilibrium of a salt.

Use Welch #4226 Temperature Equilibrium Tubes for the $2NO_2 \rightleftarrows N_2O_4$ system by immersing in (a) hot water, (b) ice-water mix, (c) either salt-ice or Dry Ice-acetone. As a project students may prepare their own tubes, Reference: *Chemistry*, 45, Jan., (1972), "Making Tubes for NO_2-N_2O_4 Equilibrium Reaction."

Prepare a saturated solution of CO_2 or use soda water to test effect of temperature rise on equilibrium system by testing with litmus or pH paper. Heat gently, increase temperature to boil out, making indicator tests. Refer to heat of solution of CO_2, Modern Chemistry, 1974, Chapter 12.

QUESTIONS: 1. How is a saturated solution defined in terms of an equilibrium condition?

2. How does the addition of sodium acetate to a dilute solution of acetic acid affect the pH of the solution? Explain.

3. How would the addition of ammonium chloride to a dilute ammonia-water solution affect the hydroxide ion concentration of the solution? Explain.

4. How would the addition of sodium hydroxide to a dilute solution of ammonia-water affect the concentrations of (a) the hydroxide ion, (b) the ammonium ion initially present? Explain.

Experiment 38 Solubility-Product Constants

PURPOSE: To show how the difference in the magnitudes of solubility-product constants of characteristic precipitates may be used to separate effectively a mixture of related ions.

APPARATUS: Funnel; graduated cylinder; ring, iron; ring stand; test tubes; wash bottle.

MATERIAL: Ethanol (denatured alcohol will do); filter paper; litmus paper; acetic acid, dilute (1:4); ammonia-water solution, dilute (1:4); hydrochloric acid, concentrated; solutions of barium chloride (0.25 *M*); potassium chromate (0.25 *M*); strontium chloride (0.25 *M*).

INTRODUCTION: The chromates of barium and strontium are insoluble according to the following data:

Salt	Ion Product	K_{sp}
$BaCRO_4$	$[Ba^{++}]\ [CrO_4^{--}]$	2×10^{-10}
$SrCrO_4$	$[Sr^{++}]\ [CrO_4^{--}]$	3.6×10^{-5}

By controlling the concentration of chromate ion added to a solution containing barium and strontium ions in identical concentration, it is possible to cause almost complete precipitation of the less soluble barium chromate. Under the conditions, strontium chromate is not precipitated and strontium ions remain in solution.

In a solution of chromate ions, such as that of potassium chromate, the existent equilibrium is

$$Cr_2O_7^{--} + 3H_2O \rightleftarrows 2CrO_4^{--} + 2\ H_3O^+$$

For this system

$$K = \frac{[CrO_4^{--}]^2\ [H_3O^+]^2}{[Cr_2O_7^{--}]} = 2.4 \times 10^{-15}$$

According to the law of mass action, increasing the hydronium ion concentration results in a decrease in the chromate ion concentration. In some qualitative analysis procedures, the chromate ion concentration is maintained at about 5×10^{-4} *M* by adjusting the pH to 5. This is achieved by using a solution of chromate ion containing acetic acid and ammonium acetate. This concentration of chromate ions is sufficient to reduce the concentration of barium ion from 0.1 *M* to 0.0001 *M* but is insufficient to exceed the K_{sp} for strontium chromate from a 0.1-*M* solution of this ion. In this simplified procedure, acetic acid is used in sufficient concentration to achieve a functional separation of barium and strontium ions. Ethanol is added to a solution of strontium chromate from which barium chromate has been precipitated. This lowers the K_{sp} of strontium chromate so that its ion-product is exceeded and precipitation occurs.

SUGGESTION: The instructor may wish to have the students calculate (a) the concentration of chromate ion required to reduce the concentration of barium ion to 1×10^{-4} *M* and (b) the value of the ion-product for strontium chromate at this concentration of chromate ion for a solution which contains 0.1-*M* strontium ion. Flame tests for barium and strontium may also be used at appropriate places in this experiment according to directions given in Part 2, Experiment 45, Flame Tests.

PROCEDURE: **1.** Add 5 ml of acetic acid to 5 ml of barium chloride solution. Stir. Add 5 ml of potassium chromate solution. Stir. Result? Explain. Filter, and wash the precipitate twice with small additions of water from a wash bottle. Puncture the filter cone and wash one-half of the precipitate into a test tube with 5 ml of water. Use another 5 ml of water to wash the remaining precipitate into a second test tube. Add 1 ml of concentrated hydrochloric acid to the mixture in one test tube. Add 5 ml of acetic acid to the mixture in the other test tube. Stir each. Results? Explain.

2. Add 5 ml of acetic acid to 5 ml of strontium chloride solution. Stir. Add 5 ml of potassium chromate solution. Stir. Result? Explain. Add ammonia-water with stirring until the solution gives an alkaline reaction with litmus paper. Result? Explain. Mix 5 ml of this solution with 5 ml of ethanol. Result? Filter and wash one-half of the precipitate into each of two test tubes as in Part 1. Add 1 ml of concentrated hydrochloric acid to the precipitate in one test tube and 5 ml of acetic acid to the precipitate in the second test tube. Stir each. Results? Explain.

3. Mix 4 ml of strontium chloride with 2 ml of barium chloride. Add 6 ml of acetic acid. Stir. Add 6 ml of potassium chromate solution. Stir. Using Hydrion paper and drops of ammonia-water solution, adjust the pH to between 4 and 5. Shake vigorously. Result? Filter and save the filtrate for Part 4. As in Part 1, wash the precipitate, puncture the filter cone and wash one-half of the precipitate into each of two test tubes. Add 1 ml of concentrated hydrochloric acid to one portion of precipitate and 5 ml of acetic acid to the other portion. Stir each. Results? Explain. Identify the precipitate.

4. Add ammonia-water solution dropwise to 5 ml of the filtrate from Part 3 until the mixture just turns red litmus to a definite blue. Result? Explain. Mix 5 ml of this solution with 5 ml of ethanol. Result? Filter. As in Part 3, wash one-half of the precipitate into each of two test tubes. Add 1 ml of concentrated hydrochloric acid to one portion and 5 ml of acetic acid to the other portion. Stir each. Results? Identify the precipitate.

FURTHER EXPERIMENTATION: Try precipitating ions of both metals from a mixed solution, made alkaline with ammonia-water using a solution of ammonium carbonate, and dissolve the precipitate in acetic acid before going on to Parts 3 and 4. This procedure is used in qualitative analysis to separate barium, strontium, and calcium from other ions. Try precipitating barium sulfate from a solution of barium ion, acidified with 1 ml of hydrochloric acid. This procedure is often used to identify barium in conjunction with a flame test for barium ion.

QUESTIONS: 1. Explain why barium chromate dissolves in hydrochloric acid. 2. Refer to the equation in the Introduction and explain the effect of addition of hydroxide ion (addition of ammonia-water solution) on the concentration of chromate ion.

Experiment 39 Hydrolysis

PURPOSE: To test the water solutions of some salts to discover which are not neutral, and to explain why this phenomenon occurs.

APPARATUS: Dish, evaporating; glass plates; test tubes.

MATERIAL: Aluminum sulfide; Hydrion papers, full range; litmus papers, red and blue; solutions of: aluminum sulfate (0.02 *M*); ammonium chloride (0.1 *M*); copper(II) sulfate (0.05 *M*); potassium carbonate (0.05 *M*); potassium chloride (0.1 *M*); potassium nitrate (0.1 *M*); sodium acetate (0.1 *M*); sodium hydrogen carbonate (0.1 *M*); sodium phosphate (0.03 *M*); sodium sulfate (0.05 *M*); zinc chloride (0.05 *M*).

INTRODUCTION: Hydrolysis is a process which involves the reaction of water with the ions of certain salts. In the slight ionization of water, equilibrium is quickly achieved and the concentrations of hydronium ions and hydroxide ions are very low.

$$2H_2O \rightleftarrows H_3O^+ + OH^-$$

Any reaction which removes either of the ions will speed the reaction producing these ions. Thus hydrolysis always shifts the equilibrium to the right, resulting in an increase in the concentration of the ion not removed. If hydrolysis removes hydronium ions by the formation of a weak acid, the solution will be basic due to the increase in hydroxide-ion concentration. If hydrolysis removes OH; ions by the formation of a weak hydroxide, the solution will be acidic due to the increase in the H_3O^+-ion concentration. If a weak acid and an equally weak hydroxide are formed by hydrolysis, the solution will remain neutral and the hydrolysis may be complete.

PROCEDURE: 1. Place 1-ml portions of each of the following solutions in separate labeled test tubes: (a) sodium chloride, (b) sodium sulfate, (c) potassium chloride, (d) potassium nitrate. Test each with strips of red and blue litmus, and with Hydrion papers. If short range indicator papers are available, close approximations of the pH of each solution may be possible. Construct a Data Table like the one shown. Record your results in the Data Table including the approximate pH.

2. Test 1-ml portions of each of the following solutions as in Part 1: (a) sodium acetate, (b) sodium hydrogen carbonate, (c) sodium phosphate, (d) potassium carbonate. Record your results in the Data Table.

3. Test 1-ml portions of each of the following solutions as in Part 1: (a) ammonium chloride, (b) aluminum sulfate, (c) copper (II) sulfate, (d) zinc chloride. Record your results in the Data Table. Now complete the last two columns of the Data Table.

4. Put a small lump of aluminum sulfide in an evaporating dish in the hood or other well ventilated place. Add water to the dish. Identify the gas that forms by its odor, and examine the precipitate. Why may this hydrolysis action be considered to be complete?

QUESTIONS: 1. Why do the solutions of some of the salts tested have a basic reaction?

2. Why do the solutions of some of the salts tested have an acidic reaction?

3. Write the equation for the net reaction in the hydrolysis of the diluate sodium hydrogen carbonate solutions.

4. If the reaction to the right (in your equation for Question 3) were complete, what would be the OH^- ion concentration?

5. What was the experimental OH^- ion con-

DATA TABLE

Solution tested	Indicator color		Approximate pH	Approximate	
	Litmus	Hydrion		$[H_3O^+]$	$[OH^-]$
$NaCl$					
Na_2SO_4					
KCl					
KNO_3					
$NaC_2H_3O_2$					
$NaHCO_3$					
Na_3PO_4					
K_2CO_3					
NH_4Cl					
$Al_2(SO_4)_3$					
$CuSO_4$					
$ZnCl_2$					

centration of the sodium hydrogen carbonate solution as indicated by the Hydrion paper?

6. What percent of the sodium hydrogen carbonate is hydrolyzed as shown by your experimental results?

$$\% \text{ hydrolyzed} = \frac{\text{Experimental } [OH^-]}{[OH^-] \text{ if hydrolysis complete}} \times 100\%$$

$$\% \text{ hydrolyzed} = \frac{\qquad}{\qquad} \times 100\%$$

7. Considering both positive and negative ions, which of the two salt solutions, $NaC_2H_3O_2$ or $NH_4C_2H_3O_2$, would you expect to be hydrolyzed more completely? Why?

EQUATIONS: Complete these equations for cation or anion hydrolysis.

1. $NH_4^+ + H_2O \rightleftarrows$
2. $Al(H_2O)_6^{+++} + H_2O \rightleftarrows$
3. $Cu(H_2O)_4^{++} + H_2O \rightleftarrows$
4. $CO_3^{--} + H_2O \rightleftarrows$
5. $C_2H_3O_2^- + H_2O \rightleftarrows$

Experiment 40 Equilibrium and Complex Ions

PURPOSE: To show how variation in pressure, temperature, and concentration affect various equilibrium systems, mainly through the study of reactions involving consideration of the equilibrium constants of complex ions and the solubility product constant of related precipitates.

APPARATUS: Balance, platform; glass rod; graduated cylinder; medicine droppers; test tubes, small, Pyrex.

ADDITIONAL APPARATUS for INSTRUCTOR'S EXPERIMENT: Beaker, (400 ml); burner and tubing; clamp, buret; flask, suction; rubber stopper, No. 7; tubing, rubber, suction; vacuum pump (or aspirator).

MATERIAL: Ammonia-water solution, dilute; hydrochloric acid, concentrated, (12 *M*); sodium fluoride; solutions of: cobalt(II) chloride (0.1-*M*); cobalt(II) chloride, saturated; copper(II) sulfate (0.1 *M*); iron(III) chloride (0.1 *M*); potassium thiocyanate (0.1 *M* in acetone.).

ADDITIONAL MATERIALS for INSTRUCTOR'S EXPERIMENT: Ethanol; ice; hydrochloric acid, dilute, (0.1 *M*); phenolphthalein; sodium chloride; sodium hydrogen carbonate.

INTRODUCTION: Transition metals such as iron, copper, and cobalt form complex ions which, unlike familiar polyatomic ions such as the NO_3^- ion, $SO_4^=$, ion and NH_4^+ ion, ionize slightly into simpler fragments (ions). This ionization is slight and its extent is indicated by the magnitudes of the ionization constants. For the tetraamminecopper(II) ion, $Cu(NH_3)_4^{++}$, the ionization constant is 5×10^{-14}.

$$Cu(NH_3)_4^{++} \rightarrow Cu^{++} + 4NH_3$$

$$K_i = \frac{[Cu^{++}][NH_3]^4}{[Cu(NH_3)_4^{++}]} = 5 \times 10^{-14}$$

The first addition of ammonia-water solution to a solution of the copper(II) ion results in the precipitation of the pale blue copper(II) hydroxide. The concentration of hydroxide ion is large enough for the K_{sp} of the hydroxide to be exceeded.

$$Cu(H_2O)_4^{++} + 2OH^- \rightarrow Cu(H_2O)_2(OH)_2\ (s) + 2H_2O$$

$$K_{sp} \text{ of } Cu(H_2O)_2(OH)_2 = [Cu(H_2O)_4^{++}][OH^-]^2 = 5.6 \times 10^{-20}$$

Further addition of ammonia-water solution causes the precipitate to dissolve with the formation of the dark blue tetraamminecopper(II) complex.

$$Cu(H_2O)_2(OH)_2 + 4NH_3 \rightarrow Cu(NH_3)_4^{++} + 2H_2O + 2OH^-$$

This shows the effect of the availability of a sufficiently large supply (concentration) of the coordinating group. For the overall reaction,

$$Cu(H_2O)_4^{++} + 4HN \rightleftarrows Cu(NH_3)_4^{++} + 4H_2O$$

the equilibrium constant is large, approximately 10^{12}.

$$K_{eq} = \frac{[Cu(NH_3)_4^{++}]}{[Cu(H_2O)_4^{++}][NH_3]^4} = 10^{12}$$

In one part of this experiment you will perform this sequence of operations. You will then add concentrated hydrochloric acid dropwise to this system to study the effects of increasing concentration of hydronium and of chloride ions. This leads to the stepwise production of 1. The regenerated copper(II) hydroxide, 2. the hydrated blue copper(II) ion, and 3. the green-yellow tetrachlorocuprate(II) ion, $CuCl_4^{--}$.

1. $Cu(NH_3)_4^{++} + 2H_3O^+ + 2H_2O \rightarrow Cu(H_2O)_2(OH)_2\ (s) + 4NH_4^+$
2. $Cu(H_2O)_2(OH)_2 + 2H_3O^+ \quad Cu(H_2O)_4^{++} + 2H_2O$
3. $Cu(H_2O)_4^{++} + 4Cl^- \rightarrow CuCl_4^{--} + 4H_2O$

SUGGESTION: Set up the Instructor Experiment showing the effect of pressure on equilibrium at the beginning of the period and have students view the results during the period. The effect of temperature on equilibrium may be investigated at a strategic time, probably toward the end after students have experimented with Co(II) complexes.

PROCEDURE: 1. *Complex ions of Cu(II).* Add dilute ammonia-water dropwise to 5 ml of the solution of copper(II) sulfate until the pale blue precipitate of copper(II) hydroxide results. Construct a Data Table like the one shown. Record the number of drops required in the Data Table. Continue

DATA TABLE

Reagent	Number of drops added	Formula of product
$NH_3(aq)$		
$NH_3(aq)$		
HCl		
HCl		
HCl		

the addition of the ammonia-water solution stirring continuously until the deep blue solution of tetraamine copper(II) results. Record the additional number of drops required. Add hydrochloric acid drop by drop with stirring until the copper(II) hydroxide is regenerated. Record the number of drops required. Continue the addition of hydrochloric acid until the blue color of the hydrated Cu(II) ion is produced. Record the number of drops required. Continue the addition of hydrochloric acid until the green-yellow tetrachlorocuprate(II) ion is produced. Record the number of drops used.

2. *Complex ions of Co(II).* Add hydrochloric acid dropwise to 5 ml of the saturated cobalt chloride solution until a perceptible color change is produced. Result? How many drops are required to change the $Co(H_2O)_6^{++}$ ion to the $CoCl_4^=$ ion? Add the dilute solution of cobalt chloride dropwise to 5 ml of the potassium thiocyanate solution (acetone) until the first perceptible color change occurs. Result? Continue the addition until a deeper color occurs. Result? This color is characteristic of the hexathiocyanatocobaltate(II) complex, $Co(SCN)_6^{-4}$. Explain the deepening of the color in terms of concentration of the hexaaquocobalt(II) ion, $Co(H_2O)_6^{++}$. Continue the addition of the cobalt chloride solution until another definite color change occurs. Result? Explain in terms of the changing concentration of water in the system.

3. *Identifying the Co(II) ion in the presence of Fe(III) ion.* Add 1 ml of iron(III) chloride solution to 5 ml of the acetone solution of potassium thiocyanate. Result? This

identifies the hexathiocyanatoferrate(III) ion, $Fe(SCN)_6^{-3}$. Mix 2 ml each of the solutions of iron(III) chloride and cobalt(II) chloride. Add 2 ml of this mixture to 5 ml of the acetone solution of potassium thiocyanate. Result? Add 0.5 g of solid sodium fluoride to the remaining 2 ml of the mixture of Co(II) and Fe(III) ions. Stir. Result? This result is due to the formation of the hexafluoroferrate(III) ion, FeF_6^{-3}. Then add this solution dropwise to 5 ml of the acetone solution of potassium thiocyanate until the color change establishing the presence of the Co(II) ion in the mixture occurs. Result? The K_i for the hexathiocyanatoferrate equilibrium is 8×10^{-3}. How does the K_i for the hexafluoroferrate equilibrium compare in magnitude with the K_i for the hexathiocyanatoferrate equilibrium?

4. INSTRUCTOR EXPERIMENT. *a.* Effect of pressure. Put 250 ml of saturated sodium hydrogen carbonate solution in a suction flask. Add several drops of phenolphthalein solution. If a pink color develops add hydrochloric acid (dilute) dropwise until the color just disappears. Stopper the suction flask and attach the side arm to a vacuum pump or aspirator. Observe periodically until the solution turns pink. Have the students explain on the basis of the following equilibrium.

$$HCO_3^- \rightleftarrows OH + CO_2$$

b. Effect of temperature. Half-fill a large Pyrex test tube with the saturated solution of cobalt(II) chloride. Heat this until the contents of the test tube undergo a color change. Have students explain on the basis of the equilibrium

$$Co(H_2O)_6^{++} + 4Cl^- \rightleftarrows CoCl_4^{--} + 6H_2O$$

Place the hot test tube in an ice-sodium chloride mixture so that the bottom half of the solution cools in the ice-salt mixture. Have students note the results and explain.

c. You may wish to dissolve $CoCl_2 \cdot 6\,H_2O$ in ethanol to show how a solvent, other than water, may affect an equilibrium. You may also wish to demonstrate the use of cobalt(II) chloride in "invisible" ink.

Experiment 41 Oxidation-Reduction Reactions

PURPOSE: To study some typical oxidation-reduction reactions, and to determine the relative strengths of some oxidizing and reducing agents.

APPARATUS: Balance, platform; forceps; medicine dropper; test tubes; wire hook.

MATERIAL: Strips 1×5 cm of copper, lead, silver, zinc; iron filings; iron(II) sulfate; potassium permanganate; sand paper; hydrochloric acid, concentrated; sulfuric acid, concentrated; solutions of: copper(II) nitrate (0.1 *M*), iron(III) chloride (0.1 *M*), lead(II) nitrate (0.1 *M*), silver nitrate (0.1 *M*), tin(II) chloride (0.1 *M*), zinc nitrate (0.1 *M*).

INTRODUCTION: Substances which lose electrons during chemical action are said to be oxidized. Those which gain electrons are said to be reduced. If one reactant gains electrons, another must lose an equal number. Thus oxidation and reduction actions must occur simultaneously and to a comparable degree.

The stronger the tendency of an oxidizing agent to gain electrons, the greater is its strength. The weaker the tendency for a reducing agent to hold electrons, the greater is its strength as a reducing agent. Thus the silver ion, Ag^+, has a strong tendency to acquire an electron to form the silver atom, Ag. The Ag^+ ion is a weak oxidizing agent.

PROCEDURE: 1. Add 5 ml of silver nitrate solution to a test tube and insert a strip of brightened copper. To 5 ml of copper(II) nitrate solution in a second test tube, add a strip of silver foil. After a few minutes, examine both pieces of metal. Results? Where a reaction has occurred, write the balanced electronic equations for the oxidation and the reduction. Then write the ionic equation for the net reaction. Which metal is the stronger reducing agent? Which metallic ion is the stronger oxidizing agent?

2. Place a strip of brightened zinc in 5 ml of copper(II) nitrate solution. Insert a strip of copper in 5 ml of zinc nitrate solution. Write the balanced electronic equations for both oxidation and reduction actions where a reaction occurs. Write the ionic equation for the net reaction. Which metal is the stronger reducing agent? Which metallic ion is the stronger oxidizing agent? What are the relative strengths of the three metals tested so far as reducing agents. What are the relative strengths of the three metallic ions as oxidizing agents?

3. Test a strip of brightened lead in 5 ml of zinc nitrate solution and a second strip in 5 ml of copper(II) nitrate solution. Similarly test zinc and copper in separate solutions of lead(II) nitrate. In which of these four combinations do reactions occur? Write the balanced electronic equations for both oxidation and reduction actions where reactions occur. Also write ionic equations for the net reactions. How does lead compare with zinc and copper as a reducing agent? How does the Pb^{++} ion compare with the Zn^{++} ion and Cu^{++} ions as an oxidizing agent? Arrange the 4 metals tested in order of their relative strengths as reducing agents, placing the strongest first. Arrange the 4 metallic ions in order of their relative strengths as oxidizing agents, placing the weakest first.

4. Note the color of a 5 ml solution of iron(III) chloride solution. Add tin(II) chloride solution, dropwise near the end, until the color of the iron(II) chloride has disappeared. Describe the color change. The Fe^{+3} ion has been reduced to the Fe^{++} ion. What was the reducing agent? What change did it undergo? Write the balanced electronic equations and the ionic equation for the net reaction.

5. Divide 2 g of oil-free iron filings into two approximately equal portions. Save one portion for Part 6, and to the other portion (test tube), add 4 ml of water and then 2 ml of concentrated hydrochloric acid. Warm (do not boil) the mixture until a moderate reaction is under way. What gas is evolved? Allow to stand until the solution is clear. Recall the colors of iron(III) chloride and iron(II) chloride solutions in Part 4. Which iron ion is produced in this reaction? What is reduced? Write the balanced electronic equations for both actions and the ionic equation for the net reaction. Which is the stronger reducing agent, Fe or H_2?

6. To 5 ml of iron(III) chloride solution (test tube), add 1 ml of concentrated hydrochloric acid and the second portion of iron filings retained from Part 5. Describe the action. Recall your previous comparison of the colors of iron(III) chloride and iron(II) chloride solutions. What reduction occurs? H_2 is the reducing agent. What is the purpose of the iron filings and hydrochloric acid? Write the pair of balanced electronic equations. Based on the reactions of Part 5 and Part 6, list H_2, Fe, and Fe^{++} in the order of their relative strengths as reducing agents.

7. Dissolve 1 or 2 small crystals of potassium permanganate in 10 ml of water. Note the intensity of the color. Recall the color of common potassium salts. Which ion of the salt is responsible for this color? Dissolve 2 or 3 small crystals of iron(II) sulfate in 5 ml of water. Acidify with 2 or 3 drops of concentrated sulfuric acid. Now add the potassium permanganate solution to the solution containing the Fe^{++} ions, a very little at a time (mix) and finally dropwise, until the color remains. The permanganate, MnO_4^-, ion is a strong oxidizing agent. The manganese(II), Mn^{++}, ion is practically colorless. What occurred during the addition of the permanganate solution? What was oxidized? What was reduced? What was indicated by the return of the permanganate color to the solution? What changes in oxidation number occurred?

EQUATIONS

1. $Zn + Cu(NO_3)_2 \rightarrow$
2. $Fe + HCl \rightarrow$
3. $FeCl_3 + SnCl_2 \rightarrow FeCl_2 + SnCl_4$
4. $FeCl_3 + H_2 \rightarrow FeCl_2 + HCl$
5. $FeSO_4 + KMnO_4 + H_2SO_4 \rightarrow Fe_2(SO_4)_3 + MnSO_4 + K_2SO_4 + H_2O$

Experiment 42 Oxidation-Reduction Titration

PURPOSE: To determine a percentage composition by means of an oxidation-reduction titration.

APPARATUS: Balance, sensitive to 0.01 g; 3 beakers, 150 ml; buret, preferably with glass stopcock; clamp, buret; graduated cylinder; ring stand; vial, shell, small size (litmus paper vial will do); wash bottle.

MATERIAL: Unknown iron(II) salt; sulfuric acid, dilute (1:6); standard solution of potassium permanganate (approximately 0.02 *M*).

INTRODUCTION: Any reaction in which there is a distinct change in some characteristic of the solution when equivalent quantities of the reactants are present may lend itself to the titration technique. Certain exidation-reduction reactions are accompanied by a distinct color change when equivalent quantities of the oxidizing ion and reducing ion are present in the solution. The iron(II) ion, Fe^{++}, is oxidized to iron(III) ion, Fe^{-3}, by the permanganate ion, MnO_4^-, when in acid solution. The MnO_4^- ion is reduced to the manganese(II) ion, Mn^{++}, in the reaction. Of these four ions, only the permanganate is intensely colored. Thus as long as Fe^{++} ions are present in a solution to which MnO_4 ions are being added, the MnO_4^- color will disappear as Mn^{++} ions are formed. When all Fe^{++} ions have been oxidized, MnO_4^+ ions will no longer be reduced to Mn^{++} and the characteristic color will reappear. Thus the first faint appearance of the pink color of the MnO_4^- ion indicates the *end point* of the titration.

In the case of oxidizing and reducing agents, the particular oxidation-reduction reaction must be known in order to express the gram-equivalent weights of the reactants. *In a given oxidation-reduction reaction, the gram-equivalent weight of the oxidizing agent or the reducing agent is equal to the gram-formula weight divided by the number of electrons lost or gained.* For example, in Part 4 of Experiment 41, the iron(III) ion, Fe^{+++}, was reduced to Fe^{++}. Tin(II) ion, Sn^{++}, was the reducing agent, being oxidized in the process to Sn^{++++}. The electronic equations for this reaction show the number of electrons gained or lost.

$$2Fe^{+++} + 2e^- \rightarrow 2Fe^{++}$$
$$Sn^{++} - 2e^- \rightarrow Sn^{++++}$$

The gram-equivalent weights of the reactants in this reaction are:

$$\text{g-eq. wt. } Fe^{+++} = \frac{2Fe^{+++}}{e^- \text{ gained}} = \frac{2 \times 56\text{ g}}{2} = 56\text{ g}$$

$$\text{g-eq. wt. } Sn^{++} = \frac{Sn^{++}}{e^- \text{ lost}} = \frac{119\text{ g}}{2} = 59.5\text{ g}$$

In this oxidation-reduction titration, you will titrate a solution of a permanganate of known concentration into a solution of a weighed sample of an unknown iron(II) salt. By computing the equivalent weights of the two reactant ions for this particular reaction, and knowing the volume and concentration of the MnO_4^- solution and the mass of Fe^{++} salt, you will be able to determine the percentage composition of iron in the unknown salt.

PROCEDURE: 1. Place about 1 g of an unknown iron(II) salt in a small vial (a watch glass will serve) and weigh accurately to 0.01 g. Record this mass in a Data Table like the one that follows. Now pour approximately half of the salt into a clean dry beaker labeled *No. 1.* Reweigh the vial and remaining salt. Record. Pour this portion of the salt into a second clean beaker labeled *No. 2.* Reweigh the empty vial and record.

2. Rinse a clean buret, first with a few milliliters of distilled water, and then with a few milliliters of the standard solution of potassium permanganate. Mount the buret in position and fill with the permanganate solution. Draw off enough of the solution to remove the air from the jet tip and record the initial reading.

3. Add about 50 ml of distilled water to the No. 1 beaker and dissolve the iron(II) salt. Add 5 ml of dilute sulfuric acid and titrate immediately until a final drop of the permanganate solution causes a pink coloration to remain. This may easily be detected if the beaker is resting on white paper and a beaker of distilled water is placed alongside for comparison. Record the final buret reading.

4. Prepare the No. 2 sample and titrate as in Part 3. Unless the buret required refilling before commencing the second titration, the initial reading for this second trial will be the final reading for the first trial.

CALCULATIONS: *Show all computations in smooth form on a separate sheet of paper.*

1. As a result of the oxidation-reduction action, the oxidation state of iron was raised from +2 to +3. Determine the change in the oxidation state of manganese by the

DATA TABLE

First mass of vial and salt		g
Second mass of vial and salt		g
Mass of empty vial		g
	No. 1	No. 2
Mass of sample of Fe^{++} salt	g	g
Initial buret reading	ml	ml
Final buret reading	ml	ml
Volume of MnO_4^- solution used	ml	ml
Mass of MnO_4^- reduced (computed)	g	g
Mass of Fe^{++} oxidized (computed)	g	g
Percentage composition of iron as Fe^{++} in salt	%	%
Average value		%

reduction of MnO^{-4} to Mn^{++}. Write the balanced electronic equations for both oxidation and reduction systems.

2. Refer to the explanation in the Introduction if necessary, and then calculate the g-eq. wt. of Fe^{++} and the g-eq. wt. of MnO_4^- for this particular oxidation-reduction reaction.

g-eq. wt. Fe^{++} = g.

g-eq. wt. MnO_4^- = g.

3. From the volume of MnO_4^- solution used with each sample and the known concentration, determine the mass of MnO_4^- used with each sample.

4. Now knowing the g-eq. wt. of Fe^{++} and the g-eq. wt. of MnO_4^- for this reaction and the actual mass of MnO_4^- reduced by each sample of Fe^{++} salt, compute the actual mass of Fe^{++} oxidized in each sample.

5. From the mass of salt and the mass of Fe^{++} oxidized in each sample, compute the percentage composition of iron as Fe^{++} in this salt for both samples. What is the average value of your two percentage-composition determinations? Record the results of all computations in the Data Table.

Experiment 43(a) Electrochemical Cells, Half-Cell Reactions

PURPOSE: To construct several electrochemical cells and study their performance.

APPARATUS: Clips, alligator; copper wire, insulated, No. 18; demonstration cell (a glass tumbler, porous cup, battery top); electrodes, carbon; glass bends (U-shaped for salt bridge); graduated cylinder (10 ml); medicine dropper; voltmeter, d-c, 0-1.5 v.

MATERIAL: Litmus paper, red; sandpaper, 1 × 5 cm; ammonia-water solution (6.0 *M*); hydrochloric acid, concentrated; solutions of: bromine water; chlorine water; copper(II) sulfate (1.0 *M*); iodine (aqueous); iron(II) chloride (Appendix); iron(III) chloride (0.1 *M*); potassium iodide (0.1 *M*) plus starch (Appendix); potassium permanganate (1.0 *M*); zinc sulfate (1.0 *M*).

INTRODUCTION: In oxidation-reduction reactions, electrons are transferred from the substance oxidized to the substance reduced. Oxidation-reduction reactions that occur spontaneously convert chemical energy into heat when the chemicals react. The reactants may be so arranged that the electron transfer will occur through a conducting wire connected between them. In this arrangement, chemical energy is converted to electric energy. Such an arrangement consists of two half-cells connected by a porous partition, or a conducting salt bridge. It is called an electrochemical cell.

In the first part of this experiment, you will construct an electrochemical cell (Daniell Cell) capable of producing an electromotive force of approximately 1 volt. To understand and interpret the performance of this cell and the others which you construct, you will need to understand the oxidation-reduction reaction which occurs in each case. Refer to the Table of Standard Electrode Potentials (Electromotive or Activity Series) in Chapter 21, Section 21.11, MODERN CHEMISTRY (1974) for specific half-cell reactions and oxidation potentials.

SUGGESTION: Students may work in pairs and different pairs may be assigned to construct and study the performance of one or more of the electrochemical cells. Toward the end of the period, the results obtained by various pairs may be reported to the class and compared with results that would be obtained by the theoretical use of the Table of Standard Electrode Potentials.

PROCEDURE: 1. *Electrochemical cell.* Construct a Daniell Cell, using a small demonstration cell consisting of a glass tumbler, an unglazed porcelain cup, and a battery top. Fill the porous cup to within 1 cm of the top with 1.0-*M* zinc sulfate solution. Place the cup in the glass tumbler and then fill the tumbler with 1.0-*M* copper (II) sulfate solution to the same level as that of the zinc sulfate solution. Brighten a copper electrode and a zinc electrode with sandpaper and clamp them into position in the battery top. Place the battery top on the tumbler so the copper electrode is suspended in copper(II) sulfate solution and the zinc electrode is suspended in zinc sulfate solution.

Connect one terminal of a d-c voltmeter to one electrode terminal on the battery top by a convenient length of copper wire. Attach another section of wire to the other voltmeter terminal. Momentarily touch the free end of this wire to the other electrode terminal on the battery top, observing the meter needle for deflection. If there is no deflection, reverse the connections to the battery top. Result? What voltage does the meter register?

The meter terminals are marked "+" and "—" to identify the anode and cathode of the electrochemical cell. Which metal is acting as the cathode? Which is the anode? Trace the path of electrons through the external circuit. At which electrode is reduction occurring? At which electrode is oxidation occurring? Consult the Table of Standard Electrode Potentials mentioned in the Introduction. Does this table support your conclusions?

Disconnect your cell, rinse the two electrodes, and return the meter. Remove the porous cup from the copper(II) sulfate solution. Rinse both containers thoroughly.

2. *Identification tests.* These preliminary tests are to be performed so that they may be used later to identify some of the products which result from the operation of electrochemical cells. They are arranged in sections to correspond to the various electrochemical cells to be set up according to Part 3. The assigned set(s) of electrochemical cell(s) should be set up and allowed to operate first according to Part 3. During this time interval, you will proceed according to Part 2.

a. For KI and $FeCl_3$ cell: Add 5 drops of ammonia-water solution to 5 ml samples of solutions of iron(II) chloride and iron(III) chloride respectively. Note the color of the precipitates formed. These will identify the respective ions. Add 2 ml of starch colloidal suspension to 5 ml of the aqueous solution of iodine. Note the resultant color. To 5 ml of iron(III) chloride add 5 ml of the solution containing potassium iodide and starch. Result? What is one identifiable product of this oxidation-reduction reaction?

b. For KI and Br_2 cell: Add 5 drops of bromine water to 5 ml of the mixture of potassium iodide and starch. Result? What is one identifiable product of this oxidation-reduction reaction?

c. Put one drop of chlorine water on a piece of red litmus paper. Result? Carefully test for the odor of chlorine in chlorine water by using the wafting motion described in Fig. F-5. Add 5 ml of the potassium permanganate solution to 1 ml of hydrochloric acid. Test for the odor of a product of this oxidation-reduction reaction by performing the odor test. Insert a piece of red litmus paper into the test tube. Result? What happened to the color of the permanganate solution?

3. *General.* For the electrochemical cell(s) assigned to you, pour 5 cm of each of the solutions into separate test tubes. Insert the salt bridge and the carbon electrodes (Fig. 43-1). Attach one end of the wire from a carbon electrode to the one terminal of the d-c voltmeter. Momentarily touch the free end of the wire from the other electrode to the other voltmeter terminal. If

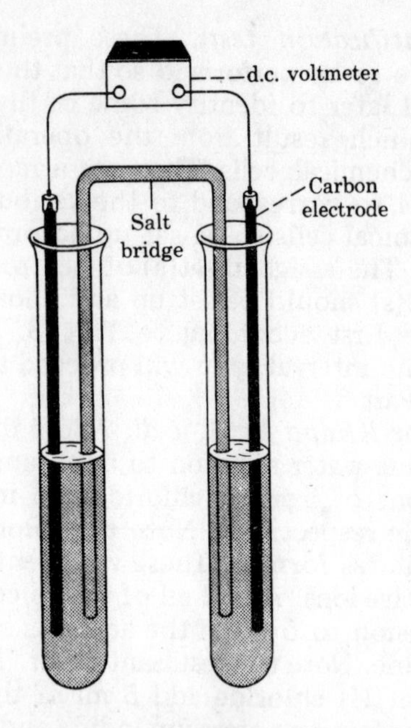

Fig. 43-1

there is no deflection, reverse the connections to the voltmeter. If there is a deflection, make a permanent connection. Construct a Data Table like the one shown. Record the observed voltage in the Data Table. Also record the solution in which solution the electrode is anode. After making the reading, disconnect the wires from the voltmeter and twist them together. Permit the reaction to proceed in the connected half-cells for 10 minutes. Record the results of the identification tests which are described in the following sections. At the conclusion of the experiment, remove the salt bridge, disconnect the twisted wires, and rinse the test tubes and electrodes thoroughly.

a. For KI and $FeCl_3$ cell: What change do you note in the test tube containing the potassium iodide-starch mixture? What is one product in this half-cell? If your experiment has proceeded to the point where the contents of the tube containing iron(III) have become almost colorless, perform the test with ammonia-water solution. What is an identifiable product in this half-cell?

b. For KI and Br_2 cell: What change do you note in the test tube containing the potassium iodide-starch mixture? What is one product of this half-cell reaction?

c. For $KMnO_4$ and HCl cell: Note any change in the color of the potassium permanganate solution. Perform the odor test for the test tube containing the hydrochloric acid. Insert a piece of red litmus paper and note the result. What is one product of this half-cell reaction?

EQUATIONS: Write complete balanced equations for these oxidation-reduction reactions.

$KI + FeCl_3 \rightarrow$

$KI + Br_2 \rightarrow$

$KMnO_4 + HCl \rightarrow$

DATA TABLE

Half-cell reactants	Identification of inserted electrode	Half-cell reaction equation	Observed voltmeter reading	Potential difference (Table of Standard Electrode Potentials)
A. KI				
$FeCl_3$				
B. KI				
Br_2		Br_2		
C. $KMnO_4$		$MnO_4 + H^+$		
HCl				

Experiment 43(b) Electrolytic Cells

PURPOSE: To construct electrolytic cells cells and study their performance.

APPARATUS: Beaker, 50 ml; copper wire, insulated No. 18; demonstration cell (a glass tumbler, porous cup, battery top); 3 dry cells; electrodes, 2 Pt; pipet, 10 ml; watch glasses.

MATERIAL: Litmus paper, red and blue; solutions of: copper(II) sulfate (0.5 *M*), phenolphthalein indicator; potassium iodide (0.1 *M*), sodium sulfate (0.2 *M*).

SUGGESTIONS: If a sufficient supply of platinum electrodes is unavailable, students should be encouraged to construct equivalent apparatus using carbon electrodes. Results for Parts 2 and 3 of this experiment may be duplicated by the use of such apparatus. A blue solution of copper(II) bromide may be used instead of copper(II) sulfate for Part 2. The test for bromine, using carbon tetrachloride, may be used for the anode product. Part 1 may be performed in a specially constructed apparatus briefly described under Further Experimentation.

PROCEDURE: 1. Assemble the demonstration cell with 0.2 *M* sodium sulfate solution in both the tumbler and the porous cup. Mount the two platinum electrodes in the battery top, one extending into the solution in the cup and the other into the solution outside the cup. Connect three dry cells *in series* as a battery, using two short lengths of copper wire. Connect the negative terminal of the battery to the platinum electrode which extends into the cup. Connect the positive terminal of the battery to the other electrode. See Fig. 43-2.

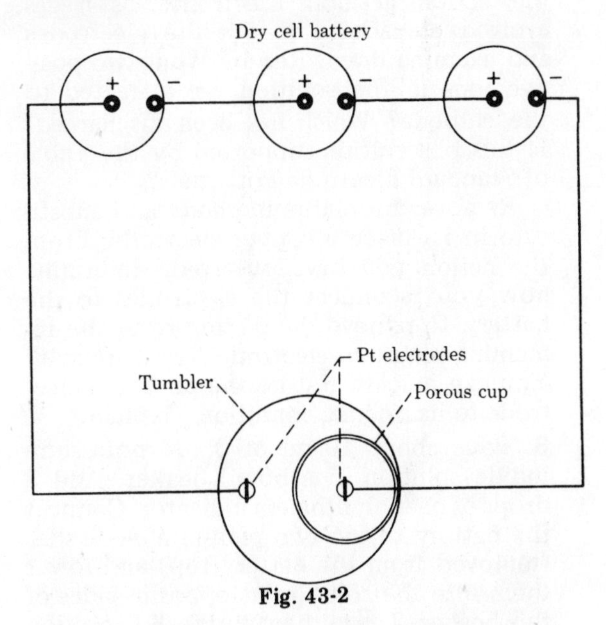

Fig. 43-2

Observe the action at each electrode. Describe it. Recall the action at the anode and at the cathode during the electrolysis of water. What ion was discharged at the cathode? What ion was discharged at the anode, and what gas was evolved? Does this action appear to be similar? Would you expect it to be? What two positive ions in the solution are attracted to the cathode? Which would you predict is more easily discharged? Evidence? Do you find agreement at the Table of Standard Electrode Potentials?

Allow the electrolytic cell to operate for at least 5 minutes. Pipet about 2 ml of solution from the porous cup onto a watch glass resting on a sheet of white paper. Add a drop of phenolphthalein. Result? Rinse the pipet and similarly test a 2 ml portion of the solution outside the porous cup, using a second watch glass. Result? Explain. Using a clean stirring rod, test the reaction of each of the cell solutions with red and blue litmus paper. Result? Explain. Discard the solution and rinse the electrodes and the two containers thoroughly, but keep the electrode assembly intact.

2. Pour the copper(II) sulfate solution retained from Part 1 in the glass tumbler (do not use the porous cup). Insert the two platinum electrodes and allow the electric current to pass for about 1 minute. Observe the action at both electrodes. Is a gas evolved at each? Life out the electrodes and examine them. Result? What two positive ions in the solution are attracted to the cathode? Which has been discharged? Is this observation supported by the Table of Standard Electrode Potentials?

Remove the platinum *anode* and substitute in its place a copper electrode. From the action you have observed, determine how you reconnect the electrodes to the battery to remove the plating from the remaining platinum electrode. Try it. Result? You can quickly restore the platinum electrode to its original condition. Explain.

3. Pour about 10 ml of 0.1-*M* potassium iodide solution in a 50-ml beaker. Add 3 drops of phenolphthalein indicator. Connect the battery to the two platinum electrodes (removed from the battery top) and lower them into the solution at opposite sides of the beaker. Leave them in the KI solution just long enough to observe a distinct action at each electrode. Is there a gas evolved at either electrode? What color changes occur? How do you explain the color change at the anode? Is this the result of oxidation or reduction? Which ion is discharged more easily at the cathode, the K^+ or the H_3O^+? Evidence? Account for the color change at the cathode. Does the anode appear to be plated? Rinse it in a little KI solution. Result? Rinse both electrodes carefully in water.

QUESTIONS: Explain the following briefly but concisely. Write the electrode reactions and the net equation for the overall electrolysis in each case.

1. The oxidation-reduction action in the Pt-Pt, sodium sulfate electrochemical cell.

2. The oxidation-reduction action in the Pt-Pt, copper(II) sulfate electrolytic cell.

3. The different color changes at the electrodes in the Pt-Pt, KI electrolytic cell.

4. How does the Table of Standard Electrode Potentials enable you to predict which of the positive ions present at the cathode of an electrolytic cell will be discharged?

FURTHER EXPERIMENTATION: The electrolysis of aqueous sodium sulfate may be explained as actual reduction and actual oxidation of water rather than as reduction of hydronium ions and oxidation of hydroxide ions. This viewpoint is an acceptable explanation since the concentrations of these ions in the neutral sodium sulfate solution is 1×10^{-7} *M*. It is consistent with the reduction of water by reducing agents such as metallic sodium and its oxidation by chlorine. The reactions are

Reduction $2H_2O + 2e^- \rightarrow H_2 (g) + 2OH^-$

Oxidation $6H_2O \rightarrow O_2 (g) + 4H_3O^+ + 4e^-$

Balancing these half reactions according to the law of conservation of electrons yields the equation

$$10H_2O \rightarrow O_2 (g) + 4H_3O^+ + 4OH^- + 2H_2 (g)$$

which produces the net equation

$$2H_2O \rightarrow 2H_2 (g) + O_2 (g)$$

The apparatus is constructed from a plastic dish according to the directions described in the *Journal of Chemical Education*, 34, 291 (1957), Teichman, Louis. It is also described in a reprint appearing in *Selected Readings in General Chemistry*, Keiffer, Wm. F.; Fitzgerald, Robt. K.; Chemical Education Publishing Co., Easton, Pennsylvania. The electrodes should be made from stainless steel rods and should be approximately 7 cm long. The dish is filled with the solution. Two test tubes are filled by sinking them in the solution and a piece of red and a piece of blue litmus paper is inserted into each test tube. The tubes are lifted to the vertical position and placed over the respective electrodes. As electrolysis proceeds, the litmus papers change indicating the production of hydronium and hydroxide ions. The gaseous products are identified by use of a glowing and a flaming splint. Before these tests are performed, the open ends of the tubes are stoppered under the solution for convenient removal. After the tests for oxygen and hydrogen are performed, the liquid contents of each test tube are poured back into the plastic dish, stirred, and litmus paper tests are again performed with the resultant mixture. Litmus paper remains unchanged indicating the stoichiometric production of hydronium and hydroxide ions. The apparatus may then be used by another student without any change of the solution.

Experiment 44 Elements of Period Three

PURPOSE: To study the properties of the elements of Period Three and some of their representative compounds.

APPARATUS: Balance, platform; beaker, 150 ml; 2 bottles, wide mouth; burner and tubing; cardboard; clamp, test tube; forceps; 2 glass plates; graduated cylinder; molecular model set (Sargent); scissors; Scotch tape; spoon, deflagrating; test tubes; tongs.

MATERIAL: Ammonium chloride; iron(II) sulfide; magnesium ribbon; phosphorus, red; sodium chloride; sodium peroxide; sulfur, roll; asbestos paper; Hydrion papers (A, B, D); litmus papers, red and blue; wooden splints; ammonia-water, dilute (1:4); hydrochloric acid, dilute (1:4); sulfuric acid, dilute (1:6); solutions of aluminum chloride (0.2 *M*); sodium hydroxide (2.5 *M*).

INTRODUCTION: The elements of Period Three illustrate the variation in properties which occurs as one goes across a period. In this period, the first element is a highly reactive metal. Then come other metals of decreasing activity. These are followed by a metalloid and then by nonmetals of increasing activity. The last element in a period is a noble gas. The properties of representative hydroxides, oxides, and binary hydrogen compounds illustrate the variations in the fundamental natures of the elements of the period.

PROCEDURE: 1. Assemble models of the crystals representative of the metals sodium, magnesium, and aluminum according to Fig. 44-1. Use the yellow spheres in the molecular model set. Nine spheres are required for the model of the sodium crystal. The construction of the magnesium crystal requires 17 spheres, while that of the aluminum crystal requires 14 spheres. Construct cardboard retainers of suitable size (approximately 8 cm in height) using tape to hold them together. The arrangements (packing) of the spheres in the cases of magnesium and aluminum represent the closest possible arrangements of identical spheres (atoms; ions). That of sodium represents a less tightly packed arrangement. Refer to Chapter 22, MODERN CHEMISTRY, 1974, and state the three physical properties of sodium which may be related to the crystal arrangement.

2. Construct a model of the silicon crystal according to Fig. 31-1 in Experiment 31. What is the electron configuration of the silicon atom? What type of hybridization produces this crystal type? Explain the great

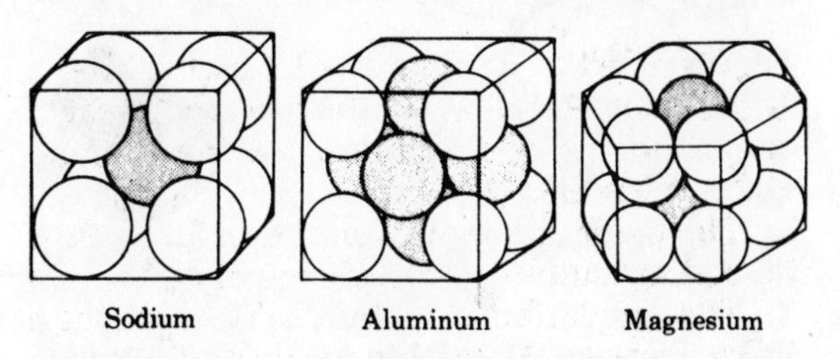

Fig. 44-1

difference in melting points that occurs between aluminum and silicon in terms of the change in crystal structure which occurs.

3. Construct models of the molecules of phosphorus, sulfur, and chlorine (see Fig. 44-2) according to the following directions: phosphorus (4 light blue spheres); sulfur (8 black spheres); chlorine (2 green spheres). How do the magnitudes of the melting and boiling points of these three elements compare with those of the first four elements of the period? Explain these in terms of the forces that hold these elements together in the solid state.

4. *a.* Add 5 ml of water to 1 g of sodium peroxide. Use a glowing splint to identify the gas produced. Test the contents of the test tube with red and blue litmus paper. Results? Test with Hydrion paper (range 11-13). Result? Approximate pH?

b. Hold one end of a 5-cm piece of magnesium ribbon with the tongs and ignite the other end in the burner flame. Hold the burning magnesium over a beaker so that the product drops into the beaker. Add 5 ml of water to the product and heat gently. Test the contents of the beaker with red and blue litmus paper. Result? Test with Hydrion paper (range 11-13). Result? Approximate pH? Compare pH for *a* and *b*.

c. Put a piece of sulfur, the size of a small pea, in the asbestor-lined bowl of the deflagrating spoon, ignite it in the burner flame, and lower it into a bottle of air. Add 10 ml of water to the bottle contents, cover with a glass plate, and shake the contents. Add a piece of red litmus paper and one of blue to the contents of the bottle. Result?

d. Repeat *c* using an amount of red phosphorus equal to the bulk of a match head. Result? What do the results of Procedures *a* through *d* indicate about the reactions of the oxides of the respective elements with water?

5. To 5 ml of aluminum chloride solution, add 1 ml of ammonia-water solution. Result? What product is formed? The gelatinous precipitate formed does not settle readily and may be regarded as a suspension. Transfer half of this suspension to a second test tube. To the suspension in one test tube, add 1 ml of sodium hydroxide solution. To the suspension in the other test tube add 1 ml of dilute hydrochloric acid. Compare the results. What property of aluminum hydroxide is thus illustrated?

6. For each reaction described in this part of the experiment, add 2 ml of liquid reagent to 1 g of solid reagent in a test tube held with the test tube clamp. Heat the test

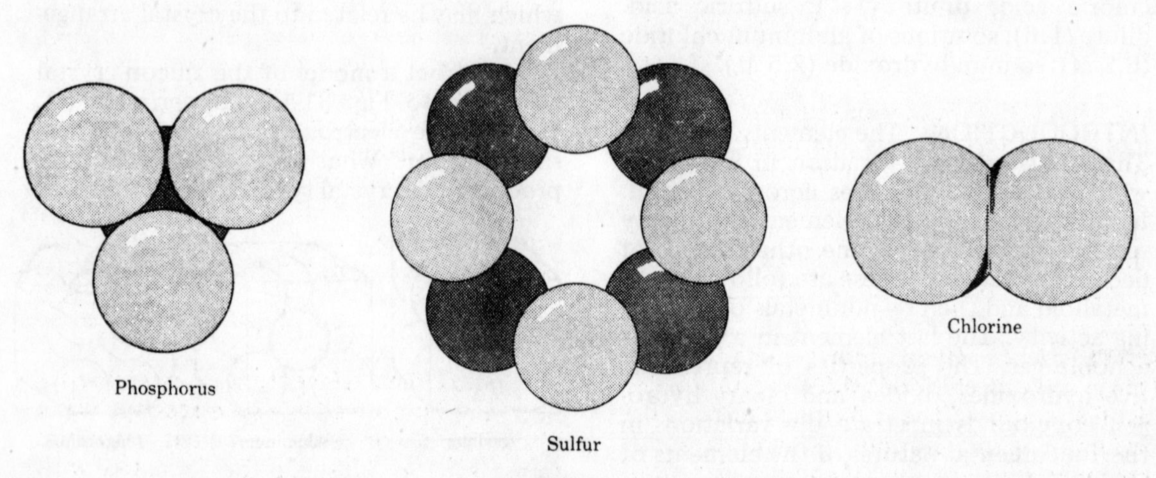

Fig. 44-2

tube gently. Then insert a piece of moistened red litmus paper and one of blue litmus paper into the vapor in the upper part of the test tube and record the results. Since the binary hydrogen compound of phosphorus is poisonous and flammable, that of nitrogen, the corresponding element in Period Two, will be substituted to show the variations in the properties of the binary hydrogen compounds of the non-metallic elements.

a. Add 2 ml of sulfuric acid to 1 g of sodium chloride and heat gently. What does the litmus paper reaction indicate? Insert a piece of moistened Hydrion paper (type A) into the vapors. Result? What is the approximate pH indicated?

b. Repeat Part *a* using 1 g of iron(II) sulfide with 2 ml of sulfuric acid. Results? What do the results of the Hydrion paper tests indicate about the relative strengths of the water solutions of the respective binary hydrogen compounds of chlorine and sulfur?

c. Add 2 ml of sodium hydroxide solution to 1 g of ammonium chloride. Heat gently and test the vapor produced with pieces of moistened red and blue litmus papers, as well as with Hydrion paper (Type A). Results? How would you expect the water solution of the binary hydrogen compounds of phosphorus to compare in acidity with those of chlorine and sulfur?

FURTHER EXPERIMENTATION: Have students test the pH of solutions of sulfuric acid (0.5 *M*) and phosphoric acid (0.33 *M*) with Hydrion paper to compare the strength of the comparable oxy-acids of sulfur and phosphorus.

EQUATIONS: Write complete balanced equations for these reactions.

1. Reactions for Part 4.
2. Reactions for Part 5 (3 equations).
3. Reactions for Part 6 (2 equations for each section; the second equation should be ionic, showing the reaction of the binary hydrogen compound with water).

Experiment 45 Flame Tests

PURPOSE: To show how certain metals may be identified by the color they impart to a flame.

APPARATUS: Burner and tubing; 2 cobalt glass plates; test tubes; 5-cm length of No. 24 platinum wire, sealed in the end of a glass tube 10 cm long. If platinum wire is not available, nichrome wire (not as satisfactory as platinum) may be used. Nichrome wire should be held with forceps.

MATERIAL: Hydrochloric acid, dilute (1:4); sodium chloride; 0.5-*M* solutions in distilled water of the A.R. grade nitrates of barium, calcium, lithium, potassium, sodium, and strontium, and of sodium chloride; unknown solutions.

INTRODUCTION: If you wish to secure good results in this experiment, your test tubes must be *scrupulously* clean. Your test tubes may be thoroughly cleaned by using the cleaning solution described in the Teachers' Edition to EXERCISES AND EXPERIMENTS IN CHEMISTRY. (CAUTION: *This cleaning solution is extremely corrosive and must not be spilled!*) After the cleaning solution has been used, the test tubes may be rinsed thoroughly in tap water and then in distilled water.

SUGGESTION: Have students examine sodium lines produced in a spectroscope using a sodium vapor lamp and then a sodium flame source. This may be repeated with mixtures of sodium and potassium.

PROCEDURES: 1. Clean a platinum wire by dipping it first into some dilute hydrochloric acid in a test tube and then holding it in the colorless flame of your burner. Repeat until the wire imparts no color to the flame. Pour 4 ml of sodium *nitrate* solution into a *clean* test tube, and dip the *tip* of the clean platinum wire into the solution, and then hold it in the flame. Observe the color of the flame just above the wire. Heat only the tip of the wire. If you heat the glass tube into which the wire is sealed, you will break the glass.

Clean the wire as before and then test a solution of sodium *chloride* in the same manner. Repeat the test, dipping the wire into a little *dry* sodium chloride.

2. Repeat Part 1, using in turn 4 ml of the solutions of the nitrates of lithium, strontium, calcium, barium, and potassium. Clean the wire thoroughly after each test. In the cases of lithium and strontium, observe which flame is more persistent and takes longer to burn off the wire. Also note the difference in the shades of color produced. When you have tested the calcium flame and then dipped the wire into hydrochloric acid and back into the flame when cleaning it, you often get an excellent flame of calcium momentarily. Record your observations in a Data Table like the one shown.

3. If two salts are present in the same solution, the color of one flame may obscure that of the other. Sometimes it is possible to absorb one color and not the other. Examine the sodium flame through at least two thicknesses of cobalt glass. Repeat, using the potassium flame with the cobalt glasses.

Flame test a mixture of the solutions of the nitrates of sodium and potassium with a clean wire. Observe the color the mixture imparts to the flame when viewed without the cobalt glasses. Repeat the test, but observe the flame as seen through the cobalt glasses. Explain any differences observed. Record your observations as before.

4. Secure an unknown solution from your instructor. Test it in the flame as in this experiment in order to identify the metallic ion present.

DATA TABLE

Metal in compound	Color of flame
sodium	
lithium	
strontium	
calcium	
barium	
potassium	
sodium (cobalt glass)	
potassium (cobalt glass)	
sodium and potassium	
sodium and potassium (cobalt glass)	
unknown metal	

CONCLUSION: Determine the identity of the unknown.

QUESTIONS: Answer in complete statements.

1. Is the flame coloration a test for the metal or for the acid radical?
2. Why do dry sodium chloride and the solutions of sodium nitrate and sodium chloride all impart the same color to the flame?
3. Describe the test for sodium and potassium when both are present.
4. How would you characterize the flame test with respect to its sensitivity?
5. What difficulties may be encountered in the use of the flame test for identification?

Experiment

46 Group II Metals and Their Compounds

PURPOSE: To study the comparative properties of some of the metals of Group II and their compounds.

APPARATUS: Balance, platform; bottle, wide mouth; burner and tubing; clamp, buret; funnel; funnel tube; glass bend; glass plate; graduated cylinder; 5 cm length of No. 24 platinum wire, sealed in the end of a glass tube (10 cm); ring stand; rubber stopper, 2-hole; test tubes, Pyrex; tubing, delivery.

MATERIAL: Barium sulfate; calcium, turnings; calcium sulfate, powder; magnesium, turnings; marble chips; filter papers; Hydrion papers (A, B, D); wooden splints; solutions of: barium hydroxide (saturated); barium chloride (0.5 *M*); calcium chloride (0.5*M*); calcium hydroxide (saturated); magnesium chloride (0.5 *M*).

INTRODUCTION: The alkaline earth metals, in general, resemble the alkali metals in their activity. They form oxides (or peroxides) and hydroxides with general similarities to those of the alkali metals. Their hydroxides, carbonates, and sulfates vary in solubility. The relative solubilities of the hydroxides explain their differences in alkalinity. The relative solubilities of their sulfates and carbonates are used in qualitative analysis in separating and identifying metallic ions.

PROCEDURE: **1.** *a.* Add a calcium turning to 5 ml of water in a test tube. Results? Perform the burning splint test for hydrogen. Result? Add a drop of phenolphthalein indicator to the test tube contents. Result? What are the two products of this reaction? Identify the solid material formed.

b. Add several pieces of magnesium turnings (about 1 g) to 5 ml of water in a test tube. Result? Heat the test tube almost to boiling. Do you see any evidence of gas evolution? If so, what gas? Cool. Add 2 drops of phenolphthalein indicator to the contents of the test tube. Result? What probable product is indicated? What do the results of a and b indicate about the relative reactivity of magnesium and calcium?

2. Set up a carbon dioxide generator according to Part 2, Experiment 32. Bubble the carbon dioxide from the generator through a test tube half full of limewater. Result? Explain. Continue to bubble the gas through the contents of the test tube until a clear solution results. Explain. Heat the contents of the test tube to boiling. Result? Explain.

3. Test 5 ml samples of the saturated solutions of the hydroxides of calcium, magnesium, and barium with Hydrion papers, both full range and the appropriate short range. What is the pH of each solution? What do these results indicate about the relative alkalinity of these compounds? Consult the Table of Solubilities in the Appendix. What trend in the solubilities of these hydroxides is indicated by the results of the pH tests?

4. To 1 g of magnesium sulfate add 5 ml of water. Stopper and shake. Result? Repeat with separate 1 g samples of calcium sulfate and barium sulfate. Results? If complete solution does not take place, filter the test tube contents. Perform the flame tests (see Experiment 45) to determine whether some solution has taken place. Results? What trend in the solubilities of the sulfates of these metals is indicated by the results of these procedures? Confirm this by consulting the Table of Solubilities in the Appendix. Consult MODERN CHEMISTRY for the solubility products of the sulfates of calcium and barium and record the values.

5. Add 1 ml of sodium carbonate solution to 5 ml of magnesium chloride solution. Result? Repeat with solutions of calcium chloride and barium chloride. Results? What conclusion can be reached about the solubilities of the carbonates of these metals? Check your results against the Table of Solubility Products in MODERN CHEMISTRY.

FURTHER EXPERIMENTATION: Investigate the comparative solubilities of the carbonates by making the stock solutions just alkaline with ammonia-water solution, and using a solution of ammonium carbonate as the precipitating agent.

EQUATIONS: Write ionic equations where appropriate.

1. Calcium and cold water
2. Magnesium and hot water
3. Reactions in Part 2
4. Reactions in Part 5

Experiment 47 Metallurgy of the Transition Metals

PURPOSE: To show how ores may undergo beneficiation and how metals are recovered from their ores.

APPARATUS: Balance, platform; beaker, 150 ml; burner and tubing; clamp, buret; glass bend; graduated cylinder (100 ml); magnet; ring stand; rubber stopper No. 2, one-hole; test tubes; tubing, delivery.

ADDITIONAL APPARATUS for INSTRUCTOR'S EXPERIMENT: Burner and tubing; clamp, buret; glass bends (2); glass tubing, Pyrex, large diameter (a large test tube with curved end removed will do); ring stand; stoppers, rubber, No. 4, 1-hole, No. 2, 2-hole; suction pump or aspirator; test tube; tubing delivery.

MATERIAL: Charcoal, wood, powdered; copper(II) carbonate; iron(II) (III) oxide (magnetite), powdered; lead(II) (III) oxide; mineral oil; sand; taconite (powdered); solution of calcium hydroxide.

ADDITIONAL MATERIAL for INSTRUCTOR'S EXPERIMENT: Lead(II) sulfide or zinc sulfide, powdered (ore samples will do); sulfuric acid, dilute (1:6); solution of potassium permanganate (0.2 *M*).

SUGGESTION: Samples of powdered taconite, and of powdered, crude sulfide ores may be obtained from metallurgical companies.

INTRODUCTION: Ores, particularly the low-grade ores, must be enriched or concentrated. The general name for the processes involved in beneficiation. The most common ores of the transition metals are oxides, sulfides, and carbonates. Oxides are generally reduced with carbon. Sulfides and carbonates are converted to oxides by heating them with excess air. The sulfides change to oxides, generally with the release of sulfur dioxide. The carbonates decompose to the oxides with the release of carbon dioxide.

PROCEDURE: 1. *a.* Mix 5 grams of powdered magnetite with 5 grams of sand on a piece of paper. Insert a magnet into the mixture. Result? Attempt to separate the components of samples of powdered taconite (Fe_2O_3 and Fe_3O_4) with a magnet. Result?

b. Mix 2.5 grams of powdered lead(II) (III) oxide, Pb_3O_4 with 2.5 grams of fine sand.

Pour the mixture into a graduated cylinder and add 75 ml of water and 25 ml of mineral oil. Shake. Result? What name is given to this process?

2. Set up the apparatus shown in Fig. 47-1. Place 3 grams of copper(II) carbonate in the Pyrex test tube and half fill the other test tube with limewater. Heat the copper (II) carbonate until a permanent change in color occurs. Result? What has happened to the limewater? Explain. What name is given to this process? Permit the contents of the test tube to cool.

3. Mix the cool contents of the test tube from Part 2 with 5 grams of powdered charcoal. Refill the second test tube half-full of limewater. Set up the apparatus (Fig. 47-1) again and heat the solid mixture. Result in the limewater? Explain. Remove the delivery tube and continue to heat the solid contents of the first test tube until they have been heated for a total of 5 minutes. Permit the contents to cool and pour them into a beaker of cold water. Result? Examine the solid material left in the bottom of the beaker. Result? What process did the copper compound undergo? What process did the carbon undergo?

4. INSTRUCTOR EXPERIMENT: Place 5 grams of either zinc sulfide or lead(II) sulfide in the central portion of the piece of Pyrex tubing, next to the retaining glass wool. Set up the remainder of the apparatus according to Fig. 47-2, half-filling the side-arm test tube with an acidified (H_2SO_4) solution of potassium permanganate. Turn on the suction or aspirator and heat the sulfide strongly. Result? What gas was produced by this process? Explain. What name is given to this process? What is the solid product left in the Pyrex tube? Continue the process for 5 minutes and then reduce the solid residue with carbon as in Part 3.

EQUATIONS

1. $CuCO_3$ (heated) →
2. $Ca(OH)_2 + CO_2$ →
3. $CuO + C$ →
4. $ZnS + O_2$ →
5. $ZnO + C$ →

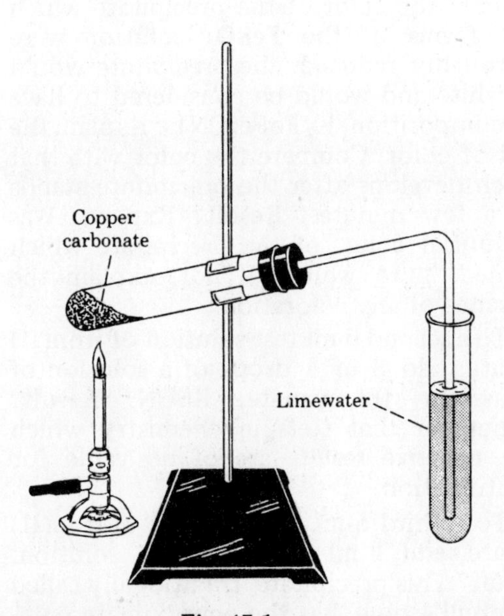

Fig. 47-1

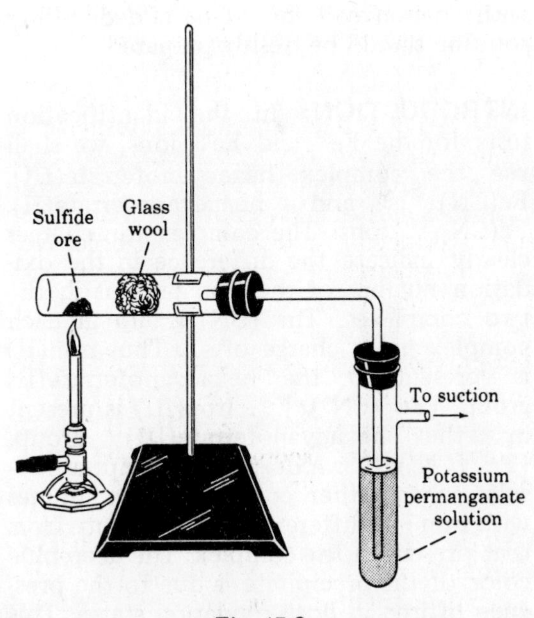

Fig. 47-2

Experiment

48 Tests for Iron (II) and Iron (III) Ions

PURPOSE: To learn how to identify iron(II) and iron(III) ions in solution.

APPARATUS: Graduated cylinder; test tubes.

MATERIAL: Solutions of: iron(III) chloride (0.1 *M*); iron(II) sulfate (0.1 *M*) or iron(II) ammonium sulfate (0.1 *M*) or iron(II) ammonium sulfate (0.1 *M*); potassium hexacyanoferrate(III) (0.1 *M*); potassium hexacyanoferrate(II) (0.1 *M*); potassium thiocyanate (0.2 *M*).

SUGGESTION: Iron(II) ammonium sulfate is perhaps a better source of Fe^{++} ions than iron(II) sulfate. The solution of iron(II) ammonium sulfate should contain 10 ml of concentrated sulfuric acid per liter. If iron(II) sulfate is used, 10 ml of concentrated sulfuric acid per liter of solution together with an iron nail should be added. Either solution should be freshly prepared.

INTRODUCTION: In the identification tests for the Fe^{++} and Fe^{+3} ions, we shall use the complex hexacyanoferrate(III), $Fe(CN)_6^{-3}$, and hexacyanoferrate(II), $Fe(CN)_6^{-4}$, ions. The complex ion charges clearly indicate the difference in the oxidation number of the iron present in the two complexes. The (CN) group in each complex has a charge of –1. Thus iron(II) is present in the hexacyanoferrate(II) group, $[Fe^{++}(CN^-)_6]^{-4}$. Iron(III) is present in the hexacyanoferrate(III) group, $[Fe^{-3}(CN^-)_6]^{-3}$. A deep-blue precipitate results when either complex ion combines with iron in a different oxidation state from that present in the complex. The deep-blue color of the precipitate is due to the presence of iron in *both* oxidation states. This provides us with the means of identifying either iron ion. If the deep-blue precipitate is formed on addition of the $[Fe(CN)_6]^{-4}$ complex, the iron ion responsible must be the iron(III) ion. Similarly, the deep-blue precipitate formed with the $[Fe(CN)_6]^{-3}$ complex indicates the presence of the iron(II) ion.

Both deep-blue precipitates are now recognized as having the same composition. The potassium salts of the complex ions are commonly used, in which case the deep-blue precipitate may be considered to have the composition, $KFeFe(CN)_6 \cdot H_2O$.

The thiocyanate ion, SCN^-, provides an excellent confirming test for the Fe^{13} ion. The soluble $FeSCN^{++}$ complex is formed, imparting a rich blood-red color to the solution.

PROCEDURE: **1.** To a 5-ml test solution of freshly prepared $FeSO_4$, or $Fe(NH_4)_2(SO_4)_2$, add 1 ml of $K_4Fe(CN)_6$ solution. Observe the color of the precipitate which first forms. If the $FeSO_4$ solution were thoroughly reduced, the precipitate would be white and would be considered to have the composition, $K_2FeFe(CN)_6$. Explain the lack of color. Compare the color with that which develops after the precipitate stands for a few minutes. Result? Explain. Was the initial color, of the precipitate which formed, pure white? If not, explain the presence of any coloration.

2. To a second 5-ml test solution of iron(II) sulfate, add 3 or 4 drops of a solution of potassium thiocyanate, KSCN. Result? Remember that tests in chemistry which give negative results are of no value for identification.

3. To a third 5-ml test solution of iron(II) sulfate, add 1 ml of $K_3Fe(CN)_6$ solution. Result? This precipitate, traditionally called Turnbull's blue, has the approximate composition, $KFeFe(CN)_6 \cdot H_2O$. What advantage does this test have over that of Part I in the identification of the Fe^{++} ion?

4. To a 5-ml test solution of iron(III) chloride, add 1 ml of the $K_3Fe(CN)_6$ solution. Result? Does a precipitate form? Do you consider this a conclusive test for the Fe^{-3} ion?

5. Add, to a second 5-ml test solution of iron(III) chloride, 1 ml of the $K_4Fe(CN)_6$ solution. Result? This precipitate, which is traditionally called Prussian blue, may be considered to have the same composition as that formed in Part 3, $KFeFe(CN)_6 \cdot H_2O$. Why may this test be considered conclusive in the identification of the Fe^{+3} ion?

6. To a third 5-ml test solution of iron(III) chloride, add 2 or 3 drops of the KSCN solution. Result? In view of the results in Part 2, do you consider this to be a conclusive test for the Fe^{+3} ion?

Record the results of each test in a Data Table like the one shown. Give color of the precipitate or solution formed.

QUESTIONS: 1. State specifically how you would make a decisive test for an iron(III) salt.

2. Which test for iron(II) ions is decisive?

3. Why must an iron(II) sulfate solution be freshly prepared?

4. Suppose you have a solution containing both an iron(II) salt and an iron(III) salt, how would you proceed to identify both Fe^{++} and Fe^{+3} ions in this solution?

DATA TABLE

Iron ion	Hexacyanoferrate(II) complex $Fe(CN)_6^{-4}$	Hexacyanoferrate(III) complex $Fe(CN)_6^{-3}$	Thiocyanate complex SCN^-
Fe^{++}			
Fe^{+3}			

EQUATIONS

1. $Fe^{++} + KI + Fe(CN)_6^{-3} + H_2O \rightarrow$

2.. $Fe^{+++} + KI + Fe(CN)_6^{-4} + H_2O \rightarrow$

3. $Fe^{+++} + SCN^- \rightarrow$

Experiment 49 Oxidation States of Transition Elements

PURPOSE: To show that typical transition metals may exist in a variety of oxidation states, each with characteristic colors. To show how these oxidation states may be changed in oxidation-reduction reactions.

APPARATUS: Balance, platform; beaker, 150 ml; burner and tubing; clamp, test tube; dish, evaporating; funnel; graduated cylinder; ring, iron; ring stand; rubber stopper, solid No. 2; test tubes; wire gauze.

MATERIAL: Iron(II) sulfate; manganese dioxide; potassium nitrate; sodium hydroxide; zinc, mossy; filter paper; litmus paper, blue; ammonia-water solution, dilute (1:4); hydrochloric acid, dilute (1:4); nitric acid, concentrated, dilute (1:5); sulfuric acid, dilute (1:6); solutions of: chromium(III) sulfate (0.16 *M*); hydrogen peroxide (3%); iron(III) chloride (0.1 *M*); manganese sulfate (0.25 *M*); potassium chromate (0.25 *M*); potassium hexacyanoferrate(II) (0.1 *M*);

potassium hexacyanoferrate(III) (0.1 *M*); potassium permanganate (0.1 *M*); potassium thiocyanate (0.2 *M*); sodium hydroxide (6 *M*); starch (colloidal); tin(II) chloride (0.1 *M*).

INTRODUCTION: The transition elements exhibit variable oxidation states and strong color. In the first-row transition metals several 4*s* and 3*d* electrons are available to be transferred to or shared with other substances. Thus several oxidation states become possible. The color of transition metals and their compounds is due to the 3*d* electrons in their structure. The compounds of chromium are all colored, the name of the element coming from the Greek word, *chroma*, meaning color. Chromium occurs in oxidation states +2, +3, and +6. Manganese compounds are also colored. Manganese occurs in oxidation states +2, +3, +4, +6, and +7. The only stable cation of manganese is the pink Mn^{++} ion. Manganates, such as K_2MnO_4, are green in color and are stable only in alkaline solutions. Permanganates, such as $KMnO_4$, are strong oxidizing agents. The permanganate ion is purple. Acid solutions of permanganate ions are useful oxidizing agents. The permanganate ion in alkaline solution may be changed to manganese dioxide, produced with a brown to black color.

The hydrated Fe^{++} ion appears to be pale green. The hydrated Fe^{+++} ion usually undergoes hydrolysis so that its solutions have a yellow-brown color. The changes in the oxidation states observed in this experiment illustrate the ease or difficulty with which the transition elements undergo changes in their oxidation states.

PROCEDURE: 1. *Chromium. a.* Add 5 ml of ammonia-water solution to 5 ml of chromium(III) sulfate solution. Result? Repeat this operation using 5 ml of sodium hydroxide solution. Result? Add an excess of sodium hydroxide solution until solution occurs. Which property of chromium(III) hydroxide is shown by this behavior? What is the oxidation state of chromium in the chromite ion (represented as either $Cr(OH)_4^-$; or the dehydrated CrO_2^-)? Save this solution for Part *c*.

b. To 5 ml of potassium chromate solution add hydrochloric acid until a definite color change occurs. Result? Explain. (Refer to the chromate-dichromate equilibrium equation in Experiment 38.) To half of this solution add ammonia-water solution until the original color is restored. Explain. What is the oxidation state of chromium in potassium chromate? What is its oxidation state in the ion produced in the acid solution?

c. To 5 ml of the alkaline chromite solution (from Part *a*) add hydrogen peroxide until a color change occurs. Result? To which chromium ion has the chromite ion been changed? What did the hydrogen peroxide do to the chromite ion?

d. Repeat the first step in Part *b* using sulfuric acid until a definite color change occurs. Result? To this solution add hydrogen peroxide until another color change occurs. Result? To which ion of chromium was the dichromate ion changed? Was it oxidized or reduced? What change in oxidation state did the chromium undergo?

e. To 5 ml of chromium(III) sulfate solution add 2 pieces of mossy zinc. Heat gently until a color change occurs. Result? This color is characteristic of the chromium(II) ion. Decant the solution and shake it with the air in the test tube until another color change occurs. Result? In which oxidation state is chromium stable in the presence of air?

2. *Manganese. a.* Add 5 ml of sodium hydroxide solution to 5 ml of manganese sulfate solution. Result? Add 10 ml more of sodium hydroxide solution. Result? What does this indicate about the nature of manganese(II) hydroxide?

b. Mix 1 g of manganese dioxide with 1.5 g of sodium hydroxide and 1.5 g of potassium nitrate in an evaporating dish. Heat until the mass melts and then let it cool. Add water to the dish and stir. Filter the contents of the dish into a cylinder half-filled with water. What is the color of the filtrate? This is the characteristic color of the manganate ion, MnO_4^{--}. To 10 ml of this solution add nitric acid until the solution is acid to litmus paper. Filter. What is the color of the filtrate? This is characteristic of the permanganate ion, MnO_4^{--}. The brown deposit left on the filter paper is manganese dioxide. What is the oxidation state of manganese in manganese dioxide, manganate ion, and permanganate ion?

c. To 5 ml of potassium iodide solution add 3 ml of sulfuric acid. Add 1 ml of potassium permanganate solution and stir. Result? Add 5 ml of collodial starch to the contents. Result? This identifies free (molecular) iodine.

3. *Iron. a.* Make a solution of iron(II) sulfate by dissolving 1 g or iron(II) sulfate in 30 ml of cold water. Do not agitate the solution unnecessarily, and do not apply heat. Divide the solution into three equal parts, using a Pyrex test tube for one part which is to be heated. To the portion in the Pyrex test tube, add 2 ml of dilute sulfuric acid and 1 ml of concentrated nitric acid. Boil the mixture *carefully* for 2 minutes. *Recall previous cautions in connection with heating corrosive liquids in test tubes.* When cool, test the liquid for iron(III) ions. Result? What purpose did the H_2SO_4, serve? What purpose did the HNO_3 serve? Had you used a solution of $Fe(NO_3)_2$ instead of $FeSO_4$, which acid could have been omitted? Why?

b. To the second portion of the iron(II) sulfate solution, add 2 ml of dilute sulfuric acid and about 4 ml of hydrogen peroxide solution. Shake the solution for a minute or two, and then test it for the presence of iron(III) ions. Result? Can you name both products of this reaction? Try the equation.

c. Shake the thrid portion of the iron(II) sulfate solution thoroughly for two minutes. Let it stand in the test tube rack for a few minutes. Then shake it thoroughly again. Now test it for the presence of iron(III) ions. What is the oxidizing agent in this action? Observe any change in appearance of the contents of the tube. Basic iron(III) sulfate, $Fe(OH)SO_4$, is formed and is only sparingly soluble. Set the tube aside to see if a brown precipitate finally appears. Can you write the equation for this reaction?

d. Reduction of iron(III) ions. To 5 ml of $FeCl_3$ solution, add $SnCl_2$ solution dropwise until the color of the iron(III) chloride solution has changed completely. Transfer a few drops of the solution to each of two test tubes. Test one portion for Fe^{++} ions. Result? Test the other for Fe^{+3} ions. If Fe^{+3} ions are still present, continue the reduction with the $SnCl_2$ solution and retest for Fe^{+3} ions. What is indicated by the presence of Fe^{++} ions? What ions are responsible? What change must these ions have undergone in the process? Can you write the equation?

EQUATIONS: Where the unbalanced equation is given, balance by using a method for balancing oxidation-reduction equations. Complete and balance all equations.

1. $Cr^{+++} + OH^- \rightarrow$
2. $Cr(OH)_3(s) + OH^- \rightarrow$
3. $CrO_4^{--} + H_3O^+ \rightarrow$
4. $Cr_2O_7^{--} + OH^- \rightarrow$
5. $CrO_2^- + H_2O_2 + OH^- \rightarrow CrO_4^{--} + H_2O$
6. $K_2Cr_2O_7 + H_2O_2 + H_2SO_4 \rightarrow K_2SO_4 + Cr_2(SO_4)_3 + H_2O + O_2$
7. $Cr^{+++} + Zn \rightarrow$
8. $Mn^{++} + OH^- \rightarrow$
9. $MnO_2 + NaOH + KNO_3 \rightarrow Na_2MnO_4 + KNO_2 + H_2O$
10. $Na_2MnO_4 + HNO_3 \rightarrow NaMnO_4 + MnO_2 + H_2O + NaNO_3$

11. $KI + H_2SO_4 + KMnO \rightarrow K_2SO_4 + MnSO_4 + H_2O + I_2$
12. $FeSO_4 + HNO_3 + H_2SO_4 \rightarrow NO$
13. $FeSO_4 + H_2O_2 + H_2SO_4 \rightarrow H_2O$
14. $FeSO_4 + H_2O + O_2$
15. $FeCl_3 + SnCl_2 \rightarrow$

SUMMARY: Copy and complete the following table, as in the example.

	Oxidation state	Electron populations		Color
		3*d*	4*s*	
Cr	0	⊘ ⊘ ⊘ ⊘ ⊘	⊘	silvery
Cr^{+++}				
CrO_2^-				
CrO_4^{--}				
$Cr_2O_7^{--}$				
Mn				
Mn^{++}				
MnO_2				
MnO_4^{--}				
MnO_4^-				
Fe				
Fe^{++}				
Fe^{+++}				

Experiment 50 Complex Ions of Copper and Silver

PURPOSE: To study some complex ions of copper and silver and to show how certain combinations are used in chemical analysis.

APPARATUS: Graduated cylinder; medicine dropper; test tubes.

MATERIAL: Acetic acid, glacial; litmus paper, red; ammonia-water solution, concentrated; solutions of: copper(II) sulfate (0.1 *M*); potassium bromide (0.2 *M*); potassium cyanide (0.2 *M*); potassium hexacyanoferrate(II) (0.1 *M*); potassium iodide (0.2 *M*); silver nitrate (0.2 *M*); sodium chloride (0.2 *M*); sodium hydroxide (1 *M*); sodium thiosulfate (0.2 *M*).

ADDITIONAL MATERIAL for INSTRUCTOR'S EXPERIMENT: Solution of hydrogen sulfide (saturated).

CAUTION: *Potassium cyanide is a deadly poison. Do not get it on your hands. It should be used only under the direct supervision of the instructor.*

INTRODUCTION: Transition metals form complex ions with ammonia molecules (NH_3), cyanide ions (CN^-), thiosulfate ions ($S_2O_3^{--}$), and thiocyanate ions (SCN^-). The transition metal is the central atom in each case. Refer to Experiment 40 which deals with complex ion equilibria and the small values of their ionization constants. In this experiment, further use of complex ions for identification and analysis will be explored. You will also investigate the role of complex silver ions in the identification of silver halogenides, several of which are used in photography. Use the following table of solubility products and ionization constants for reference.

Precipitate or complex ion	K_{sp}	K_i
½ Ag_2O ($Ag^+ + OH^-$)	2×10^{-8}	
$AgCl$	1.2×10^{-10}	
$AgBr$	4.8×10^{-13}	
AgI	1.5×10^{-16}	
$Ag(NH_3)_2^+$		6.8×10^{-8}
$Ag(S_2O_3)_2^{-3}$		6×10^{-14}
$Ag(CN)_2$		2×10^{-19}
CuS	8.5×10^{-45}	
$Cu(OH)_2$	5.6×10^{-20}	
$Cu(NH_3)_4^{++}$		5×10^{-14}
$Cu(CN)_4^{-3}$		2×10^{-27}

PROCEDURE: 1. *Copper. a.* To 5 ml of copper(II) sulfate solution add 2 or 3 ml of sodium hydroxide solution. What is the precipitate which forms? Describe its color and appearance. Add NaOH dropwise until the solution is alkaline (litmus test). Is any change observed? Write the equation.

b. To 5 ml of copper(II) sulfate solution, add 2 or 3 drops of ammonia-water solution. Result? Name the precipitate. Now add ammonia-water in excess. (How can you determine this?) What two changes do you observe? Recall the results in Part *a.* Can these changes be attributed to an excess of OH^- ions? The intense color is characteristic of what complex ion? What precaution should you observe in using this as a qualitative test for copper(II) ion?

c. Acidify 5 ml of copper(II) sulfate solution by adding 3 drops of glacial acetic acid. Then add 5 drops of a solution of $K_4Fe(CN)_6$. Result? Describe the precipitate. It may be considered to be $Cu_2Fe(CN)_6$. Recall the test for the Fe^{+++} ion. Is this a reliable, qualitative test for copper(II) ions which may be used to detect traces of copper?

d. INSTRUCTOR'S EXPERIMENT. To 5 ml of copper(II) sulfate solution, add 5 ml of saturated hydrogen sulfide solution. Result? Describe the precipitate. Under the hood, add potassium cyanide solution dropwise to 5 ml of copper(II) sulfate solution until no further precipitation is evident. **CAUTION:** *Cyanogen gas, $(CN)_2$ is formed and is extremely poisonous.* Describe the action and write the equation. Continue the addition until an excess of KCN solution is present. Result? What complex ion is formed? Write the equation for the reaction. Divide the solution into two portions. To one, add H_2S solution. Result? Recall result of use of H_2S only. To the other portion, add ammonia-water solution in excess. Result? Recall the result in Part *b.* Account for any differences observed.

2. *Silver. a.* To separate 5 ml portions of silver nitrate solution, add an equal volume of the solution of the following reagents: (1) sodium chloride; (2) potassium bromide; (3) potassium iodide. Note the colors of the precipitates formed. Name the precipitates. Save these for Parts *b*, *c*, and *d*.

b. Divide the precipitate in (*a*, 1) into three equal portions. To the first portion add 5 ml of ammonia-water solution. To the second portion add 5 ml of sodium thiosulfate solution. To the third portion add 5 ml of potassium cyanide solution. Stir the test tube contents in each case. Results? Identify the complex ions produced.

c. Repeat Part *b* with the precipitate from (*a*, 2). Results? Which reagents produce solutions of complex ions? Explain.

d. Repeat Part *b* with the precipitate from (*a*, 3). Results? Which reagents do not dissolve the precipitate? Explain. Devise a scheme for identifying the silver halogenides and briefly describe it.

EQUATIONS

1. $Cu^{++} + SO_4^{--} + Na^+ + OH^- \rightarrow$
2. $Cu^{++} + NH_3 \rightarrow$
3. $Cu^{++} + Fe(CN)_6^{-4} \rightarrow$
4. $Cu^{++} + SO_4^{--} + H_3O^+ + S^{--} \rightarrow$
5. Cu^{++} (excess) $+ CN^- \rightarrow$
6. $CuCN + CN^- \rightarrow$
7. $AgCl(s) + NH_3$ (excess) $\rightarrow$
8. $AgBr(s) + S_2O_3^{--} \rightarrow$
9. $AgI(s) + CN^- \rightarrow$

Experiment 51 Zinc and its Compounds

PURPOSE: To study the properties of zinc and some of its compounds.

APPARATUS: Burner and tubing; clamp, test tube; file, triangular; forceps; graduated cylinder; medicine dropper; ring, iron; ring stand; test tubes.

ADDITIONAL APPARATUS FOR INSTRUCTOR'S EXPERIMENT: Burner, Meker or Fisher, and tubing; crucible, sand.

MATERIAL: Zinc, mossy; zinc, sheet, strips, 1 cm × 5 cm; phenolphthalein indicator; sandpaper; wooden splints; ammonia-water solution, dilute (1:4); hydrochloric acid, dilute (1:4); solutions of: ammonium sulfide (0.2 *M*); hydrogen sulfide (saturated); sodium hydroxide (3 *M*); zinc sulfate (0.2 *M*).

ADDITIONAL MATERIALS FOR INSTRUCTOR'S EXPERIMENT: Ammonium chloride; iron nail; sawdust; sulfuric acid, dilute (1:6).

INTRODUCTION: Zinc is a self-protective metal and is used as a protective coating for sheet iron. Zinc reacts with acids. It also reacts with active metal hydroxides forming zincates and liberating hydrogen. Its characteristic oxidation state is + 2.

The hydroxides of some metals may act either as a base or as an acid. Zinc hydroxide is an example. When a strong acid such as hydrochloric acid is present, zinc hydroxide forms hydroxide ions. In the presence of a strong hydroxide, such as sodium hydroxide, zinc hydroxide forms zincate, ZnO_2^{--}, ions. Thus we may consider zinc hydroxide as either $Zn(OH)_2$ or zincic acid, H_2ZnO_2. The metallic hydroxides that behave in this manner are said to be amphiprotic.

PROCEDURE: 1. Sandpaper a piece of zinc and observe its color and luster. Bend it to note its flexibility. Test its hardness by attempting to scratch it with one of the sharp edges at the end of the file. Using forceps, hold a small piece of mossy zinc in the outer edge of the burner flame. Note the color it imparts to the flame as it oxidizes.

2. To 5 ml of hydrochloric acid, add 2 pieces of mossy zinc. Results? Perform the flaming splint test for hydrogen. Result? Repeat using 5 ml of sodium hydroxide solution. If there is no immediate sign of reaction, heat gently. Perform the flaming splint test for hydrogen after the reaction has been permitted to take place for at least one minute. Result?

3. To a half test tube of zinc sulfate solution, add 2 or 3 drops of sodium hydroxide solution. Result? Explain. Shake the tube and divide the contents into two parts. To the first half, add 6 or 8 drops of hydrochloric acid. Result? Explain.

To the second portion, add sodium hydroxide in slight excess. Result? What does this indicate about the nature of the hydroxide of zinc? The clear solution now contains sodium zincate, Na_2ZnO_2. Add a drop of phenolphthalein to the test tube. Then add dilute hydrochloric acid drop by drop until the excess sodium hydroxide is just neutralized. Result? Explain. What is the effect of adding an excess of hydrochloric acid?

4. To 5 ml of zinc sulfate solution, add two or three drops of dilute hydrochloric acid and 3 ml of hydrogen sulfide solution. Result? Does zinc sulfide precipitate in an acid solution?

To 5 ml of zinc sulfate solution, add 2 ml of ammonium sulfide solution. Result? To 5 ml of zinc sulfate solution, add just enough sodium hydroxide dropwise to form a precipitate. What is this precipitate? Shake, allow the precipitate to settle, and pour off the supernatant liquid. Add dropwise to the precipitate enough ammonia-water solution to dissolve it. The very slightly ionized complex $Zn(NH_3)_4^{++}$ ion is formed, thus reducing the concentration of Zn^{++} ions so that the excess $Zn(OH)_2$ dissolves. Now add dropwise hydrogen sulfide solution in slight excess. How can you determine this? Result?

5. INSTRUCTOR'S EXPERIMENT. Melt several pieces of mossy zinc in a large sand crucible. Use a Meker or Fisher burner, if available. Cover the surface of the molten metal with some powdered ammonium chloride and sawdust. Dip into the molten zinc an iron nail that has been cleaned by immersing it in dilute sulfuric acid and then letting it drain until it is dry. Why are dipping vats for galvanizing covered with sawdust and ammonium chloride? The crucible and zinc may be set aside to use with other classes or from term to term.

QUESTIONS: 1. Does metallic zinc burn in air?

2. What are the conditions under which ZnS may be precipitated from a solution of a soluble zinc salt?

3. What is the effect of hydrochloric acid on a precipitate of zinc hydroxide?

4. What is the effect of sodium hydroxide on a precipitate of zinc hydroxide?

EQUATIONS

1. $Zn + NaOH \rightarrow$
2. $ZnSO_4 + NaOH \rightarrow$
3. $Zn(OH)_2 + HCl \rightarrow$
4. $H_2ZnO_2 + NaOH \rightarrow$
5. $ZnSO_4 + (NH_4)_2S \rightarrow$
6. $Zn(OH)_2 + NH_3 \rightarrow$
7. $Zn(OH)_2 + H_2S \rightarrow$

Experiment 52 Cobalt Nitrate Tests

PURPOSE: To learn how to identify zinc, aluminum, and magnesium in compounds by means of the cobalt nitrate test.

APPARATUS: Beaker, 50 ml; blowpipe and tip; burner and tubing; clamp, buret; forceps; medicine dropper; ring stand.

MATERIAL: Aluminum sulfate; magnesium sulfate; zinc sulfate; charcoal block, blowpipe quality (or plaster block); unknowns containing Al, Mg, or Zn; solution of cobalt(II) nitrate (0.1 *M*).

SUGGESTION: A plaster block may be used in place of the charcoal block. To make plaster blocks, mix plaster of Paris and water to the consistency of a moderately stiff paste. Then pour enough into a flat enameled iron pan to make a layer about 1 cm deep. As soon as it begins to set or harden, cut it into blocks about 4 cm × 8 cm. Plaster blocks should be made the day before the experiment is to be performed.

INTRODUCTION: Cobalt(II) nitrate, when

heated strongly, decomposes to the oxide and combines with the oxides of certain metals to form distinctly colored complexes. With zinc, for example, it forms a *zincate*; with aluminum, an *aluminate*. The use of cobalt(II) oxide as a pigment in decorating china is an example of this action. The cobalt units with the aluminum in the china to form a blue pigment when the china is fired.

The color of the magnesium residue is faint. It should be examined near a window in a good light after your eyes have been rested for a few minutes. The eyes tire of certain colors, due to retinal fatigue, and the person may fail to see the faint tint under such a condition.

Blowpipe technique: If this is your first experience in using the blowpipe, it is suggested that you practice to develop the proper technique before beginning the experiment. Close the air ports of your burner and reduce the luminous flame to a height of 3 or 4 cm. If a support is not used, hold the end of the blowpipe in the middle of the flame so the jet flame will emerge from the side slanting downward at a slight angle. Blow with a steady pressure to produce a small, pointed, sharply defined, blue flame. Clamp the charcoal or plaster block on the ring stand, or hold it with the free hand, in a plane perpendicular to the blowpipe flame. Place it so that the sharp tip of the flame just enters the depression in the block. See diagram, Fig. F-14. Keep the cheeks puffed while blowing and learn to breathe through the nostrils without interrupting the steady pressure on the blowpipe.

PROCEDURE: 1. Make a shallow hole near one end of the charcoal or plaster block with the blunt end of the forceps. Fill the depression with zinc sulfate, add a drop of water to moisten it so it will not blow away easily, and then heat it strongly with the oxidizing flame of the blowpipe. Predict the composition of the residue. What is its color when hot? After it has cooled? Add one drop of a solution of cobalt(II) nitrate to the residue and again heat the residue strongly in the oxidizing flame of the blowpipe. If the residue is not heated strongly, it may appear blue due to the dehydration of the cobalt(II) nitrate. Blue is not the correct color and indicates that the cobalt-zinc complex has not been formed. Heat strongly again. Examine the residue. Enter the colors, before and after the addition of $Co(NO_3)_2$ solution, in a Data Table like the one shown.

2. Make a second hole in the block as before and repeat the procedure, using aluminum sulfate instead of zinc sulfate. The color you observe is characteristic of aluminum and its components. Record.

3. Make a third hole in the block and repeat the procedure, using magnesium sulfate. Rest your eyes, and then take the residue to the window for examination. Record.

4. Get a sample of an unknown salt from your instructor and test it as before. Record your findings in the Data Table. If unknowns are numbered, be sure to include the number of the one tested in your report in the Data Table. After testing the unknown, what did you determine was contained in the compound?

QUESTIONS: 1. Compose a statement which describes the cobalt nitrate tests as you have used them.

2. If you were given a sample of an unknown metal and were required to determine whether it is aluminum, magnesium, or zinc, what two possible methods could you describe for preparing the substance for a cobalt nitrate test?

DATA TABLE

Compound used	Color of residue	
	after first heating	after second heating
Zinc		
Aluminum		
Magnesium		
Unknown		

Experiment

53 Separation of Lead(II), Silver, and Mercury(I) Ions

PURPOSE: To separate a mixture of the salts of lead(II), silver, and mercury(I) and identify each metallic ion.

APPARATUS: Beaker, 150 ml; burner and tubing; clamp, test tube; funnel; glass plate; graduated cylinder; ring, iron; ring stand; test tubes; wash bottle.

MATERIAL: Litmus paper, blue; filter paper; ammonia-water solution, dilute (1:4), hydrochloric acid, dilute (1:4); nitric acid, dilute (1:5); solutions of: lead(II) nitrate (0.1 *M*), mercury(I) nitrate (0.1 *M*), potassium chromate (0.1 *M*), silver nitrate (0.2 *M*), unknowns.

INTRODUCTION: In analytical chemistry, one may be required to identify a substance, or to find out what a mixture contains. In qualitative analysis, we determine *what* is present. In quantitative analysis, we find *how much* of a substance is present.

In this experiment, we shall separate a mixture of lead(II), silver, and mercury(I) compounds by means of differences in their solubilities. We make use of the fact that the chlorides of these three metals are insoluble under similar circumstances. They may be co-precipitated as chlorides. Consequently, the group of metals is known as the *insoluble chloride group*. This experiment is an introduction to the system of analysis used by chemists.

PROCEDURE: 1. *Identification of* Pb^{++}. To 5 ml of lead(II) nitrate solution, add just enough dilute hydrochloric acid to precipitate all of the lead as lead(II) chloride. This can be accomplished by first adding about 1 ml of hydrochloric acid, shaking, letting the precipitate settle, and then adding acid dropwise. The liquid at the top will be clear enough so you can tell, as the drop strikes the surface, whether any precipitate is being formed. Shake vigorously and let the precipitate settle. Pour off the supernatant liquid.

Add enough cold water to nearly fill the test tube, and shake to wash the precipitate free from any excess acid. After the bulk of the precipitate has settled, again pour off the supernatant liquid. Test the solubility of lead(II) chloride in *hot water* by adding 10 ml of hot (not boiling) water to the precipitate and shaking. To ascertain whether part, at least, of the lead chloride has dissolved, filter the solution if it is not clear. Add about 1 ml of a solution of potassium chromate to the filtrate. Result? What insoluble product is formed? What distinguishing characteristic does it have?

2. *Identification of* Ag^{+}. To 5 ml of silver nitrate solution, add about 1 ml of dilute hydrochloric acid. Shake vigorously to coagulate the precipitate and allow to settle Add additional hydrochloric acid dropwise as necessary to insure complete precipitation of the silver chloride. When the precipitate has settled sufficiently, pour off the supernatant liquid to save time in filtering. Filter the precipitate, washing the portion that clings to the walls of the test tube into the filter cone with small additions of water from the wash bottle. Wash the precipitate on the filter paper several times with small additions of water from the wash bottle. Discard these washings (filtrates). Divide the precipitate into two parts. This may be done by puncturing the filter cone

at the point and carefully washing the precipitate from one half of the filter cone (wash bottle) into a clean test tube. Wash the second half of the filter cone into a second clean test tube. Discard the wash water by decantation after the precipitates have settled. Test the solubility of one portion of the silver chloride in hot (not boiling) water. Result? Test the solubility of the other portion of silver chloride in dilute ammonia-water solution. Is there visible evidence that the precipitate is soluble in this reagent? Shake. Filter if necessary. Verify the solubility of silver chloride in the ammonia-water solution by adding dilute nitric acid dropwise to clear liquid (shake) to neutralize the ammonia. When the odor of ammonia is no longer present, touch a drop of the solution to a litmus test strip to confirm that the environment is acidic. Result? On addition of ammonia-water solution to the silver chloride precipitate, the soluble complex, $Ag(NH_3)_2^+$, ion is formed. Interpret this procedure and the observed results in terms of this fact.

3. *Identification of* Hg_2^{++}. To 5 ml of mercury(I) nitrate solution, add enough dilute hydrochloric acid to precipitate completely the mercury as mercury(I) chloride. Filter and wash the precipitate repeatedly with cold water (wash bottle). Divide the precipitate into two parts, using the technique outlined in Part 2. Discard the wash water from each part by decantation after the precipitates have settled. Best the solubility of one part in hot (not boiling) water. Result? To the other part add 5 ml dilute ammonia-water solution. Result? Ammonia reacts with mercury(I) chloride to form insoluble *white* mercury(II) aminochloride, $HgNH_2Cl$, and metallic mercury as a *black* dispersion. This is an example of an *auto-oxidation-reduction* reaction. Carefully describe the appearance of the residue.

4. The separation of Pb^{++}, Ag^+, and Hg_2^{++}. Prepare a mixture containing solutions of lead(II), silver, and mercury(I) nitrate, about 3 ml of each. Precipitate the chlorides with dilute hydrochloric acid. Filter and wash the precipitates on the filter paper with several additions of cold water from the wash bottle. On the basis of previous tests, determine whether this filtrate should be saved or discarded. Wash the precipitate with about 10 ml of hot (not boiling) water, collecting the filtrate in a clean test tube. Pour the filtrate through the filter cone a second time. Then test the filtrate for the presence of lead. Recall the identifying test for the Pb^{++} ion in Part I. Result?

To the precipitate left on the filter, add 5 ml of dilute ammonia-water solution, collecting the filtrate. Pour the filtrate back through the filter cone a second time. Why? Test the filtrate for silver by adding dilute nitric acid until the filtrate is acidic as shown by the litmus test. Result?

Examine the residue remaining on the filter paper. Recall the action of the ammonia-water solution on mercury(I) chloride in Part 3. Result?

5. *The identification of an unknown*. Get a sample of an unknown solution from your instructor. Analyze the solution for the possible presence of Pb^{++}, Ag^+, and Hg_2^{++}, following the method outlined in Part 4. Report the metallic ions present. If the unknowns are numbered, be sure to include the number of the unknown tested in your report.

Unknown Report: Unknown number

Metallic ions present:

QUESTIONS: 1. How can you separate a mixture of lead(II) chloride and silver chloride?

2. How can you distinguish mercury(I) chloride from silver chloride?

3. Compose a statement which describes the *insoluble chloride group* tests as you have used them.

EQUATIONS

1. $Pb^{++} + Cl^- \rightarrow$
2. $Pb^{++} + CrO_4^{--} \rightarrow$
3. $Ag^+ + Cl^- \rightarrow$
4. $AgCl(s) + NH_3 \rightarrow$
5. $Ag(NH_3)_2^+ + Cl^- + H_3O^+ \rightarrow$
6. $Hg_2^{++} + Cl^- \rightarrow$
7. $Hg_2Cl_2(s) + NH_3 \rightarrow$

Experiment 54 Aluminum and its Compounds

PURPOSE: To study aluminum and some of its compounds.

APPARATUS: Balance, platform; burner and tubing; clamp, test tube; graduated cylinder; test tubes.

ADDITIONAL APPARATUS FOR INSTRUCTOR'S EXPERIMENT: Asbestos square, with hole in center; 2 clamps, buret; 2 ring stands; sand bath, large, shallow.

MATERIAL: Aluminum, chips or granules; aluminum, foil; cotton, absorbent; litmus papers, red and blue; ammonia-water solution, dilute (1:4); hydrochloric acid, concentrated; hydrochloric acid, dilute (1:4); nitric acid, concentrated; sulfuric acid, concentrated; solutions of: aluminum chloride (0.2 *M*); aluminum sulfate (0.1 *M*); ammonium sulfide (0.3 *M*); mercury(I) nitrate (0.1 *M*); sodium carbonate (0.3 *M*); sodium hydroxide (2.5 *M*).

ADDITIONAL MATERIAL FOR INSTRUCTOR'S EXPERIMENT: Ignition mixture; magnesium ribbon; sand; thermite; asbestos paper; filter paper.

INTRODUCTION: Aluminum is a self-protective metal which rapidly becomes covered with an adherent impervious layer of aluminum oxide. Hydrochloric acid and sulfuric acid react with aluminum readily, but nitric acid does not. A strong hydroxide, such as sodium hydroxide, also reacts with aluminum, setting free hydrogen and forming sodium aluminate, $NaAlO_2$.

Aqueous solutions of most aluminum salts are acid because of the hydrolysis of the hydrated aluminum ion, $Al(H_2O)_6^{+++}$, which may be regarded as a Brønsted acid according to the following reaction:

$$Al(H_2O)_6^{+++} + H_2O \rightleftarrows Al(H_2O)_5(OH)^{++} + H_3O^+$$

Aluminum hydroxide is amphiprotic.

PROCEDURE: **1.** Rub a small piece of aluminum foil with a piece of cotton moistened in mercury(I) nitrate to amalgamate the aluminum. Results? Test the unamalgamated side of the aluminum foil for any evidence of the release of heat by the oxidation reaction. Results? What is the white, flaky material which is produced?

2. Test 5 ml of solutions of aluminum chloride and of aluminum sulfate with red and blue litmus papers. Result? Explain.

3. Cover 1 g of aluminum chips or granules with water in a test tube and add a few drops of concentrated hydrochloric acid. Warm the test tube, if necessary, to start the reaction. Result? What products are formed? Repeat with sulfuric and nitric acids. Compare the results.

4. Add 1 g of aluminum chips to a test tube and then cover the metal with sodium hydroxide solution. Warm the test tube, if necessary, to start the reaction. Result? What products are formed?

5. To 5 ml of aluminum chloride solution, add 1 ml of ammonia-water solution. Result? What products are formed? Shake the test tube to flocculate the precipitate. Allow the precipitate to settle, and pour off the supernatant liquid. Transfer one-half of the precipitate to a second test tube. To the precipitate in one test tube, add 1 ml of sodium hydroxide solution. To the precipitate in the other test tube, add 1 ml of dilute hydrochloric acid. Compare the results. What property of aluminum hydroxide is thus illustrated?

6. Add 1 ml of sodium carbonate solution to 5 ml of aluminum sulfate solution. You might expect aluminum carbonate to be formed in this case, but the precipitate that forms is aluminum hydroxide. Why? (Remember that aluminum hydroxide is a weak hydroxide and carbonic acid is a weak acid.) Explain the reaction.

7. Add 5 ml of ammonium sulfide solution to 5 ml of aluminum sulfate solution. Result? Is the insoluble product the same as that formed in Part 6? Why isn't aluminum sulfide produced?

8. INSTRUCTOR'S EXPERIMENT. Set up the apparatus as shown in Fig. 54-1. Spread a layer of dry sand over asbestos paper on the table to protect the table top. In addition, nearly fill a large, shallow sand bath with dry sand. Fold a piece of filter paper into a cone and insert it in the hole in the asbestos board. Nearly fill the cone with thermite, and add starting mixture (powdered magnesium, 1 part, to barium peroxide, 9 parts), and magnesium ribbon as shown. When all is ready, have the class get at least 3 meters away from the apparatus. **Caution:** *Be very careful in executing this experiment. Be sure to stay at a safe distance.* Light the magnesium ribbon, and step aside. What sequence of reactions occurs? Results of each reaction? Examine the products when feasible. What are the advantages of aluminum-reduced iron over carbon-reduced iron? Disadvantages?

EQUATIONS

1. $Al + Hg_2(NO_3)_2 \rightarrow$
2. $Al + HCl \rightarrow$
3. $Al + H_2SO_4 \rightarrow$
4. $Al + HNO_3 \rightarrow$
5. $Al(s) + NaOH + H_2O \rightarrow$
6. $AlCl_3 + NH_3 + H_2O \rightarrow$
7. $H_3AlO_3 + NaOH \rightarrow$
8. $Al(OH)_3 + HCl \rightarrow$
9. $Al + Fe_2O_3 \rightarrow$
10. $Al_2(SO_4)_3 + Na_2CO_3 + H_2O \rightarrow$
11. $Al_2(SO_4)_3 + (NH_4)_2S + H_2O \rightarrow$

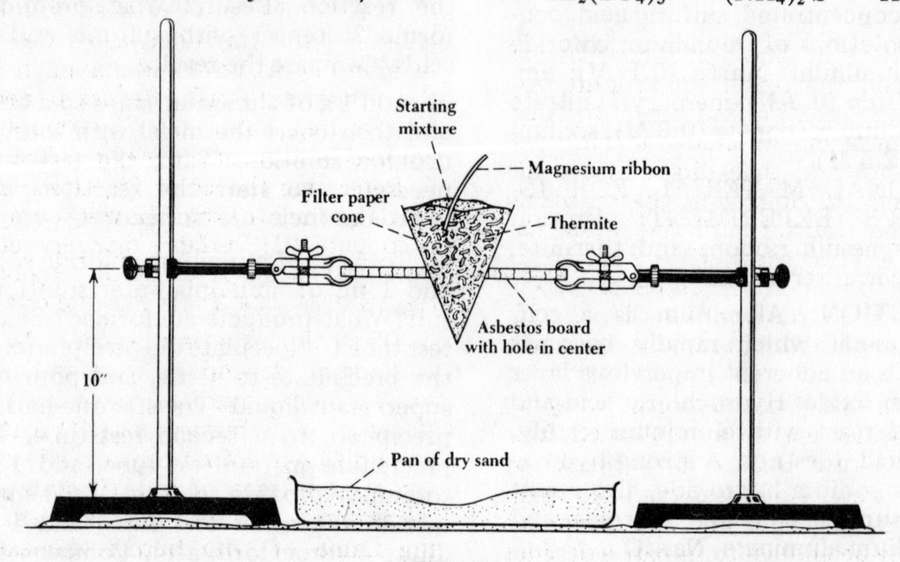

Fig. 54-1

Experiment 55 Borax Bead Tests

PURPOSE: To learn how to identify metals by the color they impart to a borax bead.

APPARATUS: Burner and tubing; dish, evaporating; 5-cm length of No. 24 platinum wire, sealed in the end of a glass tube 10 cm long.

MATERIAL: Borax, powdered; chromium-(III) sulfate; cobalt(II) nitrate; iron(II) sulf fate; manganese(II) sulfate; nickel(II) chloride; unknown salt.

INTRODUCTION: Borax is hydrated sodium tetraborate, $Na_2B_4O_7 \cdot 10\ H_2O$. When it is heated strongly, it loses water of hydration and fuses to form a colorless glassy solid. A tiny trace of certain metallic compounds, when fused as oxides with such a borax glass, imparts a characteristic color which may be used to identify the metal. The colored bead formed in the loop at the end of a platinum wire is a metaborate of the metal.

PROCEDURE: **1.** Make a borax bead as follows: Bend the tip of a platinum wire around the point of a lead pencil to form a loop about 3 mm in diameter. Heat the wire white-hot and then dip it into some powdered borax. Hold it in the oxidizing flame of your burner until the borax has melted to a clear glass. (See Fig. 55-1.) Avoid using too much borax as a large bead will simply drop off the wire. A certain amount of experimentation is necessary to get the best results.

2. Reheat the bead in the loop of wire and touch it, while hot, to a very small fragment (*not bigger than a tiny speck*) of cobalt(II) nitrate. Now heat the bead again in the oxidizing flame. The first fragment will probably be enough to impart a distinct color to the bead. If it does not do so, add another tiny speck of the cobalt(II) salt. The bead that forms should be colored, but clear and transparent. If it is black or opaque, too much cobalt(II) nitrate was used. In such an event, you must make a new bead and start over. To remove the bead from the wire, heat it strongly, hold it over an evaporating dish, and strike the hand holding the wire against the clenched fist of your other hand. Most of the bead will be dislodged and drop into the evaporating dish. Traces of the bead remaining can be removed by heating the wire and then plunging it into cold water. (CAUTION: *Do not dip the end of the glass handle in the water.* Why?) The shattered fragments of the bead can then be rubbed off between the fingers.

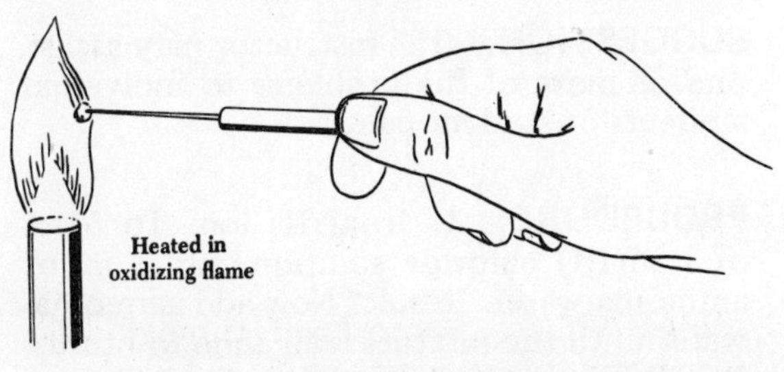

Fig. 55-1

3. Before making a new bead with a different metallic compound, clean the wire by making a borax bead and shaking it off into the evaporating dish. Repeat if necessary. The melted borax removes traces of the colored bead from the previous test.

Determine the color imparted to borax beads by traces of the following compounds: chromium(III) sulfate, manganese(II) sulfate, and nickel(II) chloride. Record your results in a Data Table like the one shown.

4. The color of a bead, colored by an iron compound, depends on whether the bead is heated in the oxidizing or in the reducing flame of your burner. Iron(II) metaborate has a different color from iron(III) metaborate. Add a trace of iron(II) sulfate to the borax bead, and then heat it in the oxidizing flame of your burner. Repeat, using iron(II) sulfate, but hold the bead in the reducing flame. (See Fig. 55-2.) Allow this second bead to cool in the unburned gas just above the top of the burner before you expose it to the air. Record the results in the Data Table as before.

5. Procure an unknown from your instructor and proceed to identify the metal it contains by the borax bead test. Record your results in the Data Table.

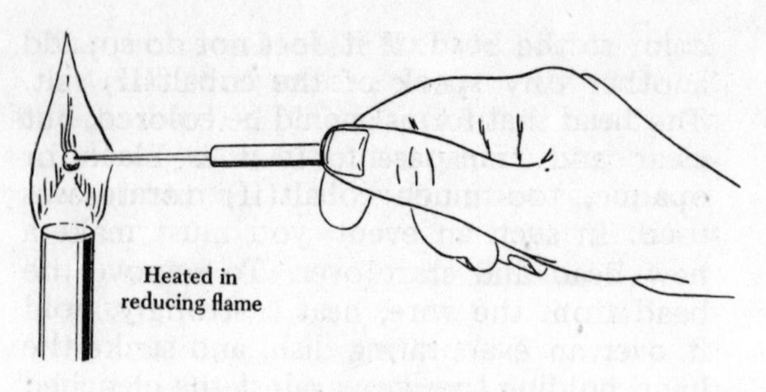

Fig. 55-2

DATA TABLE

cobalt
chromium
manganese
nickel
iron (oxidizing flame)
iron (reducing flame)
unknown

What metal was present in the unknown.

QUESTIONS: Answer in complete statements.

1. Why is the iron-bead color different when formed in the oxidizing flame rather than in the reducing flame?

2. What coloring element would you suspect in pale-green glass? What would be the likely source?

Experiment 56 Separation of Metallic Ions

PURPOSE: To devise and carry out separations of metallic ions from certain suggested pairs.

APPARATUS: Graduated cylinder; test tubes.

MATERIAL: Litmus paper, red; acetic acid, glacial; ammonia-water solution, dilute (1:4); solutions of: aluminum chloride (0.1 *M*); copper(II) sulfate (0.1 *M*); iron(III) chloride (0.1 *M*); potassium hexacyanoferrate(II) (0.1 *M*); sodium hydroxide (3 *M*); zinc sulfate (0.1 *M*).

INTRODUCTION: Some metals have amphiprotic hydroxides while others do not. Certain transition metals form ammine complexes; others do not. In the metallurgy of aluminum it is necessary to remove iron from crude bauxite before electrolysis of the purified aluminum oxide. You will devise a procedure for simulating this process by separating iron from a mixture of aluminum and iron(III) salts. Other pairs of ions for which you will devise separation procedures include Cu^{++} and Fe^{+++}, Cu^{++} and Zn^{++}, and Zn^{++} and Al^{+++}. You are to use the reagents which are supplied. The series of preliminary experiments produce the results upon which your separation procedures are to be based. You may wish to check the results of these procedures against those in Experiments 49-51, and 54. It will be necessary to filter and wash precipitates to remove residual ion traces.

SUGGESTION: The instructor may assign one or more of the problems to individual students or student pairs.

PROCEDURE: 1. Iron(III) ion. To 5 ml of iron(III) chloride solution, add 1 ml of ammonia-water. Result? Now add ammonia-water until the mixture is alkaline to litmus. Result? Explain. Repeat with 5 ml of iron-

(III) chloride solution and sodium hydroxide solution. Result? Explain. Write the equations representative of your results.

2. *Aluminum ion.* To 5 ml of aluminum chloride solution, add 1 ml of ammonia-water. Result? What products are formed? Shake the test tube to flocculate the precipitate. Allow the precipitate to settle and pour off the supernatant liquid. Transfer half of the precipitate to a second test tube. To the precipitate in one test tube, add 1 ml of sodium hydroxide solution. Result? Explain. To the precipitate in the other test tube add ammonia-water until the mixture is alkaline to litmus. Result? Explain. Write the equations representative of your results.

3. *Copper(II) ion.* To 5 ml of copper(II) sulfate solution, add 2 or 3 drops of ammonia-water. Result? Now add ammonia-water to excess (mixture alkaline to litmus). Result? Explain. Repeat with 5 ml of copper(II) sulfate solution and sodium hydroxide solution. Results? Explain. Write the equations representative of your results.

Acidify 5 ml of copper(II) sulfate solution by adding 3 drops of glacial acetic acid. Then add 5 drops of $K_4Fe(CN)_6$ solution. Result? Describe the precipitate. It may be considered to be $Cu_2Fe(CN)_6$. This is a reliable, qualitative test for copper(II) ions. This test may often be used to detect traces of copper.

4. Zinc ion. To 5 ml of zinc sulfate solution, add 2 or 3 drops of sodium hydroxide solution. Result? Shake the test tube and divide the contents into two parts. To one portion add sodium hydroxide solution to excess (alkaline to litmus). Result? Explain. To the other portion add ammonia-water to excess. Result? Explain.

5. Separation of metallic ions from ion pairs. Devise and carry through separatory procedures for the ion-pairs listed below. Prepare the test mixtures by using equal volumes of their individual solutions. In sequential form, outline the procedures you used and found to be successful in the problem(s) assigned by the Instructor. Use the space below for your outline.

a. iron(III) and aluminum ions
b. iron(III) and copper(II) ions
c. copper(II) and zinc ions
d. zinc and aluminum ions

Experiment 57 Ammonia, the Ammonium Ion, and the Nitrate Ion

PURPOSE: To prepare ammonia, study its properties, and to differentiate between the ammonia molecule and the ammonium ion. To learn how to identify the nitrate ion.

APPARATUS: Balance, platform; beaker, 250 ml; 2 bottles, wide mouth; burner and tubing; clamp, buret; clamp, test tube; forceps; glass bend; glass plates; graduated cylinder; mortar and pestle; ring stand; 3 rubber stoppers, solid No. 2; rubber stopper, 1-hole No. 4; test tubes; test tube, Pyrex; wing top.

MATERIAL: Ammonium chloride; ammonium sulfate; calcium hydroxide; iron(II) sulfate; litmus papers, red and blue; wooden splints; ammonia-water solution, concentrated; hydrochloric acid, concentrated; sulfuric acid, concentrated; solutions of: potassium hydroxide (2.5 *M*); sodium hydroxide (2.5 *M*); sodium nitrate (0.5 *M*).

INTRODUCTION: Almost everyone is familiar with the penetrating odor of ammonia. Ammonia, NH_3, is a gas at ordinary temperatures and pressures. The ammonium ion, NH_4^+, is a radical with a positive charge of one which is never found alone, but always in conjunction with a negative ion. When a solution of a hydroxide reacts with an ammonium compound, the products are a salt, ammonia, and water. If any ammonium hydroxide molecules are formed at all, they do not persist as such, but immediately decompose into ammonia and water. Some of the ammonia escapes from the solution as a gas; as a result, such mixtures have the readily detected odor of ammonia.

PROCEDURE: 1. Put 0.5 g of dry ammonium chloride on one square of paper, and 0.5 g of calcium hydroxide on another square. Smell each of the chemicals in turn. Result? Then mix the chemicals, stirring them together. Put a small quantity of the mixed chemicals in the palm of one hand, and then rub your palms together for a half-minute. Now, *cautiously*, smell the mixture in your hand. Result? Hold a piece of wet, red litmus paper just above the chemical mixture in your palm. Result? Explain.

2. Repeat Part 1, using ammonium sulfate instead of ammonium chloride.

3. Fit a large Pyrex test tube with a rubber stopper and L-tube as shown in Fig. 57-1. Gently mix 4 g of ammonium chloride and 3 g of calcium hydroxide in a mortar, and then add the mixture to the test tube. Spread the mixture in the test tube. Why? Clamp the test tube in the position shown for collecting the gas. The round end of the test tube should be slightly higher than the stopper end. Why? (What products are formed?) Heat the test tube gently and collect three dry, small test tubes of the gas and stopper them. The color change of moist strips of red litmus paper held about two inches from the open end of a test tube will indicate when it is full of ammonia. What physical properties of ammonia have you observed in this preparation?

4. Using the sample of ammonia in one small test tube, devise and conduct an experiment to determine the degree of solubility of ammonia in water. Describe your experiment and the results you obtain.

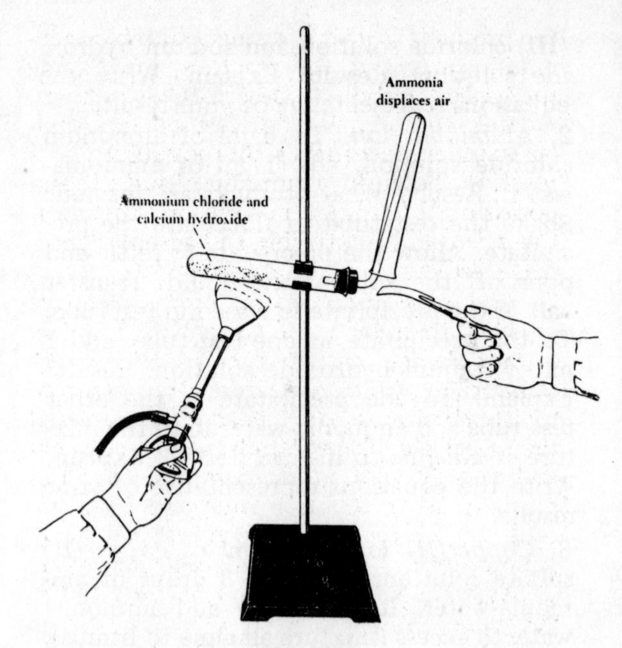

Fig. 57-1

5. Using the sample of ammonia in a second small test tube, devise and conduct an experiment to determine if ammonia burns and/or supports combustion. Describe your experiment, including the proper test tube position, and the results you obtain.

6. Adjust the generator so that ammonia can be passed into a small beaker half-full of water for a few minutes. Do not let the end of the tube touch the surface of the water. Why? Using an appropriate technique, test the solution formed with litmus paper. Result? Then pour 10 ml of the solution formed into a test tube. Boil the solution for several minutes, using a low burner flame. From time to time test the solution, using a proper method, to determine whether all the gas is expelled from solution by boiling. Result?

7. Investigate the possibility of a reaction between ammonium chloride and sodium hydroxide in solution. Determine the necessary conditions and the probable products of such a reaction. How could you identify

the products? After devising a suitable technique, carry out the reaction, identifying the gaseous product. Describe your experimental method and your results. In a similar manner, investigate the possibility of a reaction between ammonium sulfate and potassium hydroxide in solution. Carry out the reaction, identifying the gaseous product. Describe your results.

8. Add one gram of ammonium chloride crystals to a dry test tube. Using a low burner flame, heat the tube gently. At the same time, hold with forceps a strip of moist red litmus paper inside the mouth of the tube. Keep the litmus paper moist by adding a drop of water from a glass rod as needed. Look for first one, and then another, color change to occur in the litmus paper. Result? Why? What collects on the upper walls of the test tube? How did it get there?

9. Using a low burner flame, carefully heat two wide-mouth bottles until they are moderately warm to the touch. Add three drops of concentrated hydrochloric acid to one bottle and cover it with a glass plate. What happens to the concentrated hydrochloric acid when placed in a warm bottle? Take the other bottle to a distant corner of the laboratory and there add three drops of concentrated ammonia-water solution to it and cover with a glass plate. What happens to the concentrated ammonia-water solution? Bring the covered bottle containing ammonia to your work place and invert it over the bottle containing the hydrogen chloride. Remove the glass plates. Result? Explain.

10. Prepare a solution of ammonium chloride by adding 0.5 g of this salt to $1\bar{0}$ ml of water. Similarly prepare a solution of ammonium sulfate. Test each solution with red and blue litmus papers. Results? Explain the results in terms of the Brønsted acid-base concept.

11. Place 5 ml of freshly prepared iron(II) sulfate solution in a test tube. Add 2 ml of sodium nitrate solution. Mix the solutions, and then add 3 ml of concentrated sulfuric acid, holding the test tube in an inclined position so the acid will run down the side of the tube without mixing with the contents. The dense sulfuric acid sinks to the bottom of the tube. The colored layer formed where the two liquids meet serves as *test for a nitrate*. Repeat the test, using 1 nitric acid: $2\bar{0}$ water (you prepare) instead of sodium nitrate solution. Result?

EQUATIONS: Write ionic equations where appropriate.

1. Ammonium chloride and calcium hydroxide.
2. Ammonium sulfate and calcium hydroxide.
3. Ammonia and water.
4. Ammonium chloride and sodium hydroxide.
5. Ammonium sulfate and potassium hydroxide.
6. Heating dry ammonium chloride.
7. Ammonia and hydrogen chloride.
8. Ammonium ion and water.

Experiment 58 Forms of Sulfur

PURPOSE: To prepare three solid allotropic forms of sulfur, and to study the physical and chemical properties of sulfur.

APPARATUS: Asbestos square; balance, platform; beaker, 250 ml; burner and tubing; clamp, test tube; dish, evaporating;

forceps; funnel; graduated cylinder; magnifier; mortar and pestle; ring, iron; ring stand; spoon, deflagrating; test tube, Pyrex.

MATERIAL: Carbon disulfide; copper, strips of foil about 10 cm long and 0.5 cm wide; sulfur, flowers; sulfur, roll; zinc dust; asbestos paper; filter paper.

SUGGESTION: To avoid getting hot sulfur spilled on the laboratory table top, a large square of asbestos paper (or even heavy wrapping paper) may be used to cover it temporarily. A little cold water may be poured upon any burning sulfur which drops on the paper.

Since it is almost impossible to clean the test tubes used, the instructor may exchange clean test tubes for the ones used in this experiment and save the sulfur-encrusted ones for use with a later class or the class next year.

CAUTION: *The vapor from carbon disulfide is poisonous. It is very flammable, explosively so when mixed with air. Keep flames away from it.*

INTRODUCTION: Sulfur, like several other elements, exists in different allotropic modifications. Sulfur has three solid allotropic forms. Liquid allotropic forms of sulfur, of decidedly different fluidity, also exist.

PROCEDURE: **1.** Powder a lump of roll sulfur, about the size of a small pea, and dissolve it in 8 ml of carbon disulfide in an evaporating dish. Stir with a glass rod to hasten solution. Let the liquid evaporate *spontaneously* in a good draft of air in a hood or on the sill of an open window. Use a magnifier to examine the crystals. Describe their shape and appearance. Which allotropic form of sulfur is this?

2. Fill a test tube half-full of small pieces of sulfur, and melt the sulfur *at as low a temperature as possible*. During the heating, the liquid should not get much darker than a pale-straw color. Pour the molten sulfur into a folded dry filter paper cone in a funnel supported on a ring stand. Watch it as it cools. *As soon as* needle-like crystals grow across the surface, pour the excess liquid into a beaker of cold water. Unfold the filter paper *at once* and examine the crystals with a lens. Describe their shape and appearance and compare them with those obtained in Part 1. Which allotropic form of sulfur is this? Keep the crystals obtained in Part 2 for a few days and examine them closely again for any changes.

3. Fill the same test tube you used in Part 2 half-full of small pieces of sulfur and heat it, slowly at first. Note the color when the sulfur first melts, and also its fluidity. Observe any changes in color or fluidity that occur when the sulfur is heated more strongly. Its fluidity can be observed by holding the tube in a nearly horizontal position. Finally heat the sulfur to boiling, extinguish the burner flame, and pour the contents of the tube into a beaker of cold water. At this point, the sulfur may catch fire. Do not become excited, the sulfur will burn quietly. After emptying the test tube, any sulfur on it which is still burning may be smothered with a towel. Remove the product from the beaker of water and examine it. Which allotropic form of sulfur is this? Keep it for a few days and examine it again.

4. Burn a tiny piece of sulfur in an asbestos-lined deflagrating spoon. Note the color of the flame and the odor of the gas that is formed. **CAUTION:** See Fig. F-5 for the proper method of detecting the odor of a gas.

5. Heat the test tube used in Part 3 until the sulfur that stuck to the walls of the tube begins to boil. Hold a piece of bright, untarnished copper foil with the forceps, and thrust it down into the vapor from the boiling sulfur. After a few moments, remove the foil and examine it. Result?

6. Procure 0.5 g of zinc dust from your instructor. Mix it on an asbestos square with an equal bulk of flowers of sulfur.

Heap it up into a conical pile, place it in the hood, and (CAUTION), holding the burner at arm's length, ignite it with the tip of the flame of your burner. Result?

QUESTIONS: 1. What changes in the structure of sulfur molecules occur as sulfur is raised from its melting point to its boiling point?

2. What changes in structure does amorphous sulfur undergo when it stands for some time?

EQUATIONS

1. Reaction in Part 4.
2. Reaction in Part 5.
3. Reaction in Part 6.

Experiment 59 Hydrogen Sulfide and Qualitative Analysis

PURPOSE: To prepare hydrogen sulfide and study some of its properties. To show how hydrogen sulfide is used in qualitative analysis.

APPARATUS: 2 bottles, wide mouth; burner and tubing; clamp, buret; funnel; funnel tube; 2 glass bends; glass plate; graduated cylinder; jet tip; ring, iron; ring stand; rubber connector; rubber stopper, 2 hole No. 6; test tubes.

MATERIAL: Iron(II) sulfide; silver coin; filter paper; litmus papers, red and blue; ammonia water solution, concentrated; hydrochloric acid, concentrated; nitric acid, concentrated; solutions of: antimony(III) chloride (0.25 *M*); cadmium nitrate (0.25 *M*); copper(II) nitrate (0.25 *M*); hydrogen peroxide (3%); lead acetate (0.25 *M*); manganese(II) sulfate (0.25 *M*); methyl orange; zinc sulfate (0.25 *M*); stock solution of Cu^{++}, Mn^{++}, Zn^{++} (see Teachers' Edition). CAUTION: *Hydrogen sulfide is disagreeable and poisonous. Use the hood or work where there is a good draft. It is more satisfactory to do the experiment as a demonstration.*

INTRODUCTION: Hydrogen sulfide is usually prepared by the reaction between iron(II) sulfide and hydrochloric or sulfuric acid. Hydrogen sulfide forms the weak diprotic hydrosulfuric acid when dissolved in water. Saturated solutions of hydrogen sulfide are approximately 0.1 *M* with respect to H_2S. Combining the $K_{ion\ 1}$ with the $K_{ion\ 2}$ for this solution established the following relationship:

$$[S^{--}] = \frac{6.8 \times 10^{-24}}{[H_3O^+]^2}$$

This indicates that the sulfide ion concentration in hydrogen sulfide solutions varies inversely as the square of the hydronium ion concentration.

In qualitative analysis certain metallic ions may be separated from each other by controlling the hydronium ion concentration at which saturated hydrogen sulfide is added. One group, which includes Hg^{++}, Pb^{++}, Bi^{+++}, Cu^{++}, and Cd^{++} is precipitated in a solution which is acid to methyl orange. The acid color of methyl orange is red at a pH of 3.1. A second group of ions, whose sulfides do not precipitate at this pH, includes Fe^{+++}, Mn^{++}, Al^{+++}, Cr^{+++}, Ni^{++}, Co^{++} and Zn^{++}. Thier solubility products are relatively large compared to those of the first group. If all of these ions are included in the acidified sample originally treated with hydrogen sulfide, certain ones may be precipitated as hydroxides by making the filtrate alkaline with ammonia-water. These hydroxides have characteristic colors. Ni^{++}, Co^{++}, and Zn^{++} do not precipitate as hydroxides because they form complex ions such as $Zn(NH_3)_4^{++}$. The hydroxides are removed by filtration and the alkaline filtrate is again treated with hydrogen sulfide. The sulfides of these three ions do precipitate and may be identified by their color and supplementary identification procedures.

PROCEDURE: 1. Set up the apparatus as shown in Fig. 59-1 to collect the gas by air displacement. Why? Put 2 or 3 small lumps of iron(II) sulfide into the generator, and add enough water through the funnel tube to cover its lower end. Then add concentrated hydrochloric acid, a little at a time, to maintain a steady evolution of the gas. What physical properties of hydrogen sulfide do you observe?

2. Collect a test tube of the gas. Hold it mouth upward, and ignite it. Note the odor of the burning gas (refer to Fig. F-5), and observe carefully the deposit on the walls of the tube.

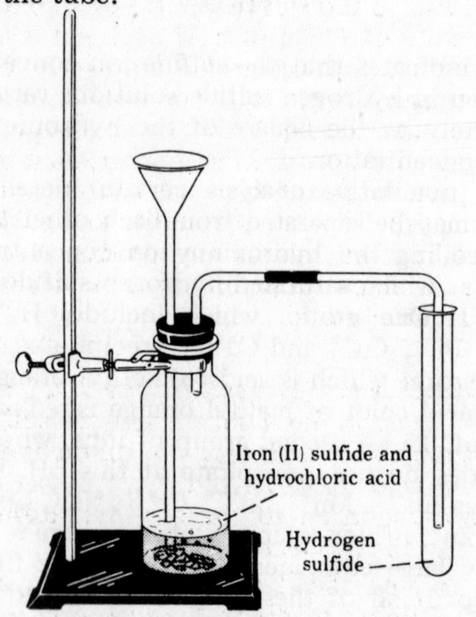

Fig. 59-1

3. Replace the glass bend at the end of the delivery tubing with a jet tip and light the gas at the end of the jet tip. Try to identify the products of combustion in this case. Are they the same as in Part 2 or different? Explain.

4. Replace the jet tip with the glass bend. Pour 50 ml of water into a wide-mouth bottle and bubble hydrogen sulfide through the water for about 5 minutes. Using a proper technique, determine the effect of this solution on red and blue litmus test strips. Result? Use a stirring rod to transfer a drop of the hydrogen sulfide solution to a silver coin. Result? The reaction that occurs serves as a test for a soluble sulfide such as hydrogen sulfide. Go on to Part 5, but save the solution you just prepared for use in Part 7 and Part 8.

5. Permit the gas from the generator to bubble through 5 ml of hydrogen peroxide in a test tube from 3 to 5 minutes or until you notice a decided change. Result? What reaction occurred? Pour the contents of the test tube into a filter paper cone in a funnel supported by a ring and ring stand. What is the appearance of the filtrate? What explanation can you offer?

6. Moisten a strip of filter paper with lead(II) acetate solution (or use a prepared test strip) and hold it at the end of the delivery tube from the hydrogen sulfide generator. Result? This reaction is a common test for hydrogen sulfide.

Remove the stopper from the generator and quickly pour the excess acid from the iron(II) sulfide. Flush the acid down the sink with water. Rinse the iron(II) sulfide remaining in the generator with water. Place the well-rinsed iron(II) sulfide in the designated container.

7. Pour about 5 ml of hydrogen sulfide solution from Part 4 into each of five test tubes. To the first one, add 1 ml of copper(II) nitrate solution; to the second, 1 ml of antimony(III) chloride solution; to the third, 1 ml of cadmium nitrate solution; to the fourth, 1 ml of zinc sulfate solution; and to the fifth, 1 ml of manganese(II) sulfate

solution. Results? Little or no precipitate will appear in the case of zinc and manganese, since their sulfides will not form unless the solution is alkaline. To the test tubes containing Zn^{++} and Mn^{++}, add two or three drops of ammonia-water solution. Results? What colors are the products?

8. *a.* To 1 ml of the mixture of Cu^{++}, Zn^{++}, and Mn^{++} solution, add nitric acid dropwise until the solution tests acid with methyl orange. Add 5 ml of the hydrogen sulfide solution from Part 4. Result? Explain. Filter to remove the precipitate. Save the filtrate for *b.* below.

b. To the filtrate, add ammonia-water until the mixture tests alkaline to litmus paper. Result? Explain. Filter. Save the filtrate for *c.*

c. To the filtrate, add 5 ml of the hydrogen sulfide solution from Part 4. Result? Explain.

EQUATIONS: Write ionic equations where appropriate.

1. Preparation of hydrogen sulfide.
2. Complete combustion of hydrogen sulfide.
3. Hydrogen sulfide and silver in the presence of air. $Ag + H_2S + O_2 \rightarrow$
4. Reaction in Part 5.
5. Reaction in Part 6.
6. First three reactions in Part 7.
7. Reactions for separation of ions in Part 8.

Experiment 60 Sulfite and Sulfate Ions

PURPOSE: To show how the sulfite and sulfate ions may be identified. To study the properties of the acids and salts of these ions.

APPARATUS: Balance, platform; bottle, wide mouth; burner and tubing; clamp, buret; clamp, test tube; funnel; funnel tube; 3 glass bends; glass plate; graduated cylinder; ring, iron; ring stand; rubber connector; rubber stoppers, 1-hole No. 4, 2-hole No. 4; test tubes; 2 test tubes, large, Pyrex.

MATERIAL: Magnesium ribbon; sodium hydrogen sulfite; zinc, mossy; filter paper; litmus papers, red and blue; hydrochloric acid, concentrated; hydrochloric acid, dilute; solutions of barium chloride (0.25 *M*); potassium permanganate (0.1 *M*); sodium sulfate (0.1 *M*); sodium sulfite (0.1 *M*).

ADDITIONAL MATERIAL FOR INSTRUCTOR'S EXPERIMENT: Copper shot; sulfuric acid, concentrated; solution of potassium permanganate (0.1 *M*).

INTRODUCTION: The oxidation states of sulfur are −2, +4, and +6. It has an oxidation state of +4 in sulfur dioxide, sulfurous acid, and in the sulfite ion. It has an oxidation state of +6 in sulfuric acid and in the sulfate ion. Sulfuric acid is a powerful oxidizing agent when hot and concentrated. Sulfurous acid and sulfites in acid solution are reducing agents. In this experiment you will perform tests which will enable you to distinguish between the sulfite and sulfate ions. You will also study oxidation-reactions in which sulfur undergoes changes in its oxidation state.

PROCEDURE: 1. *Tests for the* SO_4^{--} *and* SO_3^{--} *ions. a.* To 4 ml of sodium sulfate solution, add 5 or 6 drops of dilute hydrochloric acid. Result? Add 2 ml of barium chloride solution to the mixture. Result? Identify the products.

b. To 5 ml of sodium sulfite solution, add 5 or 6 drops of dilute hydrochloric acid. Result? Investigate the odor of the product by using the wafting motion (See Fig. F-5). Add 2 ml of barium chloride solution to the mixture. Results?

c. To 5 ml of sodium sulfite solution add 2 ml of barium chloride solution. Result? Explain. Add 5 or 6 drops of dilute hydrochloric acid to the mixture and shake the test tube. Result? Explain. Why is hydrochloric acid necessary in performing the test for these ions?

d. Test 5 ml portions of the solutions of sodium sulfate and sodium sulfite respectively with red and blue litmus papers. Results? Explain. What do these results indicate about the relative strengths of the corresponding acids?

2. *Sulfur dioxide.* Set up the apparatus as shown in Fig. 60-1 to collect the gas by air displacement. Put 2 grams of sodium hydrogen sulfite into the generator. Place a piece of red and a piece of blue litmus paper (moistened) across the open end of a test tube and put the end of the delivery tube in the test tube. Add 2 ml of dilute hydrochloric acid through the funnel tube of the generator. As soon as the litmus paper turns color, remove the delivery tube from test test tube and place it in 20 ml of water in a wide-mouth bottle. What did the litmus paper result indicate about sulfur dioxide? Add 3 ml more hydrochloric acid through the funnel tube. When gas evolution stops, remove the delivery tube from the water in the bottle. Select the test(s) from Part 1 required to identify the anion present in 5 ml of this solution. Perform the selected test(s). Results? Explain.

To another 5 ml portion of the solution add a piece of zinc. Result? If no perceptible reaction occurs, decant the solution into another test tube. Add a 1 cm piece of magnesium ribbon to the solution. Result? What do these tests indicate about the nature of the solution?

3. *Oxidation and reduction.* Potassium permanganate ($KMnO_4$) in acid solution is a vigorous oxidizing agent. In the presence of a reducing agent, the manganese in the purple permanganate ions, MnO_4^-, is re-

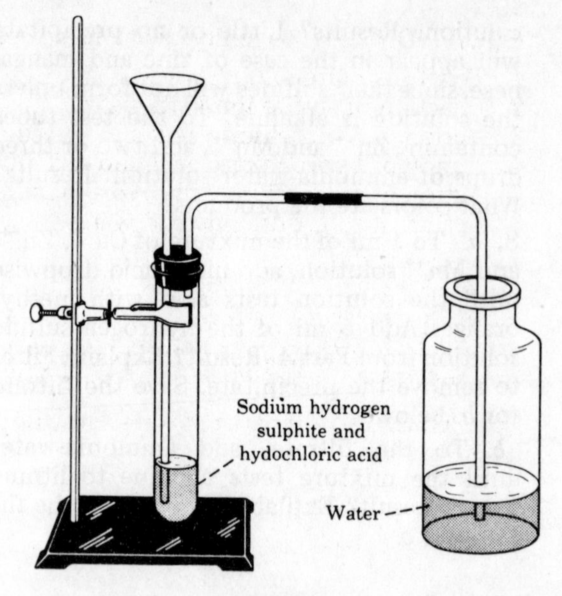

Fig. 60-1

duced to the almost colorless manganese(II) ions, Mn^{++}. To the remaining 10 ml of water solution of sulfur dioxide from Part 2, add 2 ml of concentrated hydrochloric acid. Then add potassium permanganate solution dropwise until the last drop just produces a faintly pink solution. If the solution is not clear, filter it. Test 5 ml of the filtrate for the presence of SO_4^{--} ions. Result? What change occurred in the ions present in the solution of sulfur dioxide? What action did the sulfur in these ions have on the manganese in the permanganate ions? Is the sulfur in these ions an oxidizing or a reducing agent?

4. INSTRUCTOR'S EXPERIMENT. Heat 2 g of copper shot with 2 ml of concentrated sulfuric acid in a test tube generator. Collect several test tubes of the gas and have students test its odor, reaction with litmus, and reaction with dilute potassium permanganate solution. Results? Explain. What process did the sulfur in the sulfuric acid undergo?

EQUATIONS: Write ionic equations where appropriate.

1. Test for sulfate ion.
2. Reaction of sulfite ion with water.
3. Action of hydrochloric acid and sodium sulfite.
4. Action of hydrochloric acid and sodium hydrogen sulfite.
5. Action of magnesium with hydronium ion.
6. Action of sulfur dioxide and water.

Experiment 61 Preparation and Properties of Chlorine

PURPOSE: To prepare chlorine and study its properties.

APPARATUS: Balance, platform; beaker, 250 ml; 6 bottles, wide mouth; burner and tubing; 2 clamps, buret; flask, Erlenmeyer; funnel tube; generator with delivery tube and bent jet tube; glass bends; 4 glass plates; graduated cylinder; ring, iron; 2 ring stands; 2 rubber stoppers; 2-hole No. 4; 4 rubber stoppers, 2-hole No. 6; spoon, deflagrating; test tubes; wire gauze.

MATERIAL: Antimony, powdered; bleaching powder, Ca(ClO)Cl; lead dioxide; manganese dioxide, pellets; manganese dioxide, powdered; potassium dichromate; potassium permanganate; zinc, mossy; candle; cotton cloth, colored; litmus papers, red and blue; paper, printed; paper, white; hydrochloric acid, concentrated; sulfuric acid, dilute; solution of sodium thiosulfate (0.25 *M*).

INTRODUCTION: Chlorine is prepared by the oxidation of the chloride ion. CAUTION: *Since chlorine is poisonous you will prepare very small amounts of it by using a variety of oxidizing agents.* A convenient laboratory preparation is the oxidation of hydrochloric acid with manganese dioxide. Excess chlorine may be bubbled through sodium thiosulfate solution which reduces chlorine to chloride ions, thus preventing the escape of chlorine into the room.

SUGGESTION: It is suggested that the preparation and collection of chlorine be performed by the instructor at the hood. The series of test tube preparations may be performed by the students.

PROCEDURE: 1. Set up the apparatus in the hood as shown in Fig. 61-1. Add 15 g of powdered manganese dioxide to the flask. and then pour 4$\bar{0}$ ml of concentrated hydrochloric acid through the funnel tube. The flask must be heated *very gently* to avoid too rapid production of chlorine. If a sheet of white paper is held behind the bottles, the color will indicate when they are full of the gas. What is the purpose of the HCl? Of the MnO_2? Why is chlorine led into the bottom of each collecting bottle?

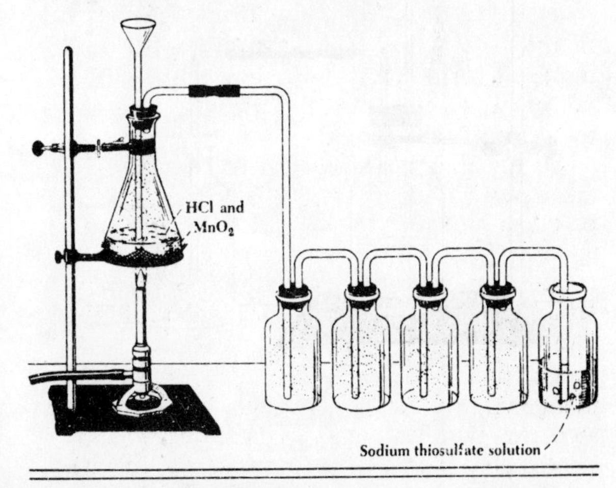

Fig. 61-1

2. When the bottles are full of chlorine, disconnect the apparatus and leave the generator in the hood. Cover each bottle of chlorine with a glass plate.

3. To one of the bottles of chlorine, add 20 ml of water, and quickly cover with a glass plate or solid rubber stopper. Shake the bottle vigorously. Result? Note the color of the water. To what is this color due? Test the effect of chlorine water on strips of red and blue litmus papers. Result? Try the effect of chlorine water on a small square of colored cotton cloth. See if the chlorine water will bleach the printing on a small square of newspaper, or a piece of book paper. Explain any differences in the effectiveness of the bleaching action you observe.

4. Set up a hydrogen generator fitted with a glass jet tube which can be lowered into a bottle of chlorine as in Fig. 61-2. CAUTION: *Do not light the hydrogen until you have determined that all of the air has been expelled from the generator. To determine this, fill a test tube with the gas by water displacement and carry it mouth downward to a flame. If it burns with a slight explosion, or "barks" it is still impure. Collect another test tube and test as before. If the hydrogen is pure, it will burn quietly at the mouth of the test tube. The jet tube is then ignited by bringing this test tube, with hydrogen burning at its mouth, to the jet tip.* Lower the jet tube of burning hydrogen into a bottle of chlorine. Does the hydrogen continue to burn in the chlorine? A moist strip of blue litmus paper may help you to identify the product. What is unusual about this reaction?

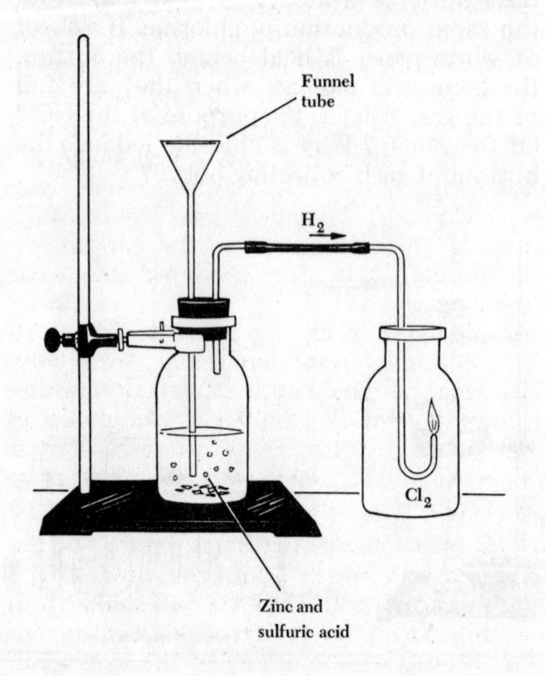

Fig. 61-2

5. Candle wax is composed of hydrocarbons. Lower a lighted candle, mounted in a deflagrating spoon, into a bottle of chlorine. Result? Identify the products of combustion. Explain.

6. Sprinkle some powdered antimony into a bottle of chlorine. Result? What is the product?

7. Half fill a 250-ml beaker with water and place it on a wire gauze mounted on a large ring on a ring stand. Heat thew ater to boiling to use as a hot water bath. In separate test tubes add 5 drops of concentrated hydrochloric acid to each of the following: (a) one pellet of MnO_2; (b) two grains of $KMnO_4$; (c) two crystals of $K_2Cr_2O_7$; (d) an amount of PbO_2 equal in bulk to a match head; (e) an amount of Ca(ClO)Cl equal in bulk to a match head. Warm each in turn in the boiling water. Observe the color of the gas produced against a white paper background. Then suspend a piece of moistened blue litmus paper in the test tube. Report the results.

EQUATIONS

1. $MnO_2 + HCl \rightarrow$
2. $H_2O + Cl_2 \rightarrow$
3. $H_2 + Cl_2 \rightarrow$
4. $Sb + Cl_2 \rightarrow$
5. $KMnO_4 + HCl \rightarrow KCl + MnCl_2 +$
6. $K_2Cr_2O_7 + HCl \rightarrow KCl + CrCl_3 +$
7. $PbO_2 + HCl \rightarrow PbCl_2 +$
8. $Ca(ClO)Cl + HCl \rightarrow CaCl_2$

Experiment

62 Preparation and Properties of Iodine

PURPOSE: To prepare iodine and to study its properties.

APPARATUS: Balance, platform; burner and tubing; clamp, buret; funnel, separatory; glass plate; graduated cylinder; ring iron; ring stand; rubber band, heavy; test tubes; test tube, large, Pyrex.

MATERIAL: Alcohol, denatured; carbon tetrachloride; iodine, crystals; manganese dioxide, powdered; potassium bromide; potassium iodide, powdered; wooden splints; phosphoric acid, concentrated; solutions of: bromine water; chlorine water; potassium bromide (0.5 *M*); potassium iodide (0.5 *M*).

INTRODUCTION: Iodine is an active, solid, nonmetallic element which forms a colored vapor when heated. It is prepared from potassium iodide, manganese dioxide, and sulfuric (or phosphoric) acid. In this experiment we will use phosphoric acid because it yields no undesirable by-products. Iodine is less active chemically than chlorine or bromine, so it may be displaced from its compounds by either of these halogens. **CAUTION:** *Carbon tetrachloride vapor is poisonous. Do not inhale the vapor.* The laboratory should be well ventilated while carbon tetrachloride is being used. Perchlorethylene may be used instead.

PROCEDURE: **1.** Mix 1 g of powdered potassium iodide with an equal bulk of powdered manganese dioxide and transfer the mixture to a Pyrex test tube. Wind a heavy rubber band around the outside lip of a smaller test tube so that this test tube will fit into the upper part of the larger generator test tube and be supported by the rubber band. Fill this smaller test tube with water. Pour 1 ml of concentrated phosphoric acid into the generator test tube and place the smaller tube inside. Heat the contents of the larger test tube *gently*. Note the color of any vapor produced in the tube. Heat for several minutes and permit the assembly to cool. Remove the smaller test tube and pour out the water. Note the color of the iodine crystals which have collected on the outside of this small test tube. What physical process does the deposition of these crystals represent?

2. With a wooden splint, scrape onto a glass plate a few iodine crystals from the test tube. Add a crystals or two of iodine to each of four test tubes. Compare the solubility of iodine in water, alcohol, carbon tetrachloride, and potassium iodide solutions. Note the color of each solution.

3. Add 3 ml of carbon tetrachloride to a test tube half-full of water, and shake the tube vigorously. What happens when you stop shaking? What term is applied to such liquids? What happens to the carbon tetrachloride? Is it more dense or less dense than water?

Add 3 ml of carbon tetrachloride to 10 ml of bromine water and shake thoroughly. Observe by the depth of color whether bromine is more soluble in water, or in carbon tetrachloride. Recall from Part 2 whether iodine is more soluble in water or in carbon tetrachloride.

4. Dissolve one or two small crystals of potassium bromide in 10 ml of water. Add 3 ml of carbon tetrachloride and shake thoroughly. Do bromide ions color carbon tetrachloride? Now add 5 ml of chlorine water and again shake the test tube thoroughly.

The carbon tetrachloride is merely a solvent and does not enter into the chemical reaction. By its color, you should be able to judge what did happen. Explain your result in terms of the halogen activity series. Similarly perform appropriate tests to show the reaction between iodide ions and chlorine molecules and the reaction between iodide ions and bromine molecules. Describe your tests, results, and reactions which occurred.

5. Place 1 ml of potassium bromide solution, 1 ml of potassium iodide solution, and 10 ml of distilled water in a separatory funnel. Add 1 ml of carbon tetrachloride and 1 drop of chlorine water. Stopper the separatory funnel and shake it. Allow the liquid layers to separate. What is the color of the carbon tetrachloride layer? What does this indicate? Remove the stopper from the funnel and draw off the carbon tetrachloride layer into a test tube. Add 1 ml of carbon tetrachloride and 1 drop of chlorine water again to the liquid in the separatory funnel, stopper the funnel, and shake. Allow the liquids to separate. Result? Unstopper the funnel and draw off the carbon tetrachloride into a second test tube. Repeat the procedure until there is a significant change in the color of the carbon tetrachloride layer. What reaction is now occurring? Why?

QUESTIONS: 1. What is the meaning of the term, "Resublimed Iodine," on a bottle of iodine crystals?

2. How do you account for the difference in the color of solutions of iodine in the solvents you tested?

3. What do you conclude about the relative chemical activities of chlorine, bromine, and iodine?

4. If you were given a solution suspected of containing both bromide and iodide ions, how could you detect the presence (or absence) of each?

EQUATIONS: Write ionic equations where appropriate.

1. Preparation of iodine.
2. Replacement of bromine by chlorine.
3. Replacement of iodine by chlorine.
4. Replacement of iodine by bromine.

Experiment 63 Halide Ions

PURPOSE: To develop a series of tests which will identify the halogenide ions, F^-, Cl^-, Br^-, I^-.

APPARATUS: Graduated cylinder; stoppers, cork, for test tubes; test tubes.

MATERIAL: Carbon tetrachloride; litmus paper, blue; ammonia-water solution, dilute (1:4); nitric acid, dilute (1:5); solutions of: bromine water; calcium nitrate (0.5 *M*); chlorine water; potassium bromide (0.2 *M*); potassium chlorate (0.1 *M*); potassium iodide (0.2 *M*); silver nitrate (0.1 *M*); sodium chloride (0.1 *M*); sodium fluoride (0.1 *M*).

CAUTION: *Carbon tetrachloride vapor is poisonous. Do not inhale the vapor.* The laboratory should be well ventilated while carbon tetrachloride is being used. Perchloroethylene may be used instead.

INTRODUCTION: The principle oxidation state of the halogens is −1. With the exception of fluorine, they may exist in other oxidation states. The specific tests which you will develop in this experiment involve the production of recognizable precipitates, oxidation-reduction reactions involving the use of halogens as oxidizing agents, and the production of complex ions. Refer to Experiments 50 and 62 for related, pertinent data.

PROCEDURE: 1. To 5 ml of each of the four known halogenide solutions in separate test tubes, add 1 ml of calcium nitrate solution. Results? Which ion(s) does this procedure serve to identify?

2. To 5 ml of each of the four halogenide solutions in separate test tubes, add 1 ml of silver nitrate solution. Results? Write the formula(s) of the precipitate(s) produced, noting the color. Save the precipitate(s) for Part 3. In which case(s) is this procedure not entirely conclusive?

3. To the precipitate(s) formed in Part 2 add 5 ml of ammonia-water and stir. Results? Explain. If solution occurs, add nitric acid until the mixture turns blue litmus paper red. Result? Explain. Which ion(s) will this procedure identify?

4. Separately test 5 ml of chlorine water and 5 ml of potassium chlorate solution according to a scheme which should serve to identify the chloride ion. Results? Explain.

5. To 5 ml of sodium chloride solution add 2 ml of carbon tetrachloride and 1 ml of bromine water. Stopper the test tube and shake it. Permit the test tube to stand. Result? Explain. To 5 ml of potassium bromide solution, add 2 ml of carbon tetrachloride and 1 ml of chlorine water. Shake and permit to settle as before. Results? Explain. To 5 ml of potassium iodide solution, add 2 ml of carbon tetrachloride and 1 ml of chlorine water. Shake and permit to settle. Results? Explain. Repeat the last step using bromine water instead of chlorine water. Results? Explain. What do the results of this series of procedures indicate about the relative strength of the halogens as oxidizing agents? Which ion(s) may be identified by the use of these procedures?

6. An alternate series of procedures that may be used to identify some of the halogenide ions appears in Experiment 50, Complex Ions of Copper and Silver. Recall Part 2 of this experiment. If you did not perform Experiment 50, perform the series of operations described in Part 2.

7. INSTRUCTOR'S EXPERIMENT. Supplement Part 5, in which potassium iodide, carbon tetrachloride, and chlorine water are used, by continuing to add chlorine water dropwise with shaking until a colorless carbon tetrachloride layer results. This is due to the oxidation of iodine to the iodate ion.

EQUATIONS: Write ionic equations.

1. $F^- + Ca$
2. Reactions in Part 2.
3. Reactions in Part 3.
4. Reactions in Part 4.
5. Reactions in Part 5.

Experiment 64 Identification of Salts

PURPOSE: To identify both the positive and the negative ions of unknown salts.

APPARATUS: Beaker, 50 ml; blowpipe and tip; burner and tubing; clamp, buret; cobalt glass; forceps; funnel; medicine dropper; platinum wire rod; ring, iron; ring stand; test tubes.

MATERIAL: Borax, powdered; charcoal or plaster block; iron(II) sulfate; filter paper; ammonia-water solution, dilute (1:4); hydrochloric acid, dilute (1:4); limewater; nitric acid, dilute (1:5); sulfuric acid, concentrated; solutions of: barium chloride (0.1 *M*); cobalt(II) nitrate (0.1 *M*); silver nitrate (0.2 *M*); unknown solids (given out by the instructor).

INTRODUCTION: A chemist may analyze a compound or mixture to find out what it contains, or to learn how much of each element is present. If you have a double laboratory period, you can probably analyze two or three unknowns by using the flame test, the bead test, or the cobalt nitrate test together with the negative ion tests.

It is suggested that you try the flame test first, since it is quicker. If you get a decisive flame coloration and can identify the metallic element present in the unknown given out, it will be unnecessary to try the bead test or the cobalt nitrate test. If no decisive flame coloration is given, then proceed with the cobalt nitrate test. If you do not find this test decisive, then try the bead test.

Next, determine whether the salt given out is a carbonate, a chloride, a sulfate, or a nitrate. An analytical chemist is expected to find all the substances present, and there may be several. As beginners, you will not be given mixtures except where you have learned a procedure for recognizing the components of such mixtures. Always record negative as well as positive results when making an identification test.

PROCEDURE: 1. Test unknown solid *No. 1* by taking up a very small particle on a platinum wire test rod and holding it in the flame as in Experiment 45. Then proceed to make flame tests with unknowns *No. 2* and *No. 3*. Complete a Data Table like the one shown. If you get a decisive test, record the results in the proper column in the Data Table. If there is no decisive flame coloration, proceed to test a sample of each unknown with the cobalt nitrate test as in Experiment 52. If neither flame test nor cobalt nitrate test gives a decisive result, proceed to make the borax bead test as in Experiment 55.

2. To a small portion of each of the unknowns, add a drop of dilute hydrochloric acid. Add additional hydrochloric acid dropwise if necessary to reach a decision. Rapid effervescence of carbon dioxide shows that the salt is a *carbonate*. Sulfites and sulfides also liberate a gas, but in each case the gas has a distinctive odor. Devise a method of identifying the CO_2 gas as it is evolved, using a platinum wire loop and clear limewater solution. Recall the limewater test for CO_2 gas.

3. Dissolve a small portion (bulk of a small pea) of each unknown in 15 ml of water in separate test tubes. If a solution is not clear, it should be filtered. Test a 5-ml portion of each solution for chloride ion by first adding to it 5 or 6 drops of dilute nitric acid (why?) and 2 ml of silver nitrate solution. A white precipitate which is soluble in ammonia-water solution and insoluble in dilute nitric acid shows the presence of a *chloride.*

4. If the unknowns did not give either a carbonate or a chloride test, then proceed to test them for sulfates as follows: to a 5-ml portion of the solution prepared in Part 3, add 5 or 6 drops of dilute hydrochloric acid (why?) and 2 ml of a solution of barium chloride. A white precipitate shows that a *sulfate* is present.

5. If one or more of your unknowns did not give a test for a carbonate, chloride, or sulfate, proceed to test it for a nitrate. Dissolve about 0.5 g of green iron(II) sulfate in 10 ml of cold distilled water. Add to it 5 ml of a solution of the unknown as prepared in Part 3. Then add 2 ml of concentrated sulfuric acid, holding the tube in an inclined position so the dense acid will run down the side of the tube without mixing. A brown layer (or ring) at the junction of the acid and the other liquids indicates that a *nitrate* is present.

(Record in the Data Table both negative and positive results for each test made on each unknown by reporting identifying color, no color, precipitate, no precipitate, odorless gas, or other identifying phrase.)

DATA TABLE

Unknown	Flame test	Bead test	$Co(NO_3)_2$ test	CO_3^{--} test	Cl^- test	SO_4^{--} test	NO_3^- test
No. 1							
No. 2							
No. 3							

Unknown Report: Unknown No. 1

Unknown No. 2

Unknown No. 3

Experiment 65 Radioactivity

PURPOSE: To show how radioactivity may be detected and how the comparative penetrating power of various radiations may be demonstrated. To show that radioisotopes are identical in chemical behavior with isotopes that are not radioactive.

APPARATUS: Simple electroscope; cat's fur; hard-rubber rod; stop watch, or watch with second hand; Geiger counter tube and associated counting apparatus (the Classmaster radioactivity demonstrator is satisfactory); 20 cardboard sheets, 4 inches square, 1/32 inch thick; 15 aluminum sheets, 4 inches square, 1/32 inch thick; 15 lead sheets, 4 inches square, 1/32 inch thick; graph paper.

ADDITIONAL APPARATUS for INSTRUCTOR'S EXPERIMENT: 2 Beakers (100 ml); 2 funnels; glass rods; graduated cylinder; 2 flasks, Erlenmeyer; 2 funnels, separatory; Petri dishes, small; 2 pipets (10 ml) with syringe bulb.

MATERIAL: Radioactive samples: radioactive isotope, if available; radioactive mineral sample, uranium metal or compound, watch with illuminated dial.

ADDITIONAL MATERIAL for INSTRUCTOR'S EXPERIMENT: Carbon tetrachloride; ethyl acetate; iodine-131 (10 microcuries) as KI; uranyl nitrate; filter paper; solutions of: ammonium nitrate (saturated); chlorine water; lead nitrate (0.1 M); potassium iodide (0.1 M); sodium carbonate (saturated); sodium hydroxide (0.1 M).

INTRODUCTION: The types of radiation emitted by radioactive materials include: alpha particles, which are helium nuclei; beta particles, which are electrons; and gamma rays, which are X rays of very short wavelength. Alpha particles will discharge an electroscope but their penetrating power is not great enough to affect a Geiger counter tube. Gamma rays have the greatest penetrating power and may be detected with the Geiger tube shield in place. This metal shield will effectively reflect or absorb most beta particles.

In one part of this experiment, the daughter products of the decay of uranium-238 will be separated from uranyl nitrate. Radioactive iodine-131 (in potassium iodide) will be used in several chemical reactions and its behavior compared with that of iodine-127 which is not radioactive.

SUGGESTIONS: If several counters are available, the class may be organized into teams to perform various, assigned procedures. For example, one team may employ Part 4 with a beta emitter while another team works with a gamma emitter. You may use the beta and gamma disks which are generally part of a demonstration kit or other sources from among those available. Teams may also be assigned to perform parts of the INSTRUCTOR EXPERIMENTS. CAUTION: The radioactive sources used in the experiment present no health hazard because the amount of radiation is small. Consult references in the *Teacher Edition* for safety procedures relating to pipeting *(these must never be pipeted orally)*, disposal of radioactive wastes, and care and washing of glassware.

PROCEDURE: 1. *Effect of radioactive materials on an electroscope.* Charge on electroscope by induction using the cat's fur and hard-rubber rod. Observe the rate of discharge of the electroscope by determining how much the leaves collapse during a fifteen-minute period. Now recharge the electroscope and place a radioactive sample beneath the leaves of the electroscope. Observe the rate of discharge of the electroscope during a fifteen-minute period. Other parts of the experiment may be performed in the intervals between these observations.
2. *Effect of radioactive materials on a Geiger counter. a. Background count.* Set the Geiger counter apparatus in operation. Note the frequency of clicks when there are no radioactive materials near the counter tube. To what are these counts due? In accurate work this background count must be subtracted from all other measurements.

b. Intensity of radiation. Place the radioactive sample at such a distance from the Geiger counter tube that you obtain the maximum count reading which the apparatus can measure. Take the reading. Remove the radioactive sample, and place the illuminated dial of a wrist watch the same distance from the counter tube. Take the reading. If some uranium metal or uranium compound is available, place it the same distance from the counter tube. Take the reading. If some radioactive ore or a radioactive isotope is available, test its radioactivity in a similar fashion. Take the reading.
3. *Absorptive effect of air on beta particles.* Place a radioactive sample 2 inches from the counter tube. Determine the count. Now place the sample 4 inches from the counter tube. Again determine the count. Continue to move the sample away from the counter tube in 2-inch intervals up to a distance of 24 inches. Make a count reading for each position and record the measurements in a Data Table like Data Table 1. Do not forget to subtract the background count in each case if it is significant.

CURVE: On a piece of graph paper plot a curve of these data, using the distances as abcissas and the counts as ordinates. How far can beta particles travel through the air before being absorbed? What type of radiation still reaches the counter tube from the radioactive sample?

4. *Absorptive effect of other materials on beta radiation.* Place the radioactive sample close to the counter tube so as to obtain the maximum reading of which the counter is capable. Record this count in a Data Table like Data Table 2. Now place one sheet of cardboard between the sample and the counter tube. Make a count reading. Continue to place additional sheets of cardboard between the sample and the counter tube, making a count reading after the addition of each sheet. Use a total of 20 sheets of cardboard.

Repeat the experiment, but use sheets of aluminum instead of cardboard. Make readings when 1, 2, 3, 4, 5, 7, 10, 12, and 15

DATA TABLE 1

Distance	Count	Distance	Count	Distance	Count

DATA TABLE 2

Cardboard				Aluminum		Lead	
No. Sheets	Count	No. Sheets	Count	No. Sheets	Count	No. Sheets	Count
0		11		0		0	
1		12		1		1	
2		13		2		2	
3		14		3		3	
4		15		4		4	
5		16		5		5	
6		17		7		7	
7		18		10		10	
8		19		12		12	
9		20		15		15	
10							

sheets of aluminum are placed between the counter and the radioactive sample.

Repeat the experiment, but use sheets of lead this time. Make readings when 1, 2, 3, 4, 5, 7, 10, 12, and 15 sheets of lead are used.

CURVE: Plot curves of these data on the same sheet of coordinate paper, using the number of sheets of various materials as abscissas and the counts as ordinates. Use different colored pencils to draw the graph lines so that the curves may be identified.

Which is the most effective material for absorbing beta radiation? What must be the relative thickness of cardboard, aluminum, and leads to produce absorption of beta radiation?

5. INSTRUCTOR'S EXPERIMENTS: *a.* Separation of thorium-234 and protactinium-234 from uranium-238. Uranium-238 decays in the sequence:

$^{238}_{92}U \rightarrow {}^{4}_{2}He + {}^{234}_{90}Th$

$^{234}_{90}Th \rightarrow {}^{0}_{-1}e + {}^{234}_{91}Pa$

$^{234}_{91}Pa \rightarrow {}^{0}_{-1}e + {}^{234}_{92}U$

The beta radiations from a sample of uranyl nitrate are being given off by the daughter products. The alpha particles are not detected by the Geiger counter. The procedures used separate the daughter products of uranium-238 by preferential solubility. To $2\overline{0}$ ml of a saturated solution of ammonium nitrate, add 5 grams of uranyl nitrate. Dissolve by stirring. Transfer 15 ml of the resultant solution to the separatory funnel. Test the remaining 5 ml for beta activity, using a small Petri dish as the container. Add 75 ml of ethyl acetate to the separatory funnel and shake for 1 minute. Draw off the lower aqueous layer. Transfer 5 ml of this solution to a small Petri dish. Draw off 5 ml of the ethyl acetate layer to another Petri dish. Test both samples for beta activity. Results?

b. The chemical behavior of a radioisotope. Iodine-131 is a beta-ray and gamma-ray emitter. Dissolve $1\overline{0}$ microcuries of this isotope in $1\overline{0}$ ml of water. Pipet 5 ml of this solution into a small Petri dish and test it for radioactivity with the Geiger counter. At the same probe distance, test for the different types of radiation by using the tube, first with the shield removed and then with the shield in place. Results? What does this indicate about the relative penetrating power of beta and gamma radiation? With the shield in place, test for the penetrating power of gamma radiation using Part 4. Record your results in a Data Table like Data Table 3.

6. Place 25 ml of potassium iodide solution in each of two small flasks. Add the 5 ml of the radioactive sample from the Petri dish to one of these. Add $3\overline{0}$ ml of lead nitrate solution to each flask and stir. Add excess lead nitrate solution after the initial precipitate settles tc insure complete precipitation. Filter and wash each precipitate (wash bottle). Test each precipitate and 5 ml of each filtrate for radioactivity with the shield covering the Geiger tube. Results? Explain.

A further experiment may be tried by the reaction of each precipitaet with $1\overline{0}$ ml of saturated sodium carbonate solution. The yellow lead iodide precipitate is converted to white lead carbonate which is removed by filtration. After washing, these precipitates as well as the initial filtrates are tested for gamma radiation.

7. Dilute 1 ml of the remaining radioactive solution to 25 ml. Add 3 drops of sodium hydroxide solution. Add 2 crystals of non-radioactive potassium iodide and stir into solution. Measure the gamma activity of 5 ml of this solution in a Petri dish. Pour 15 ml of this solution into a separatory funnel. Add 10 ml of carbon tetrachloride and 3 drops of chlorine water. Shake the separatory funnel and permit the carbon tetrachloride layer to settle. Result? Explain. Separate this layer from the water layer. Test 5 ml samples of each layer in small Petri dishes with the Geiger counter. Results? Explain. What do the results of these procedures show about the chemical properties of radioisotopes?

FURTHER EXPERIMENTATION: The Union Carbide MINIGENERATOR and the corresponding instruction manual may be purchased from W. H. Curtin Scientific Co., P.O. Box 1546, Houston, Texas 77001 or from the Welch Scientific Supply Co., 7200 N. Linder Avenue, Skokie, Ill. 60076. It is available in two systems: Cesium-137 yields Barium-137m (2.6 minutes half-life) and Tin-113 yields Indium-113m (100 minutes half-life). Among the twenty five experiments is one on the half-life of these short-lived isotopes, which are readily available for as many as 1000 repeated uses by use of the MINIGENERATOR.

DATA TABLE 3

Cardboard				Aluminum		Lead	
No. Sheets	Count	No. Sheets	Count	No. Sheets	Count	No. Sheets	Count
0		11		0		0	
1		12		1		1	
2		13		2		2	
3		14		3		3	
4		15		4		4	
5		16		5		5	
6		17		7		7	
7		18		10		10	
8		19		12		12	
9		20		15		15	
10							